WATERFOWL IN AUSTRALIA

WATERFOWL

IN AUSTRALIA

By H. J. Frith

HONOLULU
EAST-WEST CENTER PRESS

First published in 1967 by
ANGUS & ROBERTSON LTD
89 Castlereagh Street, Sydney
54 Bartholomew Close, London
107 Elizabeth Street, Melbourne

Published in the United States
by East-West Center Press, Honolulu

PRINTED IN AUSTRALIA
BY HALSTEAD PRESS, SYDNEY

To my father

RICHARD FRITH

who taught me about birds

FOREWORD

MY personal interest in this book on Australian waterfowl has many roots. First there is my long association and friendship with the author, Dr Harry Frith, whom I admire for his unusual combination of toughness and an instinctive sympathy for wild creatures. Then there is my affection for the Anatidae, surely one of the most fascinating of bird families. Third, there is my grateful delight in the places where waterfowl are to be encountered. In this great grey land of Australia, where it is only too easy to travel for days—indeed for weeks—without seeing natural water, lagoons and estuaries, rivers and swamps have an almost mesmeric attraction.

Then again, now that the flood of publications forces a biologist to forage more and more in library stacks and reprint boxes, there is my gratitude to anyone who gathers into a single volume all one wants to know about a group. Last but by no means least there is my pleasure in illustrations by really good artists and photographers. Harry Frith is extremely fortunate in having the talents of Betty Temple Watts and Ederic Slater at his call.

This book is above all a compendium of first-hand information. In dealing with two or three species only has the author had to depend substantially on the data and observations of others. For the rest he has relied almost entirely on the results of his own field studies and those of his divisional team-mates. As a result his writing has that special authority which comes only from an author's intimate personal acquaintance with his living subjects. With its added scientific solidity, I have no doubt at all that *Waterfowl in Australia* will be hailed as a landmark and a classic in its field.

At one stage in my biological career I worked on termites, and I would like to draw attention to the debt owed to these maligned insects by many Australian ducks, and other of our birds which nest in hollow branch stubs. The extent to which our ducks nest "in trees" amazes overseas ornithologists who are familiar with closely related species. When it comes to trees, these men think in terms of conifers, or hardwood species like oaks, beech and maple, which do not have our eucalypts' habit of losing branches while still, so to speak, in the prime of life. Sometimes these shed branches are solid; more often than not they are hollow, due to the activity of *Coptotermes* colonies, so that their breaking away leaves a convenient "spout". Were it not for these live-tree infesting termites, and their extreme abundance in Australia, many of our ducks, not to mention our parrots and cockatoos, would have a very hard time house-hunting, and would probably be much less abundant than they are.

Several times in his pages Harry Frith draws attention to the need for conservation action if future generations are to be assured the pleasure of seeing this or that species in reasonable abundance. And he makes the point, very clearly and definitely, that enough is now known about the ecology of Australian waterfowl to provide the blueprint of a practical conservation policy. Any policy, to be effective, must be based on genuine co-operation between the States, and between various departments and authorities within the States, as readers of this book will be led to realize. The goodwill and the desire to do the right thing are there. What is lacking is the organization needed to turn the goodwill and desire into intention and determination.

To draw up a master plan for waterfowl conservation in Australia would mean a lot of hard and detailed work for quite a few people. The programme would of course have to be based on the preservation of waterfowl habitat, in its necessary variety. As I see it, one thing alone will take us beyond the phase of generalizations and platitudes. This is the preparation of an annotated map showing the actual areas of habitat which need to be preserved, with others perhaps that would require some degree of rehabilitation. A useful start has already been made in some States, particularly Victoria.

Such a map, if it was indeed to act as a starting point for a working programme and not degenerate into an ikon for pious resolvers, could only be prepared with the co-operation of those State agencies responsible for water-resource management and agricultural development. This is because the maintenance of waterfowl habitat in the desired ecological state will require not only positive action but here and there a restraining hand on developmental plans. Natural habitat cannot be conserved without some restraint on development, which it is obviously wise to ensure early in the piece. Experience in other countries shows that if no one halts the progressive destruction of natural habitats, when the public realizes the full extent of its loss there will be a demand for at least some of the habitats to be artificially recreated—quite practicable in the case of wetlands—at whatever the cost.

If the essential steps in developing an Australia-wide waterfowl conservation programme are to be taken before it is too late, I foresee the need for a catalyst in the form of some national organization, with no special axe to grind other than to see the minimum necessary action taken. The finger rather points to the recently formed Australian Conservation Foundation, with which I am associated; and I only hope that body will find a way of doing something to help ensure the safety of this delightful group of birds and the peace-bringing places on which they depend for their survival.

FRANCIS RATCLIFFE

Canberra, September 1966

PREFACE

THIS book is a contribution from the C.S.I.R.O. Division of Wildlife Research. Much of the data has been collected as part of my official duties as an officer of that Division.

I have the good fortune to have had Dr S. J. J. F. Davies and Mr L. W. Braithwaite as colleagues in some studies and have had the valuable field and laboratory assistance of Messrs B. K. Brown, J. McKean, J. Burt, and G. Booth, all of that Division, at various times.

In addition, I have profited from discussions with other waterfowl workers, particularly Mr H. J. Lavery of the Queensland Department of Primary Industry, Mr M. C. Downes of the Victorian Fisheries and Wildlife Department, Mr D. G. Tulloch of the Northern Territory Administration, and Dr E. R. Guiler of the Tasmanian Animals and Birds Protection Board; all have very generously allowed me to use parts of their unpublished data. Dr D. L. Serventy of the C.S.I.R.O. Division of Wildlife Research has helped with details of distribution in Western Australia, and Mr K. Miers of the New Zealand Department of Internal Affairs has done the same for that country.

I have been fortunate in having the invaluable co-operation of Mrs Betty Temple Watts, who has prepared the coloured plates, and in the skill of Mr Ederic Slater, who is responsible for most of the photographs. A small army of other collaborators have provided field records and notes on ducks in their districts and many landholders have given free access to their properties; their help is gratefully acknowledged.

My own interest in waterfowl is of long standing and has taken many forms, including those of shooter, conservationist, research biologist, and bird-watcher. During the development of this interest in waterfowl I have lived in north-eastern New South Wales, the

Riverina, and near the mountain lakes of the Southern Tablelands, New South Wales; all good waterfowl districts. It has been possible to study waterfowl in widely different regions of Australia, to traverse every part of it, and to visit New Guinea, Indonesia, the Subantarctic, and several Northern Hemisphere countries in search of the elusive ducks.

After all this, whilst writing this book, it has been a source of surprise and some dismay to discover how little we really know about Australian waterfowl. May the efforts of the coming young biologists, professional and amateur, be more productive in the next thirty years.

Canberra, 1966 H. J. Frith

CONTENTS

ILLUSTRATIONS

COLOUR PLATES

OTHER PLATES

DISTRIBUTION MAPS OF SPECIES

OTHER ILLUSTRATIONS

INTRODUCTION

THE numbers of Australian waterfowl are declining. This decline was inevitable when the continent was first subjected to European settlement, the streams dammed and swamp lands drained in the interests of agriculture, and sheep and cattle began to trample the nesting habitat on the edges of those lagoons that were allowed to remain. The tempo of change is increasing, both in the scale of drainage and agricultural development, and in the mobility of the shooter and the power of his firearms; even the most remote refuges of waterfowl are now freely accessible.

The public and Governments are aware of the increasing speed of the decline of waterfowl populations, but many of the tools with which to halt it are lacking. One such tool is a comprehensive account of the biology of Australian waterfowl. There have been significant advances in research during the past decade and much of the information needed for conservation is available, but it is scattered widely in numerous scientific journals or is too briefly summarized in general books on the world's waterfowl.

Until 1951 little work, other than of a taxonomic nature, had been undertaken on Australian waterfowl. In that year the Victorian Government began studies of wild-duck movements and management, and in the same year the Commonwealth Scientific and Industrial Research Organization undertook regional studies of the ecology of wild ducks in the inland. The work continues, and has been expanded, to include work on the tropical species in Northern Territory and regional studies of the ecology of wild ducks in south-eastern New South Wales.

In 1961 waterfowl work was begun in north Queensland by the Queensland Department of Primary Industry. Surveys of Cape Barren Geese have been conducted by the Tasmanian Animals and Birds Protection Board since 1958, and in 1964 work on the ecology and behaviour of that species was begun by Monash University, Melbourne. In 1964 the Department of Fisheries and Fauna of Western Australia began a survey of waterfowl habitat in that State. In all States groups of naturalists have assisted by careful surveys and population counts in their areas, providing very useful background data.

The amount of work is increasing, but clearly there is scope for much more effort.

Nomenclature

The nomenclature of the R.A.O.U. Official Checklist has been followed in this book, except where this has been superseded by the recent account of the world's waterfowl by J. Delacour,[26] with two exceptions. I have placed the Freckled Duck in a new monogeneric tribe, Stictonettini, of the Anserinae and have followed the *Checklist of New Zealand Birds* in treating the New Zealand Brown Teal as subspecies of the Chestnut Teal, *Anas castanea.* The vernacular names are those that the writer has encountered personally and they are listed without comment. The name at the head of each life history is the one that seems to have the widest usage in Australia, although sometimes very marked differences occur in different places. The adoption of uniform vernacular names for the same species throughout the continent is very desirable.

Descriptions

Each species is described in some detail so that the bird in the hand can be identified with certainty. Of more practical importance, however, is "Field Identification" which is based on sounds made, general behaviour, and marks that are visible to an observer, under average light conditions, when mixed flocks of several species are seen briefly as they flash overhead or as they sit far out in the glare of the sunshine on water. Although it needs some practice, all Australian waterfowl can be identified when seen only as a silhouette on the horizon. Near at hand, and specifically within shotgun range, they are all very distinctive and easily recognized.

Distribution Maps

The construction of accurate and meaningful distribution maps is always difficult and especially so in Australia. The special difficulties in Australia are that the majority of the observers live in the southeast corner of the continent and there are vast areas that ornithologists seldom visit and never reside in; it is only from a local resident that exact data on the status of local birds can be had. Also a great number of Australian ducks are nomadic,[35] some species in all years, and of others a small part of the population is involved in movement only in years of unusual weather. This means that many ducks could, at one time or another, be found anywhere in the continent, yet it is not logical, on a distribution map, to give the same value to an area in which an isolated bird turns up, never to be seen again, as to one where thousands of that species live and breed permanently. It is also sometimes difficult to assess that isolated record in the absence of local residents.

The most recent comprehensive work that includes Australian waterfowl (Delacour 1954-64)[26] gives several misleading ideas of their distribution, because the author was forced to rely solely on published records and had no personal experience in this country. As one example: we see the continental range of the Magpie Goose as "Australia and Tasmania", and the map shows the whole continent and Tasmania shaded to illustrate the range. In fact the Magpie Goose, at present, has a very restricted range indeed in the northern near-coastal districts; there are a few recent records of isolated wanderers in the south-east and south-west and two such records from Tasmania fifty years ago. It has never been seen in the greater part of the continent. One should not criticize the author, but rather sympathize with him in his problem.

In this book I have examined all the published records that I have found, and many unpublished ones, having discussed birds with numerous landholders and other residents in isolated districts. I have been able to travel extensively in little-known parts of the country and have tried to assess each spot record in the light of what is known of the species, its habitat needs, and general ecology, as well as the usual distribution of habitat in the continent. The aim has been to show a distribution map that gives some idea of the usual abundance and regularity of occurrence of the species concerned in the continent. (It has not been attempted for extra-continental occurrences.)

Such an approach cannot be uniform for each species, must be, to some extent, based on opinion rather than on precise data, and for several species will undoubtedly be modified in the future. For a few species, the rare ones, where records are scarce and the birds seldom seen, it is impossible to do more than to show these localities.

Illustrations

Correct identification, under all conditions, is one of the first essentials for the hunter for his sport, and the bird-watcher for his pleasure, and for the conservationist. Accordingly the book is illustrated copiously with paintings and photographs.

Colour Plates. The colour plates show male and female of each species where the sexes are dimorphic, but where they are not only the male is shown. The eclipse plumage is shown where it is known to exist. They are painted from life by Mrs Temple Watts. The live birds used as models are in the collection of the Division of Wildlife Research C.S.I.R.O., where all species of Australian Anatidae are held. The collection is unique in this respect. Reference skins of each species were also available.

Photographs. At least one photographic portrait of each species is included. The ideal in bird photography is a portrait showing the species in its habitat. Wild waterfowl are, however, difficult subjects because of their wariness and of assorted technical difficulties, including harsh reflection from the water surface. Accordingly, in the few cases where photographs of sufficient quality of wild birds have not been available, portraits have been secured of captive birds in the collection.

Identification Plates. The identification plates are my own work, since I was dissatisfied with the others that are currently available. I make no pretence of artistic ability but do believe the postures and plumage patterns are correct. They are based on photographs, film, and my own experience in the field.

Life Histories

A substantial part of the book consists of descriptions of the life history of each species. The aim is to document as much as is known of the bird's ecology with emphasis on its conservation. The quality of these accounts varies greatly, since some species have been quite extensively studied whereas there has been little work done on others. For this reason the sources of the data are not mentioned for some species. In these cases it is to be inferred that the source is incomplete or unpublished data collected by myself and my colleagues during our travels and studies of other waterfowl. It has been one of my ambitions to observe and to work on every Australian species, and this has been partly achieved. All have been observed and all but two, the Cape Barren Goose and White Pigmy Goose, have been worked on. Fortunately these two are at present under study by others.

Measurements

The length recorded for each species is the straight line distance from the tip of the bill to the tail-tip; wingspread is the distance from wing-tip to wing-tip, the bird being held under firm tension; wing length is the distance from the wing bend to the tip of the longest primary. Bill length is the distance from the end of feathering to the tip of the bill. Tarsus measurements are not included because workers, including myself, have used a wide variety of measurements and large series of standard measurements are not available.

Voice

The significance of the sounds made by Australian waterfowl has not been studied; I know of no species for which one could list all the sounds made, the postures adopted, and their significance, except perhaps the Chestnut Teal, and that work was done in Germany. I have then merely listed the sounds most commonly heard and not tried to interpret them.

The description of birds' voices is difficult because none can be rendered precisely in musical terms. It is usual to describe them phonetically, or in words, or to liken them to supposedly familiar sounds, but this has many difficulties; "quack" and "honk" have different meanings to different people. For these reasons diagrams of sonograms have been shown in this book where they have been available.

Sonograms give a diagrammatic representation of the sound. They show the frequency in kilocycles per second (the "pitch"), the amplitude ("loudness") and duration—with experience, from this information the actual sound can be imagined.

In the diagrams the vertical scale shows the frequency, the horizontal scale the duration, and the intensity of the shading the relative amplitude.

THE FAMILY ANATIDAE

THE family Anatidae comprises the Swans, Geese, and Ducks, a homogeneous group of web-footed, aquatic birds known collectively as "Waterfowl". The family is a large one and world-wide in distribution.

The Australian continent is the poorest of all in respect to waterfowl. There are 148 species in the world and of these only nineteen are native to Australia; there are also two occasional visitors and two introductions. This may be compared to North America which has 61 breeding species, 4 regular visitors, and 15 occasional visitors.[67] Even Great Britain has 47 species, including a few introduced feral ones.

Two waterfowl, the Garganey and the Northern Shoveler, which are not native to Australia, have occasionally been reported in the wild, and two others, the Mute Swan and Mallard, have been introduced and small feral populations exist. These birds are described here in case they are encountered in the field. Any records of any of them would be of great value to those concerned with the conservation of waterfowl.

Classification

Many Australian waterfowl are closely related to species that occur in other countries—for example, the Teal, Shovelers, and Black Duck groups are more or less cosmopolitan—but there are six endemic genera not closely related to any other so far as is known. These are: Cape Barren Goose, *Cereopsis*, Magpie Goose, *Anseranas*, Freckled Duck, *Stictonetta*, Pink-eared Duck, *Malacorhynchus*, Wood Duck, *Chenonetta*, and the Musk Duck, *Biziura*.

Modern classification of the numerous species of the family Anatidae has taken basic behavioural characters together with non-adaptive structural features into consideration, and the birds are now classified into more natural groups than they were before.[27]

The family is now divided into three subfamilies:

I. Subfamily ANSERANATINAE. Formed by the unique species, the Magpie Goose *Anseranas semipalmata*, which has many anatomical features that, at present, are considered to set it apart from all other waterfowl, even by some to the extent of making it a separate family.

II. Subfamily ANSERINAE. Members of the subfamily are distinguished by possessing a "gooselike" shape, posture, and long neck. The tarsus is reticulate in front and they have a single annual moult, and no important sexual differences in plumage, voice, and structure of syrinx. Displays are simple and similar in both sexes. The subfamily includes the tribes Anserini (Geese), Cygnini (Swans), Cereopsini (Cape Barren Goose), Stictonettini (Freckled Duck) and Dendrocygnini (Tree-ducks). All of these, except the Anserini, have at least one representative in Australia; two are confined to it. Several Australian ducks are popularly known as geese—Mapgie Goose, Pigmy Goose, Cape Barren Goose, and Maned Goose—but none is a true goose and the similarity is only superficial.

III. Subfamily ANATINAE. All other waterfowl. The members of the group have a tarsus usually scutellate in front, a double annual moult, and sexual differences in plumage, voice, and the structure of the syrinx. The displays are usually elaborate and different in the two sexes. The subfamily includes the tribes Tadornini (Shelducks), Anatini (River or Dabbling Ducks), Somateriini (Eiders), Aythyini (Pochards), Cairinini (Perching Ducks), Mergini (Scoters, Goldeneyes, and Mergansers), and Oxyurini (Stiff-tailed Ducks).

In Australia there is at least one representative of each tribe except for the Somateriini (Eider Ducks), and the Mergini (Scoters, Goldeneyes, and Mergansers). The Eiders are restricted to the Northern Hemisphere and the most northern parts at that. They are sea ducks adapted to deep diving off rocky shores and are quite at home in even the roughest and coldest seas. The Scoters, Goldeneyes, and Mergansers are confined to the cold parts of the Northern Hemisphere but for two isolated species of Merganser, one in South America and one in the Auckland Islands to the south of New Zealand. They are mainly freshwater ducks, and are even more adapted to feeding under water than the Stiff-tailed Ducks. The Mergansers eat mainly fish. Perhaps in Australia that niche is occupied, to some extent, by Cormorants and Darters.

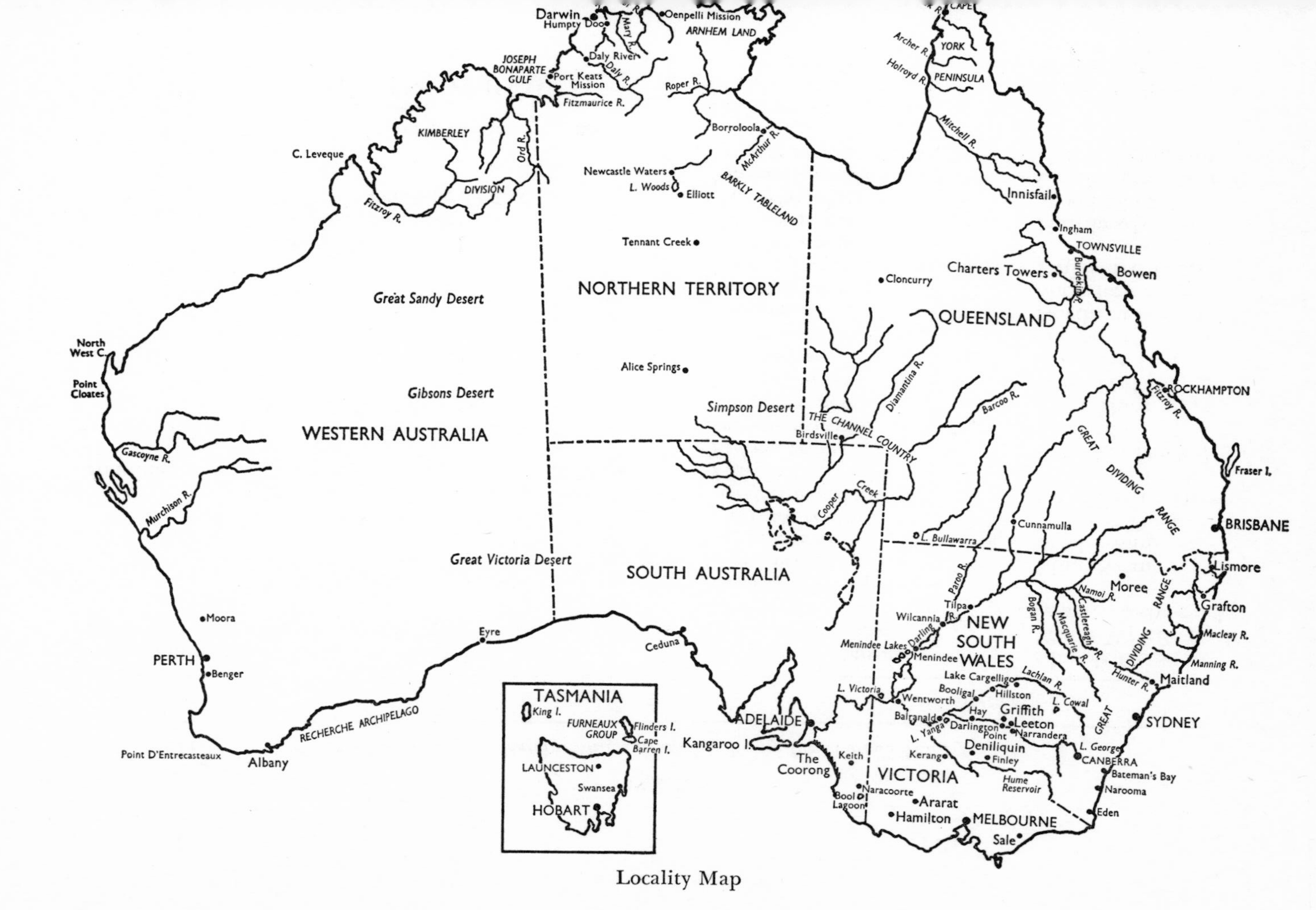

Locality Map

TABLE I

Classification of the Australian Anatidae Among the World's Waterfowl

Subfamily	*Tribe*	*Species*	
Anseranatinae	Anseranatini (Magpie Goose)	*Anseranas semipalmata*	Magpie Goose
Anserinae	Dendrocygnini (Tree-ducks)	*Dendrocygna arcuata*	Water Whistle-duck
		Dendrocygna eytoni	Grass Whistle-duck
	Anserini (Geese)	No Australian species	
	Cygnini (Swans)	*Cygnus olor*	Mute Swan
		Cygnus atratus	Black Swan
	Stictonettini (Freckled Duck)	*Stictonetta naevosa*	Freckled Duck
	Cereopsini (Cape Barren Goose)	*Cereopsis novaehollandiae*	Cape Barren Goose
Anatinae	Tadornini (Sheldgeese and Shelducks)	*Tadorna tadornoides*	Mountain Duck
		Tadorna radjah	Burdekin Duck
	Anatini (Dabbling Ducks)	*Anas platyrhynchos*	Mallard
		Anas superciliosa	Black Duck
		Anas gibberifrons	Grey Teal
		Anas castanea	Chestnut Teal
		Anas querquedula	Garganey
		Anas clypeata	Northern Shoveler
		Anas rhynchotis	Shoveler
		Malacorhynchus membranaceus	Pink-eared Duck
	Somateriini (Eider Ducks)	No Australian species	
	Aythyini (Pochards)	*Aythya australis*	Hardhead
	Cairinini (Perching Ducks)	*Chenonetta jubata*	Wood Duck
		Nettapus pulchellus	Green Pigmy Goose
		Nettapus coromandelianus	White Pigmy Goose
	Mergini (Scoters, Goldeneyes, and Mergansers)	No Australian species	
	Oxyurini (Stiff-tailed Ducks)	*Biziura lobata*	Musk Duck
		Oxyura australis	Blue-billed Duck

The classification of the Anatidae, down to the level of the tribe, is summarized in Table I, which shows the placement of all the Australian species.

Movements

In the Northern Hemisphere, although some undertake only local or erratic movement, most waterfowl are characterized by regular migrations. The term "migration" refers to a large-scale movement, in which the whole or most of the population is involved, from a breeding to a wintering area, and return, each year. Migration seems to have developed in regions where survival or reproduction is more successful if the population does move to some other area for part of each year and is commonest where there are marked and regular changes in the environment in different seasons.[68]

Thus in North America most waterfowl breed during the spring and early summer in the northern parts of the continent, some as far as northern Alaska and, at the beginning of the northern autumn, move out and fly south to spend the winter in the warmer, more southern areas. In the late winter and early spring they return, flying north to their ancestral breeding grounds. The individuals follow very definite and constant routes on their travels, year after year, and many return to the same swamp or waterhole to breed each year.

The movements are very regular, so that the expected dates of arrival or departure are known to within a few days. In some species the winter and summer ranges overlap, but in many they are widely separated so that when the birds leave their summer breeding grounds they go completely and are not seen there again until the flocks come swinging back in the following spring. Such regular mass movements are spectacular and have become deeply ingrained in the folklore of many Northern Hemisphere countries. I was once privileged to see the first returning wedge of Canada Geese swing over a Canadian prairie village—excitement at the sudden forecast of approaching spring was intense, all work ceased, and the people watched until they had disappeared over the northern horizon.

In Australia, although massive movements of waterfowl do occur, they are usually erratic in both direction and timing. Some species are reasonably sedentary, spending their whole life in the district in which they were hatched, and there is a small-scale regularity of movements in others, but most waterfowl are nomadic. They disperse in all possible directions from their breeding or feeding place whenever it becomes unsuitable and do not necessarily return there again.

Key to Plate I

INTRODUCED AND VAGRANT WATERFOWL

1. Mute Swan.
2. Mute Swan, immature.
3. Mallard, male.
4. Mallard, male in eclipse.
5. Mallard, female.
6. Garganey, male in eclipse.
7. Garganey, female.
8. Garganey, male.
9. Northern Shoveler, male in eclipse.
10. Northern Shoveler, female.
11. Northern Shoveler, male.

B.T.W. 1966

Some species may be the commonest birds in a particular district at one time, but then move on and may not be seen there again, in numbers, for years.[41]

Clearly regular annual phenomena, such as changes in day length and seasonal changes in temperature, can have little value in the explanation of the erratic and multidirectional movements of many Australian waterfowl, and most observations suggest that rainfall, and its effects on the availability of food, is the most important factor in determining their movements.

The proximate factors initiating irruptive movements, common in Australian waterfowl, are usually thought to be considerations of food or behavioural responses to crowding. Clearly the drastic changes that occur in the extent of waterfowl habitat in Australia could affect both for waterbirds. Large swamps dry, causing very great concentrations of birds and great concentration, and later disappearance, of food supplies. Many species, however, occur in very dense groups and continue breeding as the swamps decline in level until, ultimately, many nests must be deserted and young die in the dry swamps.

This event has been frequently seen both in the dry inland and in the tropical north and, under such conditions, it is difficult to accept crowding as an important factor in initiating movement. One might expect that a behavioural response to terminate breeding would operate before the ultimate need for the population to move. A further difficulty in accepting crowding as a factor to initiate movement arises from the droughts and dry periods that are of frequent occurrence in Australia. At these times the only means of survival available to waterfowl is to gather into immense concentrations on the relatively few remaining suitable water areas. A movement response triggered by crowding might be expected to operate selectively against the birds under these conditions, even though to remain in the concentrations does increase the danger of mortality due to botulism.

The results of all single species ecological studies of Australian waterfowl suggest that food, ultimately determined by rainfall, is the major factor that controls the movements of the birds. In most cases the food supply is directly geared to the rainfall, which replenishes the swamps, leading to the appearance of aquatic plants or, by the inundation of dry land, makes dry land plants available to the birds. The birds usually remain in the area until the food supply is exhausted.

The development of nomadism among Australian waterfowl, and

many other birds, is undoubtedly an adaptation to the erratic climate that prevails over the continent. In another chapter the distribution of waterfowl habitat will be described and it will be shown how this varies greatly in extent and distribution from year to year. Areas that are extensive swamps in one year, owing to heavy rain or flooding of the rivers, dry and may then remain dry and parched for several years. If a duck in the interior had regular seasonal movements in specific directions then more often than not it would find no water at the end of its travels and perish.

There is, however, a strong bias in the nomadic movements towards the coast, particularly in the south-east, each summer. These areas are more regularly and constantly watered than elsewhere and therefore more reliable habitats. In the same way some species in the tropical north have a strong east to west bias in their movements. In the north swamps are more reliable on some of the eastern rivers than elsewhere, and the birds tend to concentrate here in the winter, dispersing westwards when the summer monsoons begin.

The highly developed nomadic tendency of many species presents rather delicate problems in the conservation and management of their populations. Breeding, movement, and gross changes in the population, both locally and throughout the continent, can occur with practically no forewarning, at almost any time.

Plumage

Little is known of the sequence of moults and plumages of Australian waterfowl. I know of no comprehensive study of any species.

Anseranatinae. The Magpie Goose, *Anseranas semipalmata,* has one moult each year and is thought to be unique among waterfowl in having a gradual moult of the primaries, so that at no time is the bird flightless. Other waterfowl pass through a flightless period soon after breeding.

Anserinae. The Swans, Geese, and Tree-ducks, in general, have one moult a year, after the breeding season, during which the whole plumage is changed and for a period the birds are flightless. Observations in the field of the Black Swan, *Cygnus atratus,* the two Tree-ducks, *Dendrocygna arcuata,* and *D. eytoni,* and the Cape Barren Goose, *Cereopsis novaehollandiae,* show that Australian species conform to the remainder of the subfamily; the position with the Freckled Duck, *Stictonetta naevosa,* is not yet known.

Anatinae. There is a good deal of variation in the plumage succession of the ducks and the brief account given here is very generalized.

Ducks in general have two moults each year. After breeding the males separate from the females, many desert them entirely, and moult. This post-nuptial moult involves a complete change of the body, tail, and wing feathers. In the Northern Hemisphere many males, particularly in the genus *Anas*, shed their bright breeding plumage and appear in a dull "eclipse" plumage. So far as is definitely known only three Australian species, the Shoveler, *Anas rhynchotis*, the Chestnut Teal, *Anas castanea*, and the Blue-billed Duck, *Oxyura australis*, assume eclipse plumages, but there is some evidence that several others may also pass into an eclipse after breeding, for example, the Mountain Duck, *Tadorna tadornoides*, and the Green Pigmy Goose, *Nettapus pulchellus*. The point has been well made by Humphrey (in Delacour[26]) that in many of the species in which there is thought to be no eclipse plumage, it might actually exist, but, by being very similar to the nuptial plumage, has escaped notice. The point would merit detailed study in Australian waterfowl.

During the post-nuptial moult the birds become flightless and, in the Northern Hemisphere, many species congregate into very large moulting flocks at this time. In Australia the only duck known to form moulting concentrations is the Mountain Duck, *Tadorna tadornoides*, which gathers on large lakes. Although there are persistent rumours that Wood Ducks, *Chenonetta jubata*, also sometimes gather on large lakes in moulting flocks, this has not yet been reliably reported. Most ducks in Australia undergo the post-nuptial moult as individuals scattered over a large area, and during a long period, so that after breeding a few moulting birds only may be found in any concentration. This extended moulting period confers an obvious selective advantage on the birds. If the whole population of a species, dependent on temporary water, were to moult at the one time the species as a whole could be endangered in many years by premature disappearance of the water.

Soon after the wing feathers have grown again in the eclipse, or post-nuptial, plumage ducks moult again to assume the nuptial plumage. This moult results in the renewal of all the feathers except those of the wings. In the Northern Hemisphere the pre-nuptial moult, as the name implies, occurs before the breeding season, that is, in the winter and is quite regular. In inland Australia the breeding season, in some species, is erratic and may occur at any time of the year, according to the weather. How the moults are fitted in to this irregular breeding season is not known. It seems probable that, on many occasions, the two must overlap; otherwise favourable opportunities for breeding would be missed. Clearly there is much study to be done on moult of waterfowl in Australia.

Breeding

The breeding seasons of birds, generally, are timed to occur when conditions are most favourable for the survival of the young and the population. Breeding is controlled by secretions from the pituitary gland, and it was shown many years ago that this could be stimulated by increasing the amount of light reaching the eye. In the temperate regions of Europe and North America it is widely held that the increasing daylight in spring is a major factor in initiating the predominantly spring breeding season. The exact timing of egg-laying is then modified by other factors in the environment, such as the availability of nesting sites and food.

In much of Australia, particularly the inland, many birds have quite erratic breeding seasons that may occur at any time of the year in widely differing light regimes. Clearly under these conditions light, as a stimulator of breeding, can have no general application and it is necessary to look to factors in the environment to explain the timing of the breeding season.

The breeding of many waterfowl in Australia is very closely linked with rainfall, and there is no doubt that rainfall, and its effects on the breeding habitat and food, are the major factors in determining the breeding seasons.[40] In the south, where there is predominantly winter rainfall, most ducks breed in the late winter and spring; in the tropical north, where there is a summer wet season, the breeding season is in late summer and autumn; in the inland, where rainfall is erratic, so is the breeding season and it can occur at any time of the year that there is rain or flood. As one example, the Black Duck, *Anas superciliosa,* breeds in October and November in southern Australia, but in May and June in northern; in the inland some birds breed in spring each year, but should there be exceptionally high water-levels at any time they have the capacity to breed again, and sometimes very extensively, at that time.

The effects of the rainfall are often more important to the waterfowl than the rain itself. Ducks often breed far out on the New South Wales plains in very dry weather, having received their stimulus through alterations in the local water-level caused by rainfall hundreds of miles away at the headwaters. Similarly they may remain sexually inactive under heavy local rain if it does not alter the level of the billabongs. In the life histories of each species the regulation of the breeding season, so far as it is known, will be dis-

The billabongs of the inland rivers are of extreme importance to many waterfowl. When they are low (*upper*) most birds move, but a nucleus remains in the small pools; when they flood (*lower*) very extensive breeding follows.

Photos by author

Upper: Many waterfowl from the inland billabongs find dry-season refuge in the billabongs of the New South Wales and Queensland coasts.

Lower: The senile rivers of the north coast of Australia and the southern coast of New Guinea support very great numbers of tropical species and also provide drought refuge for ducks from the south. *Photos by author*

cussed, but here it is useful to compare briefly the breeding sequence of species in different areas.

In inland New South Wales there is a clear connection between the water-level and the waterfowl breeding season. Some species, the Musk Duck and Blue-billed Duck, are restricted to the very few permanent swamps and seem to have had less need to adapt to irregular changes in habitat. They have regular breeding seasons in spring, and no matter how wet or dry the season is or how high the swamps rise, the dates are not varied very greatly, though the duration of the breeding season is affected by the water-level. The Wood Duck, which lives in the forests and river margins and is not dependent on swamps or billabongs, has a breeding season that is independent of alterations in water-level. The birds feed entirely on green herbage and their breeding season is timed to occur when this is abundant. Sexual activity, and ultimately breeding, begins at any time of the year that there is heavy rain and food is abundant in the newly germinated herbage. The other ducks, which live in the

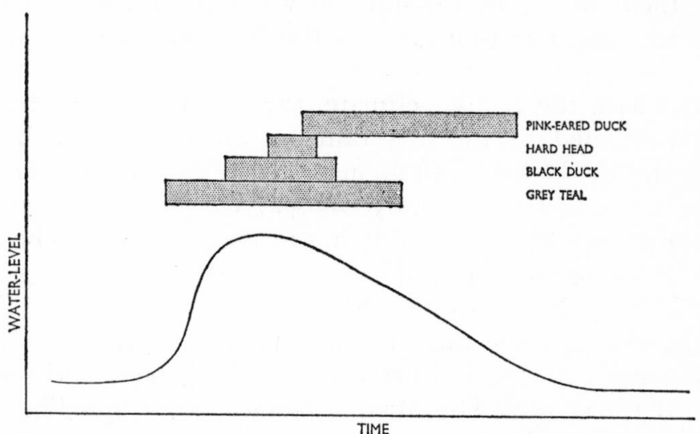

Idealized diagram to show the relationship of the breeding seasons of some common ducks to changes in water-level in inland billabongs.

billabongs and lagoons, are almost independent of rainfall itself but are stimulated to breed by changes in water-level that may be induced by rain or snow or manipulation for irrigation some hundreds of miles away. When a suitable rise in water-level occurs breeding follows, and it is more meaningful to refer to a particular species' place in a set sequence of breeding seasons than to allot it a separate month. The Grey Teal has an immediate response to a rising water-level and begins sexual activity and lays eggs within a few days of its first being evident. The Black Duck does not react so rapidly, but if the rise is sustained it follows the Grey Teal. The Hardhead, *Aythya australis,* which lives in deep water, also begins sexual activity as the water rises, but delays nesting until it is certain that the deepest lagoons and creeks are going to be filled. The Pink-eared Duck, *Malacorhynchus membranaceus,* lives in shallow water and depends on plankton for food; its food is abundant only in drying residual floodwaters. It begins sexual activity when the water-level rises, but generally delays nesting until the water has risen enough to overflow the banks and create expanses of floodwater; breeding then occurs in the declining pools. If the flood is not great enough to overflow the banks then very few Pink-eared Ducks breed.

The main reason for this connection with water-level in inland New South Wales seems to be to ensure that suitable habitat exists for the ducklings. If any of these species had a regular breeding season, or were stimulated to go through the whole breeding cycle by rainfall itself, more often than not when the ducklings were hatched there would be no suitable water for them to live in.

Similarly, in subcoastal areas of the Northern Territory, in the tropical north, although there is a superficial regularity in breeding coincident with the regular climate, the sexual cycle of the waterfowl is stimulated by the first rains of the wet season, but nest-building and egg-laying await an appropriate response of the habitat due to rain.[49] The Green Pigmy Goose, *Nettapus pulchellus,* living in permanent lily lagoons, merely has to wait for them to be replenished; the ground-nesting Whistle-ducks wait until tall grass has grown for cover in the forests. The Black Duck breeds at the end of the wet season, when the level of the swamps has been stabilized and it is certain the ground nests will not be flooded and the ducklings' food has grown. The Magpie Goose, whose breeding habitat disappears completely during the dry season, begins sexual activity with the first storms of the wet, but has an extended period of breeding behaviour as the swamps fill and later decline and the swamp vegetation grows and finally achieves a critical density for the elaborate nest construction. The Burdekin Duck, *Tadorna radjah,* also begins sexual activity in the early wet season, but does not breed until the swamps are declining in April and May, no doubt having waited until animal life, its food, is abundant in the declining muddy pools near which it breeds.

In other districts, where the seasons are fairly regular, the breeding seasons of ducks are superficially regular, but this may be a coincidence, and further study could easily disclose an effect similar to those mentioned above.

Distribution

Waterfowl are found throughout Australia and probably no district is without one or more species at some time of the year. The detailed distribution of each species will be described in a later section when the life history of the birds is discussed. However, to generalize, although many Australian waterfowl are nomadic and in times of drought or flood may wander widely, there are three fairly distinct types of distribution, largely determined by the climatic zones of the continent.[42] Each zone has a number of very characteristic species. Some are essentially restricted to the northern tropical regions, some are mainly found in, and some restricted to, the southern temperate regions of mainly winter rainfall, and others have a continental distribution, being found throughout it, as resident birds or as nomads, at one time or another, and need the resources of the whole continent to live.

The waterfowl characteristic of these zones or distribution patterns are summarized below.

TABLE II

Classification of Australian Waterfowl According to their Generalized Distribution Pattern

Northern	*Southern*	*Continental*
Magpie Goose	Cape Barren Goose	Grey Teal
Grass Whistle-duck	Black Swan	Pink-eared Duck
Water Whistle-duck	Mountain Duck	Black Duck
Burdekin Duck	Chestnut Teal	Hardhead
Green Pigmy Goose	Freckled Duck	Wood Duck
White Pigmy Goose	Shoveler	
	Musk Duck	
	Blue-billed Duck	

Northern. The typically northern species are nomadic within the tropical zone but seldom leave it. In times of drought in the tropics there may be irruptions to the south and inland generally, but these occasions are rare and, in the main, the species with a northern distribution are seldom seen beyond the tropical zone. The exception is the Grass Whistle-duck, which, while most numerous in the tropics, does have a few scattered colonies throughout the eastern part of the continent generally, and some individuals travel widely each year.

Diagram showing the types of waterfowl distribution in Australia: from top, Northern, Continental, Southern.

The usual range of a northern species extends from King Sound in the west to about the Clarence River in the east; inland it rarely extends beyond the zone of *Eucalyptus* into the *Acacia* scrubs.

Southern. The southern species are less strongly restricted to the south than the northern ones are to the tropics; for example, the Black Swan, one of the most typical southern species, of which enormous populations exist in southern New South Wales, Victoria, and Tasmania, is also able to survive in small breeding colonies as far north as Townsville, Queensland, well into the tropical zone. Droughts are more common in the south than in the tropics, and accordingly irruptions northward of southern species are more common than irruptions southward of northern species.

The typical range of a southern species is from about Geraldton in the west to Brisbane in the east. The range does not extend far inland in the west or across the Great Australian Bight, avoiding the great deserts, but in the east it widens to follow the Darling River and its tributaries to the east coast. The Black Swan is a borderline case—there are tropical colonies and nomads wander widely, but the main distribution is overwhelmingly southern.

Continental. The species with continental distributions vary greatly in the way they utilize the country. The Black Duck is widely distributed as a resident breeding species, the Hardhead and Wood Duck are mainly southern but move throughout the continent quite frequently, in response to dry weather in their main habitats. The Grey Teal and Pink-eared Duck are extreme nomads, wandering throughout the continent in great numbers, though the greatest populations are usually in the south-east.

Nesting Sites

The nesting habits of Australian waterfowl can be summarized. In each case the italic type infers that this is the sole, or by far the commonest, nesting site of the species.

I. In swamp vegetation	*Magpie Goose,* Black Swan, *Musk Duck, Blue-billed Duck, Freckled Duck, Hardhead.*
II. Open nests on land	*Black Swan, Water Whistle-duck, Grass Whistle-duck, Cape Barren Goose,* Black Duck, Grey Teal, Chestnut Teal, *Shoveler.*
III. Open nests on raised sites (tree stumps, etc.)	Black Duck, Grey Teal, Chestnut Teal, Shoveler, *Pink-eared Duck.*

IV. Concealed under rocks, etc. on the ground, in holes in the ground	Chestnut Teal, Mountain Duck.
V. Holes in trees	*Mountain Duck, Burdekin Duck, Black Duck, Grey Teal, Chestnut Teal,* Pink-eared Duck, *Wood Duck, Green Pigmy Goose, White Pigmy Goose.*

The typical nest is merely a scrape in the ground, in debris or in a tree hollow lined with down. The only Australian waterfowl that construct a more elaborate nest are the Magpie Goose, Black Swan (sometimes), Musk Duck, Blue-billed Duck, Freckled Duck and Hardhead.

Feeding

Nearly all Australian waterfowl feed in, or on the edges of, water, and only four consistently collect large quantities of food on dry land. These are the Magpie Goose, which grazes far from water at some seasons and at others moves across sunbaked plains digging for bulbs of the spike rush, and the Wood Duck and Grass Whistle-duck, which feed on emergent aquatic plants to some extent but secure most of their food by grazing open grasslands far from water. The Black Swan, Cape Barren Goose, and Mountain Duck also graze pastures and crops.

In the Northern Hemisphere Mallards and some other River Ducks, at some seasons, secure much food from dry land by feeding in harvested grainfields on the waste grain. The numbers involved are enormous and in some places, such as the wheatfields of the Prairie Provinces of Canada and the Mississippi Valley, the waste grain is of considerable value in maintenance of the populations. In Australia the Wood Duck is the only waterfowl that consistently feeds in stubble fields. The development of the habit in the Wood Duck is easy to understand, considering its normal food-gathering methods of grazing across open land. It is difficult to imagine why the Black Duck, which is abundant throughout areas where cereals are grown, has not developed the habit. I have seen very few instances of Black Ducks feeding in grainfields and these have always been in abnormally dry seasons and have involved very small numbers of birds. Usually the Black Ducks are associated with Wood Ducks, suggesting that they are capable of learning the habit from them. If field feeding among Black Ducks did become widespread it would, to some extent, compensate for the losses of feeding habitat as the more productive swamps are drained.

The location of feeding of the species restricted to water habitats varies, as does the food eaten. Magpie Geese, Black Swans, Wood Ducks, and Pigmy Geese feed almost entirely by grazing seedheads, buds and other plant parts; Freckled Ducks, Black Ducks, Grey Teal, Chestnut Teal, and Shoveler secure most food by stripping seed from emergent plants but also freely dabble in shallow water and mud for animals; none of these dive for food. The Pink-eared Duck is completely a surface feeder, filtering the surface water for small items. The Water Whistle-duck and Hardhead feed mainly on the surface but frequently dive in deep water, whereas the Blue-billed Duck feeds mainly by diving and the Musk Duck entirely by diving. The Cape Barren Goose, Grass Whistle-duck, Mountain Duck, and Burdekin Duck seldom feed in water except at its edge.

The food eaten includes numerous aquatic and dry-land plants and aquatic animals. There is no evidence that any Australian waterfowl selectively feeds; in all those that have been studied the composition of the food eaten closely parallels the abundance and availability of the food items in the chosen feeding habitat. Some waterfowl are entirely vegetarian and some subsist almost entirely on animal material. The food eaten by the Australian species is summarized below.

I. Entirely vegetable	Magpie Goose, Black Swan, Cape Barren Goose, Wood Duck, Green Pigmy Goose, White Pigmy Goose, Grass Whistle-duck, Water Whistle-duck.
II. Predominantly vegetable	Freckled Duck, Black Duck, Grey Teal, Chestnut Teal, Hardhead, Blue-billed Duck, Mountain Duck.
III. Predominantly animal	Burdekin Duck, Shoveler, Pink-eared Duck, Musk Duck.

The types of animals eaten are remarkably uniform among the different species of waterfowl in different localities although, of course, the species of the different animal classes vary a good deal locally. Insects are most important, principally beetles and water-boatmen and lesser numbers of aquatic fly larvae. Molluscs and crustaceans are of considerably less importance to most Australian waterfowl and none seems to have become specialized to their utilization.

Although a great number of plants are eaten the number of plant families that are really important individually to waterfowl is quite small. The diagram below suggests the relative importance of various plant families to waterfowl generally in two regions. The figures are derived from the average contents of stomachs of very large samples of birds, containing all the local species, in the inland, mainly the Riverina, and in the tropics, mainly north-east Queensland and subcoastal Northern Territory. The figure can be taken to indicate approximately the order of importance of various plants and animals to waterfowl generally in the two regions.

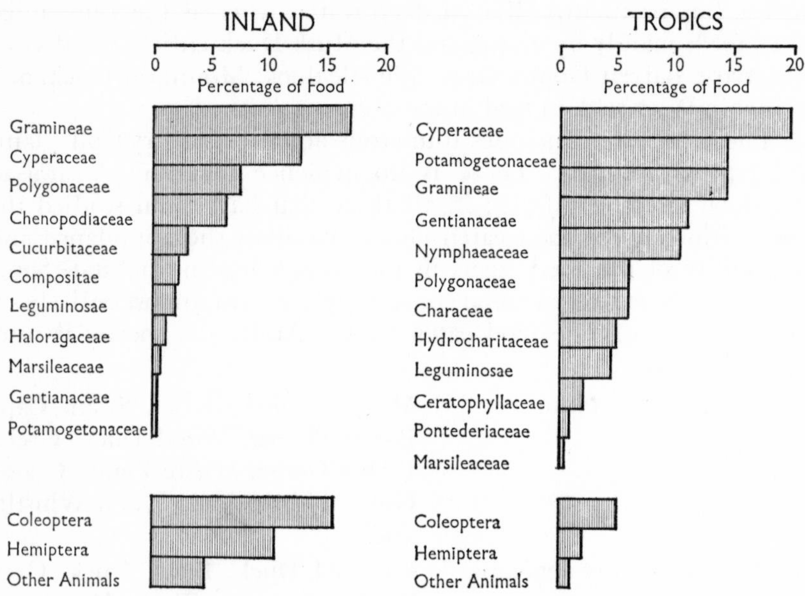

Average composition of the food of waterfowl in tropical coastal districts and in the southern inland, mainly the Murray-Darling Basin.

Both in the semi-arid inland and the wet tropics sedges and grasses are of major importance; they are the most important plant families in both areas. In the inland, they are the only really important plant families and the remainder of the food is made up of insects and a very wide variety of dry-land and swamp plants, none being of outstanding importance on its own. In the tropics, owing to the wide development of permanent rich lagoons, plants characteristic of these provide very important food sources; these include water-lilies, hyacinth, and pondweeds.

Many waterfowl have rather similar food habits, at least superficially, and when large mixed flocks occur on the same swamp it might seem that they are competing for the same food, but this is usually not so. Each species tends to collect different food items or the same items from quite different parts of the swamp. Thus in a generalized situation in an inland cumbungi swamp examination of the food being eaten shows that, typically, the Wood Ducks would be feeding away from the swamp on pasture lands, the Swans partly on pasture and partly on cumbungi shoots. The Grey Teal would be subsisting on grasses, smartweeds, and small insects, and the Black Ducks on larger insects as well as these plants. The Blue-bills would be eating some sedge and many midge larvae, while the Hardheads would be diving into deep water for large insects and large molluscs. The Musk Ducks would be diving into deeper water again for crayfish, large mussels, and deepwater weeds; the Pink-eared Duck would be filtering minute particles from the water surface, and the Freckled Duck filtering algae from shallow water. When one particular food is very abundant many species may concentrate on it, but only in time of drought, when food is scarce, does real competition occur between species.

DISTRIBUTION OF HABITAT

THE three-million-square-mile land mass of Australia extends from far into the tropics to the southern mid-temperate region and provides a wide range of climate and environment, but, despite this, it is the poorest continent of all with respect to the number of kinds of waterfowl it supports.

One of the main reasons for this poor representation of waterfowl is that the physiography and latitudinal placement of the continent have not favoured the development of large and varied areas of waterfowl habitat. The continent is flat, or nearly so, having missed the great land upheavals that produced lofty mountains in the other continents. There are no permanent snowfields and few opportunities for high land to induce rainfall on its slopes to replenish swamps. Most of the rain that falls does so on narrow northern and eastern coastal strips and rapidly drains into the sea.

The tropical areas of the continent are too far south to share the well-distributed and constant rain of the wet tropics, and the southern regions are too far north to benefit from the steady rains of the mid-temperate regions. The continent is within the zones of the south-east trade-winds and the prevailing westerlies. The north coast is also subject to summer monsoonal rainfall and the southern districts receive much rain from winter depressions from the Southern Ocean. The result is that in the north rainfall is predominantly in summer, with a pronounced winter dry season, and in the south it is mainly in winter. No rainfall system extends far inland and most of the interior, having low rainfall and a very high evaporation rate, is arid. There are comparatively few permanent streams and the flow of surface water, in most of the country, is limited to periods immediately after heavy rain. The average annual run-off corresponds to a depth of only $1\frac{1}{3}$ inches of water over the whole continent; this can be compared to $9\frac{3}{4}$ inches for all other land surfaces or 9 inches for the United States of America.

Although there is some overlap and some of the borders are not distinct, it is most convenient to consider the distribution of waterfowl habitat in Australia in four major regions and a number of drainage systems within each region.

The four regions are:

(i) Central Region
(ii) Southern Region
(iii) Murray-Darling Region
(iv) Northern Region

They are characterized by differences in annual rainfall distribution, quantity and reliability, annual temperature, slope of the land and drainage.

Central Region

The Central Region occupies one and three-quarter million square miles, more than half the continent, and is virtually useless to waterfowl. It is arid, with no permanent surface water, and much of it is desert. Although many streams are marked on maps these are nearly always dry, sandy beds, and the lakes are salt-encrusted dried mud. The streams that drain into Lakes Eyre, Callabonna, and Frome rise in the districts of low and unreliable rainfall and drain into the most arid part of the continent where the annual rain is seven inches and the annual evaporation is over a hundred inches. They seldom flow and when they do surface water does not persist for long. Some of the more eastern rivers, however, the Georgina, Diamantina, Mulligan, and Cooper, in their lower reaches form a network of channels, "the Channel Country", which often receives some water, and in the rare periods of flood they inundate eight million acres, leaving numbers of semi-permanent waterholes. At such times the region produces significant numbers of typically inland ducks, but the over-all contribution to the continental populations is small.

In the west a series of large but intermittent rivers flow towards the Indian Ocean. They flow only briefly after the infrequent heavy rains and leave pools that provide some breeding habitat for Grey Teal and Black Ducks and Pink-eared Ducks, but, over all, the area is of little use to waterfowl. The rest of the Central Region consists of the great deserts.

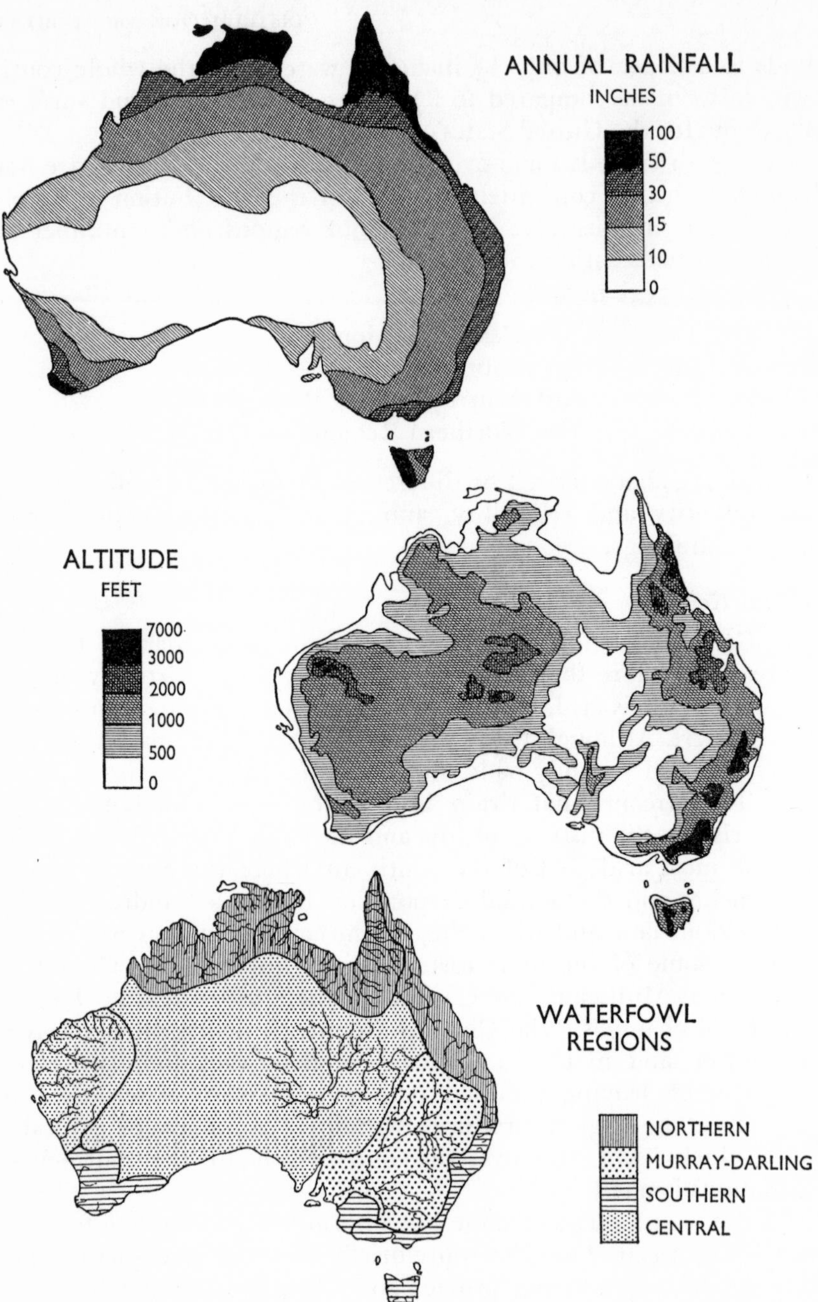

The waterfowl regions of Australia, based on the drainage systems, compared to the distribution of rainfall and the altitude of the continent. The maps are based on those of the *Atlas of Australian Resources* (Department of National Development).

Southern Region

The Southern Region is the part of Australia that has been most intensively settled and developed for agriculture and industry. Much of it was formerly good waterfowl habitat, but this has been greatly decreased by drainage.

No region in Australia is completely self-supporting with regard to waterfowl, but two parts of the Southern Region, Tasmania and south-west Western Australia, more closely approach this state than any other. Most of Tasmania is hilly and although it has many lakes they are generally too deep and cold to be good breeding habitat. Waterfowl breeding is mainly in the streams, pools, and swamps of the midlands and the northern and eastern coastal districts. The island supports large breeding populations of Black Swans, Mountain Ducks, Black Ducks, and smaller numbers of Grey Teal, Chestnut Teal, and Blue-billed and Musk Ducks. Each summer there is an influx from the mainland of Black Duck, Grey Teal, Mountain Duck, and some Hardheads. In times of drought on the mainland this influx can be very great and includes Pink-eared Duck and the other less common species.

South-western Australia is isolated from the rest of the continent by the great deserts. The numerous small streams are intermittent in flow because of summer drought. Inland there are many brackish and salt-water pools and, near the coast, many permanent and semi-permanent swamps, though many more have been drained. Black Duck, Grey Teal, and Black Swans are abundant breeding species, Blue-billed and Musk Ducks are widely distributed, and Pink-eared and Freckled Ducks and Shovelers occur in smaller numbers. The Mountain Duck is numerous and the Chestnut Teal common, particularly in the salt-water estuaries, and Wood Ducks have been increasing in the past few years. The area seems to be largely self-supporting and contributes little to the rest of the continent, though there is sometimes a movement of Grey Teal to the eastern States.

The value of the southern regions of eastern Australia to waterfowl varies greatly from place to place. The largest rivers are on the New South Wales North Coast. These flood almost annually and there are numerous swamps behind the river levees in the middle and lower regions, particularly on the Richmond, Clarence and Hunter. This area was formerly a very important waterfowl district, but continued drainage and diversion works have destroyed most of the habitat. At present this work continues at an accelerated pace, following disastrous floods in 1956, and it is certain that the

North Coast will become even less significant, in the near future, as a waterfowl-producing district, than it is today.

Farther south, between the Hunter Valley and the east Gippsland district, the coastal strip is only a few miles wide and the rivers mostly small, their valleys are steep and run-off is rapid. There are numerous lakes and lagoons close to the seashore, but most are salt or brackish and provide little breeding habitat for waterfowl. Although the coastal strip between Gippsland and the vicinity of Hamilton, Victoria, was once an important breeding and refuge area for waterfowl, it has been greatly altered by settlement. The most important swamps in Victoria formerly occurred round Port Phillip Bay, but these have all been drained for many years.

In the western part of the region, from the Coorong to Western Victoria, there are numerous swamps, potholes, and lakes that receive adequate rainfall and provide useful breeding habitat for ducks. Many of these are in south-east South Australia, where an extensive drainage and agricultural development programme is rapidly destroying many of those that remain. This area has a significant breeding population of Musk and Blue-billed Ducks, Wood Ducks, Black Ducks, Grey Teal, and Black Swans. It is the most important breeding area in the continent for Mountain Ducks and contains one of the largest strongholds of the rare Freckled Duck in the continent. Smaller numbers of Chestnut Teal, Shovelers, and Hardheads breed there fairly regularly.

Murray-Darling Region

The Murray-Darling Region is the source of most of the waterfowl bred in southern Australia. The Murray-Darling river system is the greatest in Australia and drains nearly half a million square miles of country. The rivers rise in the eastern highlands and quickly fall to flat, or nearly flat, flood-plains, across which they meander for hundreds of miles before joining the Murray River or disappearing into sands or reedbeds. As the senile rivers wander across the plain they have developed extensive systems of billabongs, swamps, and effluent streams. The effluents, in turn, meander across hot, dry plains until they disappear or rejoin the parent stream or another river.

The extent of waterfowl habitat in the area depends entirely on rainfall on the eastern highlands, hundreds of miles to the east or south of the plains. There is rarely sufficient local rain to replenish swamps. In years of abundant rain or snowfall on the eastern highlands the rivers flood, filling the swamps and billabongs and sending floodwaters far across the plains, where every depression and claypan is filled and converted to a temporary swamp. The more frequent and extensive the flooding, the more extensive and reliable the habitat. When the life histories of the various ducks are read later in this book, it will be appreciated how closely the breeding, food, and movements, and hence the numbers, of the important game species are controlled by these fluctuations in river level and the extent of flooding.

There are four distinct waterfowl breeding areas in the Murray-Darling Region: the Riverina, the Macquarie-Gwydir System, the Bulloo-Paroo System, and the Lower Darling. The Riverina includes the Murray River and its tributaries, the Lachlan and Murrumbidgee, and the smaller Ovens and Goulburn rivers, which drain the region of most regular rainfall and are permanent streams. Although the Lachlan frequently ceases flowing and the Murrumbidgee occasionally does so, they never dry up. The streams rise sufficiently to fill many of the lagoons and billabongs nearly every year and major floods occur frequently; for example, the Murray River at Wentworth has experienced thirty major floods in the sixty years ending 1956.

The main tributaries of the Darling—the Macquarie, Gwydir, and Castlereagh rivers—are permanent streams in their upper reaches, but do not flow far across the plains before discharging into swamps and reedbeds. These form waterfowl breeding areas that are important but only a small fraction of the size of the Riverina. In times of flood the area is increased and water reaches the Darling River.

The Bulloo, Paroo, and Warrego rivers rise in areas of low rainfall, seldom flow, and discharge into large shallow swamps, claypans, and channels before reaching the Darling. The Bulloo never reaches the Darling, and the Paroo and Warrego rarely do so. Flooding, especially large-scale flooding, is less frequent than in the other subregions, but when it does occur large areas of duck habitat are created. Some of the lakes at the end of the Bulloo and Paroo, once filled, can retain water for several years and form valuable inland breeding areas and, later, refuges. Below Menindee the Darling forms very extensive systems of meanders, effluents, lakes, and billabongs, which when flooded create very large areas of waterfowl breeding habitat, especially towards its junction with the Murray River.

The Murray-Darling Region is the most important duck breeding area in Australia. It produces very large numbers of Black Ducks, Pink-eared Ducks, Grey Teal, Hardheads, Wood Ducks, and Black

Swans. Musk Ducks and Blue-billed Ducks occur whenever the habitat is suitable; the less common Shovelers and Freckled Ducks are found as breeding species; Mountain Ducks are common, particularly in the south-west, and there are small colonies of Chestnut Teal; Grass Whistle-ducks and Water Whistle-ducks occasionally visit.

Northern Region

The Northern Region, much of which is still in its primitive condition, produces very large numbers of tropical ducks as well as providing valuable drought refuge for birds breeding in the Murray-Darling Basin. The region extends from the Kimberley Range to the New South Wales coast, more or less following the 20-inch isohyet. The inland border is fairly well marked by the isohyet, but the southern border, on the New South Wales coast, is indistinct. I have chosen the Clarence River as the boundary because that river is the extreme southern limit of distribution of two tropical waterfowl, the Burdekin Duck and the White-quilled Pigmy Goose. However, many of the swamps are ecologically similar to those of the Hunter River and a case could be made for extending the border to that river. The region is dominated by the summer monsoons and has many large rivers that flood each summer but cease flowing during the pronounced winter dry season when most other surface waters also disappear.

The amount of habitat varies from place to place. The north-western region from the Kimberleys to Cape Arnhem contains the largest rivers—the Fitzroy, Ord, Daly, Mary, and South Alligator—and many smaller but still considerable streams. Most of the hinterland is elevated in the form of sandstone plateaux, but lagoons are numerous and the rivers have very extensive plains which flood each wet season, forming vast areas of breeding habitat.

The rivers on the west of the Gulf of Carpentaria fall abruptly from high plateaux and form few swamps or flood plains, though there are numerous lagoons and billabongs, but the rivers on the southern and eastern sides of the Gulf flow across flat land and form more extensive plains. Numerous meanders and effluent streams connect the different rivers; the intervening plains are high and form grasslands rather than the sedge swamps of the north-west region. Lagoons are numerous, but the main water habitats are in the form of extensive salt-water mangrove swamps and creeks and large claypans, periodically inundated by salt water.

In north-eastern Queensland, although the rivers are similar

Upper: Inland lakes are normally dry, but when water flows in from the supply creek they are important breeding places.

Lower: In contrast, many tropical lagoons provide permanent rich habitat. This one is near Townsville, north Queensland.

Photos by Ederic Slater

Upper: Dove Lake, Tasmania. High mountain lakes normally support a few Chestnut Teal and Mountain Ducks, but are too deep and cold to be of great value to waterfowl, except in very dry seasons.

Lower: Cumbungi swamps, like Barrenbox, N.S.W., are the only permanent swamps in the inland. Most have been artificially created for storage and control of irrigation water.

Photos by Ederic Slater

ecologically to those of the south-east slopes, they differ in having their maximum flows in the summer and there is a very small flow at other times, due to the marked dry season. On Cape York Peninsula the hills approach the coastline very closely and there is very little waterfowl habitat; the main development is around Townsville and the Burdekin River valley and on the New South Wales northern rivers.

The most numerous waterfowl of the Northern Region are the Magpie Goose and the two Whistle-ducks, which occur in great numbers everywhere, but the numbers are greatest on the plains between Darwin and Arnhem Land. Geese are common in most permanent lagoons, and Burdekin Ducks occur among the mangroves and brackish streams. Black Ducks are widely distributed as a breeding species; their numbers are not great in the Timor Sea subdivision, but in north-east Queensland they are the commonest duck. In addition to its value as a breeding area for tropical species the Northern Region, especially the eastern half, is a very valuable drought refuge for southern birds of all species.

Although the four waterfowl regions of the continent have been described separately it would be a mistake to believe that they operate independently. The tropical species, it is true, are fairly well restricted to the Northern Region but sometimes irrupt southwards for refuge. The southern species, the most numerous and important waterfowl of Australia, at one time or another need the whole of the continent for living space and utilize each region. They are bred mainly in the Murray-Darling Basin but each summer move into the favoured areas of the Southern Region as the inland waters decline, and in times of drought move in vast numbers to the Northern Region also for survival.

The paucity of and irregularity in occurrence of rainfall and habitat have led to the development of novel adaptations in Australian waterfowl to enable them to cope with the erratic environment. Many do not have regular breeding seasons or permanent breeding areas; they are nomadic, wandering all over the continent, and have very flexible food habits, eating almost anything that might be available at the time. Some others are very highly specialized to utilize one particular type of water. These adaptations and their significance in conservation will be discussed in the account of the life history of each species.

CONSERVATION

AUSTRALIA, a semi-arid continent with little rain and few large rivers or swamps, probably never had a very great population of waterfowl, except in the tropical north. Certainly the explorers, unlike the early travellers in North America, whose journals are full of descriptions of astounding numbers of ducks, geese, and swans, never remarked on great flocks. For the most part, when travelling through the Murray-Darling Basin, the best waterfowl area of southern Australia, they were hungry, so presumably unable to shoot large numbers of ducks.

The waterfowl populations in the inland, whilst not large and, no doubt, fluctuating wildly in response to the changes from flood to drought, as they do today, were thoroughly adapted to survive these conditions, by having a very rapid rate of increase in flood and strongly developed nomadic abilities to seek out a refuge, even during the greatest of the droughts, and also sufficient flexibility of behaviour to enable a small number of birds to hang on in the few remaining swamps should the far-flying nomads meet disaster. One might imagine that the populations were quite delicately balanced and that it would not need much interference with their resources to upset this balance.

The interference was provided by the advent of European man in 1788 and his first probings inland in the early nineteenth century. As the explorers floated down the inland rivers or struggled among the lignum channels and were followed by settlers and their sheep to trample the lagoon and billabong edges, a decline in waterfowl numbers became certain. Only seventy years after Captain Sturt was swept from the Murrumbidgee into the Murray River, the first waterfowl, the Magpie Goose, was extinct locally.

For birds that are regularly shot for sport it is easy to imagine that this is the main cause of scarcity, and in some cases this is probably so, but anyone who has seen the enormous fluctuations in duck numbers in Australia in a series of wet and dry years must be impressed with the recovery powers of the populations of birds. One must doubt whether shooting at the present level is a very potent factor in the over-all decline of wild ducks, except in some special cases and districts. For instance, shooting could probably eradicate the Freckled Duck, Magpie Goose, and Pigmy Geese; it has been involved in the critical situation that existed for the Cape Barren Goose and in the virtual eradication of the Burdekin Duck from settled districts.

Under the Commonwealth Constitution the management of the fauna is a matter for the individual States. It is, however, apparent that when one State produces most or many of the ducks that spend their summers and dry seasons in the neighbouring States, and some in very distant States, close co-operation in management is called for at a very high level to co-ordinate the efforts. The only co-ordinating body at present, is the Australian Waterfowl Committee, which is composed of a research worker or administrator from each State and from the Commonwealth. It meets biennially, but has no executive power at all; it does, however, provide a useful forum for debate.

Efficient management must be based on careful research, and it will be apparent to the reader of this book how inadequate is our knowledge of even the life history of some species and that the details of population regulation of very few are known in even approximate terms. We are hazy about the distribution of some. The number of qualified biologists working on waterfowl is very small; there are not half a dozen among all the States combined. At this level it will be quite some time before we solve all the problems of waterfowl conservation and management. Research provides the tools for successful, rather than hit-or-miss, conservation, so it is fortunate that there has been sufficient done, at least, to recognize the most urgent needs—particularly the most pressing ones of habitat retention and restoration and of the over-all importance of maintaining the flow of the inland streams.

There are several conservation problems involving single species of Australian waterfowl, and these will be discussed in the life histories later in this book; species for which special approaches are needed are the Cape Barren Goose, the Freckled Duck, and perhaps the Magpie Goose. In general terms, however, conservation of waterfowl demands the recognition of only two distinct zones or groups of species, the tropical and the southern. Of these the tropical zone is the simplest and, fortunately, effective measures there will be of immense value to the birds of the southern zone.

The tropical north is still largely in its virgin condition; there has been little agricultural development and large-area cattle-raising is the most important industry. This type of land utilization does not seriously compete with waterfowl. The area is also favoured with a mild climate and bounteous rain, so that stock dams and other artificial water-storage areas are rapidly colonized by aquatic plants and provide excellent waterfowl habitat.

The problems of the south are more pressing and more complex and need action on a very wide front, biological, geographic, and political. Most of the common game ducks in eastern Australia are derived from three or four quite small areas of inland New South Wales, and developments there, adverse to waterfowl, have a significance far beyond that region and that State. Preservation of these breeding grounds is the most pressing problem.

The most important breeding areas are in the lagoons, billabongs, swamps, and creeks of the inland rivers; the Murray, Murrumbidgee, Lachlan, and Darling, and the Macquarie, Gwydir, Bogan, Paroo, and Bulloo. These rivers twist and wind across the endless flat plains, losing themselves in mazes of channels to emerge again and continue until some reach the sea and others disappear into the sand or into immense depressions of hard salt-encrusted clay—usually shown hopefully on maps of Australia as lakes, and coloured blue.

Usually the swamps, claypans, and plains are dry and parched and the billabongs have a few inches of muddy water in the bottom, but when heavy rain falls on the mountains or snow melts, hundreds of miles away, water courses down the rivers, out through every effluent creek, into every swamp, lagoon, and lake and the breeding habitat is created. The ducks are adapted to utilize this and to breed at any time of the year that it occurs, despite the local weather.

In times of very heavy rain on the catchments the effluents cannot carry the flow, and floodwaters, only a few inches deep, creep for many miles across the flat plains, filling every depression and claypan to form temporary, but vast, expanses of breeding habitat. Duck breeding becomes extensive, the local birds are reinforced by nomads from elsewhere, and really great numbers of birds are produced and ultimately spread all over eastern Australia and sometimes western and northern Australia also. The very next year could be a drought; the creeks will remain dry and the domestic stock that escaped drowning in one year may perish from thirst the next summer.

Under these conditions there is virtually no breeding of ducks and little refuge inland, and the birds in the area must find somewhere else to exist.

Breeding and refuge areas of Grey Teal and other game ducks in eastern Australia. The majority of the birds are bred on the inland river system with vertical shading. The areas shown black are refuges occupied annually, and the dotted areas are refuges also occupied in years of drought.

Conservation of breeding habitat in the inland is not so much a matter of reserving swamps to provide undisturbed conditions, though no one would deny the value of this also, as of ensuring that the inland rivers continue to fluctuate in level frequently, so replenishing the lagoons, billabongs, and depressions on the plains, and creating the correct breeding habitat for the different species, each of which breeds at a different stage of the flooding. Not many inland lagoons have been drained, but their water supply has been greatly decreased in volume and frequency. For irrigation it has been necessary to dam the rivers and to control their flow, diverting vast volumes of water to irrigate crops rather than to fill billabongs. For flood control, levees have been built to protect great low-lying areas from flooding, and throughout the length of each river its flow is reduced by pumping to reticulate water across the plains for stock. The result has been a great decrease in the frequency of filling of many swamps, lagoons, and billabongs, and a corresponding decrease in the numbers of ducks breeding.

One cannot, nor would one wish to, deny the legitimate needs of the nation for water-conservation works, but one can deplore the lack of consideration that is usually shown to wildlife-conservation problems by the planners of these schemes. The large bodies of water held by dams in the highlands are practically useless for ducks. They are too deep to permit feeding other than at the edge and, because of their purpose, are always built where the banks are very steep and usually rocky, so that the edge is minimal. They are usually in cold highlands where few aquatic plants and insects thrive and there is no cover on the shore and edges. They provide negligible waterfowl habitat.

Of more concern, however, is the water after it leaves the highland dams and finds its way downstream through the various water-conservation structures. Waste irrigation water could flood billabongs, and many of the inland storage areas, weirs and levees for flood control, irrigation and disposal of irrigation water, could provide invaluable waterfowl breeding habitat and still serve their primary purpose, sometimes with only quite minor modifications in their structure and operation. It is certain that if fauna authorities were consulted during the planning stages of water-conservation schemes the essentials of the birds' breeding habitat in many cases could be maintained, or even improved, rather than destroyed.

Most of the waterfowl are nomadic, some entirely so and others whenever necessary, and for survival they need not only secure breeding grounds, but also secure refuges for the usual dry summers and more extensive ones for droughts when they might have to support almost the whole surviving duck population of the continent for some time. If the refuge areas are inadequate then the position of the remaining ducks is critical.

Important inland refuges are a few permanent swamps, like the artificial lakes at Menindee, New South Wales, and the cumbungi swamps of the Murrumbidgee River, around Kerang, Victoria, as well as the land-locked waters of the Murray River west of Balranald, New South Wales. These inland refuges, however, are not great enough to provide shelter for all the inland ducks in even a normal summer, and coastal refuge areas are also essential. The most important coastal refuges for ducks from inland New South Wales are the districts between Adelaide, South Australia, and Sale, Victoria, extending inland to include the swamps of the Naracoorte and Keith districts in South Australia and the large clear lakes of western Victoria, the valleys of the northern rivers of New South Wales from the Hunter to the Tweed, and the coastal plain of the Burdekin River, between Bowen and Townsville in north Queensland.

These refuge areas have all been decreased greatly by drainage, and, both inland and on the coast, domestic stock graze to the edge of most waters that remain and have completely destroyed the cover. In places cattle and feral buffalo even wade into the water to carry the destruction further. What cover remains on the shore is usually infested with feral pigs, foxes, and cats, none of which are very agreeable to ducks.

When virgin land is converted to a thriving agricultural and pastoral region the wildlife must suffer; it always has and most probably always will. In Australia, however, we are fortunate in having seen the great, and largely fruitless, expenditure in trying to bring back wildlife that has gone in many parts of the world and, presumably having learnt from this, can take action before it is too late.

Not all agricultural developments have been adverse to waterfowl; some have even been beneficial locally. There is little doubt that the introduction of improved pastures and grain crops, as well as the creation of hundreds of thousands of ground tanks in the inland, has favoured the Wood Duck in many districts and probably even extended its range into areas that it could not inhabit because there was no surface water and little green grazing. In the tropics Lavery[69] considers that the grazing of lagoon edges by domestic stock has provided more suitable feeding and roosting habitat for Grass Whistle-ducks than formerly existed. The irrigation schemes of inland New South Wales are disastrous to the billabong and lagoon breeding grounds of Grey Teal, but, as a by-product, these irrigation schemes have produced several large cumbungi-choked swamps of drainage water that provide an extensive and ideal habitat for Blue-bills and Musk Ducks and valuable drought refuges for all species. Development of agriculture on the subcoastal plains of the Northern Territory destroys the habitat of the Magpie Goose, but water-storage areas for the rice crops now provide the largest refuge and breeding areas for the Green Pigmy Goose in the country.

However, development in the main is adverse to waterfowl, and in the early surge of enthusiasm in the nineteenth century much land was drained that has not fulfilled agricultural expectations and could now be restored to swampland without a great loss to the nation's economy. In this connection one immediately thinks of the great areas of formerly excellent productive swamps on the North Coast of New South Wales that now grow coarse tussocks and produce small amounts of highly subsidized butter. Such land could be resumed or purchased with public funds for restoration. The authorities are aware of these possibilities and some land is being restored to waterfowl production. Victoria, particularly, has recognized the need and is actively effecting a series of Reserves and Sanctuaries throughout the State, but the amount of land being reserved in the continent is not enough.

The selection of areas to be preserved, or restored, depends on surveys of the distribution of habitat in the continent, as well as on knowledge of the birds' movements and habitat needs. Fortunately, although a great deal of work remains to be done in these directions, the principles are now sufficiently well known for ignorance of them not to be the limiting factor in habitat restoration.

In addition to the preservation or restoration of habitat, its creation on a very useful scale is possible. Schemes to create duck habitat are widespread in North America and in New Zealand and have been carried out with notable success, but there has been little done in Australia. I was impressed with one effort spontaneously made by the Bowen Gun Club (North Queensland), primarily to provide better shooting for themselves but incidentally assisting numerous waterbirds and the duck situation in their region greatly. A bank constructed on the seaward end of a useless salt-pan, by preventing tidal influence, permitted the water to become fresh and swamp vegetation to develop, providing a very large and useful refuge for many ducks. Their example could profitably be followed in many other places on the east coast.

Even more widely possible is the planning of water-storage dams on farms to provide waterfowl habitat as well as serving their primary function. Most such dams now are rectangular and bare, stock being allowed access freely to the banks. With a little thought to each situation, many could be made useful small breeding areas for a few ducks and refuge for many others. The essentials are that there should be a shelving margin to provide some shallow water, since all our ducks feed in shallows and most prefer to; few can feed in water more than eighteen inches deep. Where natural drainage lines are dammed to provide farm water-supplies it should be remembered that an irregular edge can provide much more feeding and resting areas than neat straight lines. Cover on part of the edge is essential and can easily be provided by fencing, so that stock cannot trample the edges; a small island is very useful for a predator-free nesting site.

Conservation is a team effort and cannot be left to the Government alone. Increased awareness on the part of the shooter that if he shoots out of season and exceeds his bag, or consistently shoots at and cripples, but does not recover, birds out of range, it is his own sport he is damaging, is already apparent. Sportsmen's organizations with high ideals are formed and are prepared to train their members in the utilization of game, and in ethics, and their potential should not be underemphasized. Wild-duck populations are declining, but there is no need for this to continue if the public, sportsmen, and Governments, aware of the problems and the most urgent needs, work together to conserve the birds.

FIELD IDENTIFICATION

I have been surprised to see duck-shooters who, from a mixed flock of swift-flying birds, could select the sex of the particular species they wished to fire on, but I have been just as surprised to find many shooters who could not identify the birds in their bags. Some only know the Black Duck and Grey Teal, and call everything else "widgeon"—a Northern Hemisphere bird.

Swift, accurate identification is essential for the shooter and the naturalist alike, particularly so for the shooter, since many species are not legal game and their shooting is both an offence against the law and against conservation generally. The difficulties associated with identifying distant ducks in mixed flocks are usually exaggerated—all species of waterfowl in Australia are distinctive and very easily determined by concentration on a few simple field marks. These marks are described in some detail in the account of the life history of each species, but the principles of duck identification are summarized here.

Habitat

The habitat can only give a very general clue to a duck's identity, because there is almost complete overlap, but there are a few special cases. In summer Blue-billed Ducks and Musk Ducks are seldom seen away from dense swamps; Pink-eared Ducks are usually on shallow open water and Hardheads in deep water; Green Pigmy Geese are usually among water-lilies; Water Whistle-ducks are usually in the water, but Grass Whistle-ducks usually on land.

Flock Action

The shape of the flock and the manoeuvres of the birds can be very helpful, but must be learnt first by experience as there are many variations. Among the large waterfowl, Black Swans and Mountain

Ducks fly in long lines, skeins, or sometimes loose Vs, but Magpie Geese seldom do and move in loose groups. Teal fly in dense flocks that twist and wheel, but Pink-eared Ducks have more open flocks that move more directly with less twisting; Black Ducks, Shovelers, and Hardheads fly straight and purposefully. Pigmy Geese fly in loose groups, each bird twisting about within the group. Whistle-ducks fly in very tight flocks, often elongated; they do not swoop about much.

Size

Unless the observer is very close to the bird, attempts to judge its size are usually futile, since it is impossible to maintain one's standards. The best that can normally be done is to group the birds into three size groups.

Large: Black Swan, Magpie Goose, Cape Barren Goose, Mountain Duck.

Medium: Black Duck, Freckled Duck, Burdekin Duck, Shoveler, Hardhead, Wood Duck, Water Whistle-duck, Grass Whistle-duck, Musk Duck.

Small: Grey Teal, Chestnut Teal, Pink-eared Duck, White Pigmy Goose, Green Pigmy Goose, Blue-billed Duck.

Behaviour

Some aspects of behaviour can provide clues but should never be relied on alone to more than narrow the field, as there is much overlap. Some characteristic situations of waterfowl are helpful in this way.

Grazing away from the water: Magpie Goose, Grass Whistle-duck, Cape Barren Goose, Mountain Duck, Wood Duck.

Frequent diving: Hardhead, Musk Duck, Blue-billed Duck, Water Whistle-duck, Green Pigmy Goose.

Perching: Most ducks can be found sitting on fallen timber and fence-posts in the water, but only the Magpie Geese, Mountain Ducks and Burdekin Ducks are seen perched in tall trees.

Sound

The voice of most species is very distinctive and a certain identification; there are many variations to be learnt and in many the sexes differ, but, once identified, the sounds of calls and of wing-beats are very valuable field guides. They are difficult to describe on paper, but some hints on which the observer should base his own standards are mentioned below.

The wings of a Shoveler make a very distinctive clap, those of a Hardhead whirr, and the Whistle-ducks' wings whistle in flight. Three ducks whistle, vocally, in flight: the Pink-eared Duck, Water Whistle-duck, and Grass Whistle-duck; in each case the sound is very distinctive. The Green Pigmy Goose "chirrups" and the White Pigmy Goose "trumpets". The only ducks that really "quack" are female Black Ducks (the male hisses) and female Teal. The female Black Duck makes a loud and raucous quack that is very distinct from the softer "laughing" notes of the Teal. The Magpie Goose and the Mountain Duck honk in flight, on the ground, or water, and the sounds are very distinctive. The Burdekin Duck "rattles", the Cape Barren Goose "honks" and the Freckled Duck "grunts", the Wood Duck "mews" and the Black Swan "bugles".

The observer who would know his ducks, is urged to make a practice of associating the sounds heard with the birds that make them, and he will find his identification much quicker, simpler, and more certain.

Silhouette

In many cases the silhouette of a bird, even at extreme distance, can positively identify it, for example, Hardheads' wings are farther back on the body than those of Black Ducks and Teal. The Black Duck's neck is much longer than that of the Teal. Compared to a Black Duck, a Freckled Duck's back is humped in flight and on the water it has a much larger head. Pink-eared Ducks fly with their heads up more than any other duck. Whistle-ducks have a very characteristic shape with humped back and depressed head and neck, and long legs.

Colour

Colour is usually of little value for systematic field identification unless the birds are very close, but there are some special cases where it can provide a helpful clue or even be diagnostic.

Shoveler. Any blue colour on a duck's plumage shows it is a Shoveler, but, more important, the bright yellow legs are obvious and diagnostic.

Blue-billed Duck. Even at extreme binocular range a blue bill identifies male Blue-billed Ducks, but Hardheads' bills also can appear blue under some lighting conditions, so care is needed.

Black Duck. Flashes of iridescent green are often seen from the wings of Black Ducks at rest or in flight.

Freckled Duck. In the breeding season the bright red bills of males can be seen for great distances.

Chestnut Teal. The iridescent green heads of male Chestnut Teal are striking even at long range.

Plumage Pattern

The pattern of the plumage, the distribution of light and dark areas, is the basis of duck identification in the field. All nineteen species of Australian waterfowl have distinctive patterns and all can be readily identified by concentration on one or two characters. The most important are the presence of a speculum, white areas on the wings and their position, and the contrast between underwing, body and neck.

In the plates that follow the plumage patterns of waterfowl are shown diagrammatically and the most useful distinguishing features listed. These diagrams are intended to show the essential diagnostic features that can be seen on a bird at a couple of hundred yards' range in moderate light. Where it is necessary to draw attention to a mark it is exaggerated and unnecessary detail is excluded. The diagrams are not to scale because size is less important than the field marks in identification.

WATERFOWL ON THE WATER

1.	Black Swan.	Slender neck, red bill.
2.	Magpie Goose.	Black head and neck, white shoulders.
3.	Cape Barren Goose.	Light colour, prominent cere.
4.	Mountain Duck.	Male: Dark head, light breast, neck ring. Female: White eye spot.
5.	Wood Duck.	Male: Posture, pale sides, dark head. Female: Posture, mottled sides.
6.	Burdekin Duck.	White head, neck and sides, dark back.
7.	Black Duck.	Light throat, face pattern.
8.	Freckled Duck.	High crown, dark colour.
9.	Hardhead.	Male: Dark body, white undertail, white eye. Female: Dark body, white undertail, dark eye.
10.	Grass Whistle-duck.	Long neck, plumes.
11.	Water Whistle-duck.	Dark body, plumes.
12.	Shoveler.	Male: Large bill, white flank. Female: Large bill.
13.	Chestnut Teal.	Male: Dark head, white flank. Female: Dark face, shape.
14.	Grey Teal.	Light face and throat.
15.	Pink-eared Duck.	Large bill, light body, forehead.
16.	Green Pigmy Goose.	Male: White face, dark neck. Female: Light sides, no white over eye.
17.	White Pigmy Goose.	Male: White body, neck ring. Female: Pale neck, white over eye.
18.	Blue-billed Duck.	Male: Shape, blue bill. Female: Shape.
19.	Musk Duck.	Male: Shape, lobe. Female: Shape.

1
2
3
4
5
6
7
8
9
10
11
12
13
14
15
16
17
18
19

1
2
3
4
5
H.J.F. 1965

SWAN, GEESE, AND SHELDUCKS IN FLIGHT

1. Black Swan.	Long neck, white wing-tips.
2. Cape Barren Goose.	Uniform light grey, dark wing-tips.
3. Magpie Goose.	Above: White mantle and tail. Below: Black neck, white body.
4. Burdekin Duck.	Above: White head and neck, white wing patch. Below: White head and neck, dark wing-tips.
5. Mountain Duck.	Above: Dark head and neck, white wing patch. Below: Light breast, white underwings. Female: White eye spot.

DUCKS IN FLIGHT

1. Grass Whistle-duck.	Shape, long legs, light body.
2. Water Whistle-duck.	Shape, light shoulders.
3. Black Duck.	Face pattern.
4. Hardhead.	Male: White wing stripe, white eye. Female: White wing stripe, dark eye.
5. Freckled Duck.	High crown, uniformly dark.
6. Shoveler.	Male: Shoulder patches, bill. Female: No shoulder patches, bill.
7. Grey Teal.	Light face, wing stripe.
8. Wood Duck.	Male: White wing stripe, light shoulders. Female: White wing stripe, lighter head.
9. Pink-eared Duck.	Bill, white rump.
10. Blue-billed Duck.	Male: Shape, dark, blue bill. Female: Shape, lighter colour.
11. Chestnut Teal.	Male: Very dark head, wing stripe. Female: Dark face, wing stripe.
12. Green Pigmy Goose.	Male: White wing patch, dark neck, face patch. Female: White wing patch, white face.
13. White Pigmy Goose.	Male: White wing-tips, white neck, dark crown. Female: White wing stripe, pale neck.

1
2
3
5
4
6
8
7
9
11
10
12
13
H.J.P. 1965

2
1
3
5
4
6
8
7
9
11
10
12
13
H.J.F 1965

DUCKS OVERHEAD

1. Grass Whistle-duck.	Shape, light underside.
2. Water Whistle-duck.	Shape, dark underside.
3. Black Duck.	Light throat, white underwings.
4. Hardhead.	Male: White wings, dark head, white eye. Female: White wings, dark head, dark eye.
5. Freckled Duck.	Dark with lighter wings.
6. Shoveler.	Male: Bill, yellow legs. Female: Bill, dark legs.
7. Grey Teal.	Pale throat, underwing pattern.
8. Wood Duck.	Male: Wing patch, black abdomen. Female: Wing patch, light abdomen.
9. Pink-eared Duck.	Bill, white tail edge, striped body.
10. Blue-billed Duck.	Male: Shape, dark body, blue bill. Female: Shape, dark body.
11. Chestnut Teal.	Male: Dark head, underwing pattern. Female: Dark throat, underwing pattern.
12. Green Pigmy Goose.	Male: Wing patch, white body, dark neck. Female: Wing patch, white body, pale neck.
13. White Pigmy Goose.	Male: White underside, white wings. Female: White body, dark wings.

Magpie Goose

Anserανas semipalmata (Latham)

References

Anseranas Lesson, Man. d'Orn., 2, p. 418, 1828.
Anas semipalmata Latham, T.L.S., 4, p. 103, 1798. (Hawkesbury River, N.S.W.

Other Names

Pied Goose, Wild Goose, Semipalmated Goose, Black-and-white Goose.

Description

ADULT MALE. Head, neck, and wings, rump and tail, black; upper wing coverts, mantle, rump, and belly, white; legs yellow, with partly webbed toes; bill and bare skin of face, flesh or reddish more or less; bill is strongly hooked; eye brown. In the dry season most white plumage is stained red-brown from stagnant water. There is a prominent cranial knob which tends to be larger in males than in females, but there is considerable overlap and it is a more reliable gauge of age than of sex. In adult males the windpipe can be felt looped under the skin extending down the breast; it does not extend outside the breastbone in females or juveniles, with the exception that in very old females there is one very small loop close to the neck.

ADULT FEMALE. The plumage is as in the male.

IMMATURE. The juvenile plumage is the same as the adult, but the white parts are more or less mottled with brown or grey.

GOSLING. Head, except the lores, which are bare, and neck cinnamon red, paler and extending farther above than below. There is a dark-grey stripe on the upper neck which merges with the dark grey of the back and sides of the body. Underside white; undertail and underwing pale grey; bill and legs claret, but at 3 to 5 days old yellow.

Size

	Weight gm.	*Length mm.*	*Wingspread mm.*	*Wing mm.*	*Bill mm.*
Adult Male					
Maximum	3195	920	1794	450	92
Minimum	1838	750	1289	368	72
Average	2766	864	1549	419	80
Number measured	*402*	*249*	*238*	*165*	*74*
Adult Female					
Maximum	2770	814	1638	418	82
Minimum	1405	712	1283	356	63
Average	2071	775	1430	389	73
Number measured	*359*	*220*	*217*	*177*	*56*

Voice

Both sexes have a loud and resonant honk, louder and higher in pitch in the males than in the females. It may be uttered as a series of spaced deliberate calls, with the head uplifted, or in rapid repetition (concerting) in which several birds may join in. Typically, in flight and on the ground, a call by the male is answered immediately by one or more females.

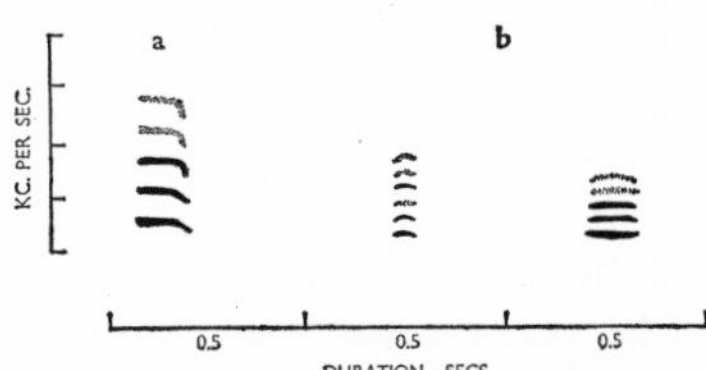

Diagram of sonogram of the Magpie Goose:
(*a*) male, (*b*) two separate females.

Routine

Magpie Geese are usually found in groups or flocks, though there is no social structure larger than that of the individual family. Congregations on the ground may be very large, and at least one of 80,000 has been seen, but normally the congregations are of 5,000 or so, and groups flighting to and fro usually not more than 200 or 300. Except when roosting, in tight clusters, the flock is very active feeding across the plains or dabbling in mud at the edge of lagoons. Threatening and fighting between individuals is very frequent.

They are more often found away from water than in it. In the wet season some swim in lily lagoons, but most are found in dense spike-rush swamps where the water is inaccessible beneath the vegetation over which they clamber and walk. In the dry season some swim or wade in shallow swamps, but most feed in the soft mud on the edge or walk far across the dry plains. They walk strongly and well, but their flight is slow, heavy, and laboured. They can perch with great agility on very thin twigs but in the wild seldom have cause to do so.

Unless disturbed by shooting they are tame and easily approached. When alarmed they raise their heads and necks erect and move close together, and the flock walks off together; if pressed they break into a run and fly, but seldom fly far. Often the first birds aloft have landed before the far side of the flock has flown. To get the heavy body aloft it is necessary to crouch to the ground before jumping into the air with flailing wings to flap heavily away. Sometimes momentum is gained by running into the wind with beating wings.

They are most active in the early morning and late afternoon. At these times, except when located in a dense swamp, they have a marked preference for feeding in open places well away from cover, presumably as a protection from predators; dingoes have been seen to rush from cover and attack and sometimes secure geese. At dusk, feeding complete, they fly back to their roosting places in successive groups.

Field Recognition

The size, posture, and bold black and white colour make it impossible to confuse the Magpie Goose with any other Australian bird.

At extreme visual distance, in poor light, they might conceivably be confused with Black Swans or Strawnecked Ibis, but need not be. In swans the neck is long and slender, very unlike the short silhouette of the goose; the swan's wings are slender, but those of the goose are distinctly rounded; the swan's wing-beat is slower and the flight is more laboured than that of the goose. With ibis the very rapid wing-beat gives the whole flock a very different appearance to the slow flapping motion of the Magpie Goose.

Relationships

It is usually thought that the Magpie Goose is very different both in anatomy and behaviour from all other waterfowl, and it is classified as the sole member of a separate sub family, the *Anserana-*

tinae. Von Boetticher,[98] working from anatomical evidence, considered that in evolution it branched off from the ancestors of the Anatidae before the true geese and ducks were differentiated. His opinion is followed by Verheyen,[96] Delacour,[26] Woolfenden[101] and more recent authors. Some have wondered is it more closely related to the Screamers, Anhimidae, than to the Anatidae, and Woolfenden has gone so far as to suggest a separate family, Anseranatidae, for it. Taxonomic significance is placed on the long convoluted windpipe, the semipalmated feet, the strong hooked bill, the successive moulting of the primaries, the structure of several bones, and some superficial observations on behaviour of captive birds.

That the Magpie Goose is different from other waterfowl is undoubted. Nevertheless, in the field, one is more impressed with their similarities to the Anserinae than with the differences. Their habits and behaviour are in many ways remarkably Anserine and many of the characters that have been used to widely separate them from the Anserine geese could, just as easily, be interpreted as the result of evolution moulding a "normal" goose to life in a dense tropical swamp.[25]

The half-webbed feet have been assumed to be an adaptation to perching in trees, a habit setting them apart from other geese. Although Magpie Geese do perch in trees, in the wild they do not do so habitually, and the feet are much more likely to be adapted to the great amount of walking they do across bare plains in the dry season and for climbing over tangled masses of spike-rush in the wet season, as well as for the construction of their rather elaborate nests, which are themselves presumably the result of adaptation to breed in, virtually, the only situation partially protected from predators in the environment. They rarely swim, having little need to in the tropical swamps, so do not require full webs for that purpose.

The strongly hooked bill, which is different from those of other waterfowl, is precisely the development one could expect in a bird forced to dig for part of its food in hard baked clay, as does the Magpie Goose. The actions in the use of the bill when digging are similar to those of the Anserine geese that dig in soft mud. Much has been said of the unique long convoluted trachea between the muscles of the breast and the skin, but the difference in trachea, although spectacular, is really not much greater than that which exists between other members of the Anserinae; some swans and the Freckled Duck also have convoluted windpipes; in the former inside the sternum, in the latter outside it.

The gradual moulting of the primaries, which is unusual in waterfowl, could logically be considered an adaptation to the bird's life. They moult at the end of the breeding season at a time when the swamps are fast drying out. Simultaneous moult of the wing feathers, making them flightless, would lead to a very real danger of the birds being stranded and helpless in a dry swamp.

When the dynamic nature of some of the characteristics used to classify the goose is clearly recognized it appears that the bird is probably much more closely related to the Anserinae than is usually accepted.

Habitat

The life of the Magpie Goose is more closely and obviously linked to changes in specialized habitat than that of any other Australian waterfowl, so it is appropriate to discuss this in some detail and to base the description on the subcoastal plains of the Northern Territory, where the birds are much more numerous than elsewhere.

In that region the streams, in their lower courses, are senile and meander across their flood-plains. They are bordered by well defined levees beyond which the plains fall gradually to higher forested land, dividing the valleys. For convenience the flood-plains can each be divided into two zones; high black soil and low black soil. The high black soil is the part of the plain that is subject to transient flooding, only, from the river; the low black soil is the part that is low-lying, usually farther from the river. It also receives water from creeks and springs debouching into the plains and forming swamps nearly every wet season. The relative extent of the two zones varies from year to year according to rain and flood.

The distribution of habitats on the plains is largely determined by the water conditions on it during the wet season.[48] Where there is almost permanent water more than about four feet in depth there is a deep water vegetation dominated by lotus *Nelumbo*, spike-rush *Eleocharis* (called bulgaroo in Queensland), and water-lilies *Nymphaea*. In water that is three to four feet deep and dries to damp soil in the dry season, tea-tree *Melaleuca* forest grows, particularly on the edges of the plains. The forest may have a ground cover of spike-rush, water-lilies and aquatic herbs, and mangroves *Bauhavia*, which often form a narrow belt between it and the plains.

Where the water is less than about three feet deep and dries out completely in the dry season, low black-soil swamps develop. These swamps are dominated by spike-rush and wild rice *Orzya*, but also contain large numbers of other aquatic plants and are of great importance to the geese. Where the plains are not flooded at all, or to a very shallow depth, a high black-soil grassland develops composed of couch *Cynodon*, millet *Echinochloa, Panicum, Paspalum*, numerous other grasses, and a great variety of sedges, but very few herbs.

Although the boundaries of some of these floras vary considerably from season to season, in correspondence with the extent of flooding, the sequence between the woodland and the river channel remains the same. The plains are lowest where they intrude as bays into the high country at the effluence of the small creeks, it is here that the tea-tree forests and permanent lagoons are usually found. The latter often run some distance across the plain as deep channels, sometimes broken into several discrete lagoons, all carrying the deep-water flora. The rest of each bay supports a low black-soil swamp extending as far as the floodwaters permit, towards the rising ground of the river levees. Both the levees and the inner edges of the low black-soil swamps, where these do not directly abut on the woodland, are covered with high black-soil grassland. Transient lagoons form on the grasslands after heavy storms, but the high black soil is wholly flooded only when the river overflows its banks after heavy rains on the headwaters.

Each of the habitats has a particular significance for the geese. The tea-tree forests are used as roosts, and breeding may occur in those with an under-storey of spike-rush. The permanent lagoons are refuges for the birds, and where they are very extensive great concentrations of geese occur on them in the dry season. As well as being breeding habitat for the geese, the areas of low black-soil swamp produce a crop of wild rice at the end of the wet season, much of which is stripped by feeding geese. The high black-soil grasslands are important feeding grounds when the grasses are seeding in the middle of the wet season, but are rarely used at other times.

Elsewhere Magpie Geese live in similar habitats and all the swamps favoured by geese that I have seen in northern Australia and New Guinea have been characterized by very dense spike-rush and abundant grasses. Although the swamps in southern Australia where Magpie Geese formerly existed have been very much altered by drainage and agriculture it is still possible to see that they, also, were of a very dense nature, with spike-rush as one of the dominant plants, and that permanent lagoons and grasslands were available near by.

Distribution and Movements

The Magpie Goose is to be found as a breeding species in northern Australia, between the Fitzroy River in Western Australia and Bowen in Queensland, and in southern New Guinea. Within this region breeding is confined to the flood-plains of the coastal rivers and is generally within fifty miles of the coast, though occasionally there is some breeding in more inland areas, as near Cloncurry, Queensland, and Elliott, Northern Territory. In these inland swamps breeding only occurs in exceptional years, but the underlying factors are not yet understood.

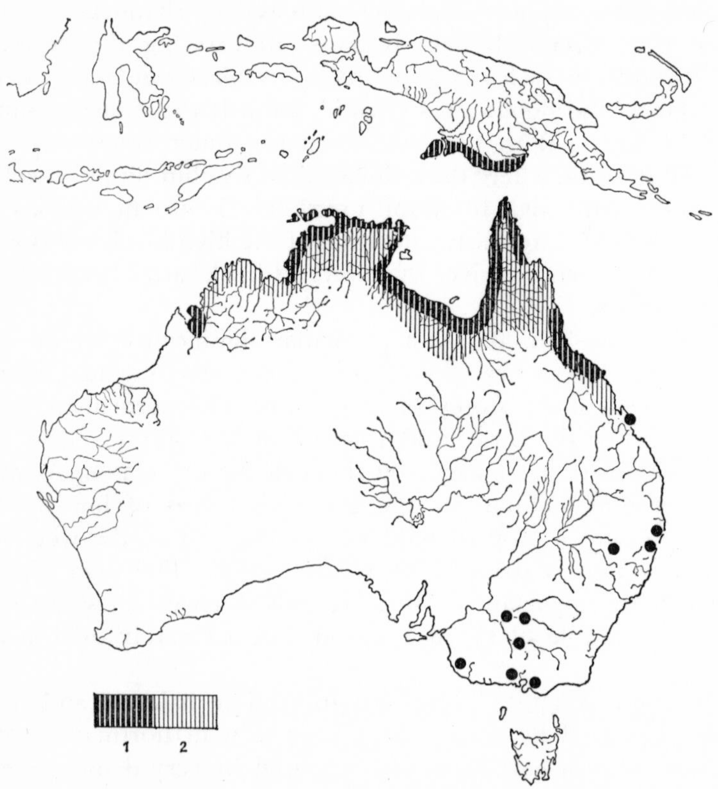

DISTRIBUTION OF THE MAGPIE GOOSE

The darkest area shows the present breeding range and the lighter shading the normal nomadic range, though in some years rare vagrants occur throughout the continent, except in the central deserts. The spots show the location of former breeding colonies that have been destroyed.

The greatest area of flood-plain is found between Darwin and Arnhem Land, and most of the geese remaining in Australia breed there; between 1955 and 1958 there were about 350,000 geese in that area. There are colonies of geese on every river between the Fitzroy and the Murgenella whenever suitable low black-soil swamps occur, but the size and number of the colonies vary greatly according to the hydrology of the rivers. By far the biggest colonies in this region are found on the Daly, Mary, and Adelaide rivers, although those on the latter river are now being affected by settlement and agriculture.

The rivers of the northern and eastern coasts of Arnhem Land are relatively small and do not have extensive plains, and the numbers of geese on them are not great, though Thompson reported a large colony on the Glyde River. The birds breed on Melville Island but not on Croker Island, Goulburn Island, or Groote Eylandt. They occur occasionally on the Rose River and regularly on the Roper. They are present in considerable numbers on the rivers of the Gulf of Carpentaria and west coast of Cape York, but their numbers there are not accurately known. In north-east Queensland they occur wherever there are suitable swamps, but not in great numbers, to as far south as Bowen.

Before 1900 geese were much more widely distributed than they are today. The northern distribution was as it is now, but breeding colonies existed down the east coast and in parts of the south and east. Breeding occurred on the Clarence River, New South Wales, Darlington and Westernport, Victoria, and Bool Lagoon, South Australia, at least. Inland breeding occurred near Moree, New South Wales, on the lower Lachlan and Murrumbidgee rivers, and on the Murray River near its junction with the Murrumbidgee River. The birds in the more southern colonies were shot for food and poisoned in large numbers when they invaded crops, and their habitat was altered or destroyed by grazing animals and drought. The geese had disappeared from Victoria and South Australia by 1911 and soon afterwards in the other southern regions. Today they are only seen there as very rare vagrants from the north.

The movements of Magpie Geese are controlled by seasonal changes in the availability of food and nesting habitat, but tradition also probably plays a part. Since young geese stay with their parents until the following wet season, and have been observed with them in the breeding colonies, it is unlikely that they would ever have to travel to or from the breeding colonies or dry-season refuges unaccompanied by experienced geese.[23] The movements are only over short distances but are made in a variety of directions, so it is simpler to assume that each young bird learns the direction of movement rather than that each navigates in an inherited direction. The movements are probably not a random scatter but are directed by the experience of adult birds moving between the breeding colonies and the refuges where they have passed the dry season.

In the dry season each flock occupies a roosting place or camp on the plains, on the edge of a billabong or occasionally in the trees surrounding a swamp, and flies out each morning and evening to feed. The feeding range of each flock remains fairly constant, but the composition of the flock does not—many birds flying over a flock join it and may return with it to its camp. Sometimes several flocks from different camps feed in the one place and it seems largely a matter of chance to which camp each bird or group returns.

The feeding range of the flock depends on the food available at that time of the year; in the dry season they congregate where the underground bulbs of spike-rush are most abundant, this means in the large swamps that occur on some rivers and the small permanent lagoons on others where they feed in the mud round the edges or on the dry soil of the low black-soil swamps. In the wet season they are less dependent on the rush bulbs and spread more widely. Thus the great concentrations of the large permanent swamps disperse and the geese distribute themselves over the other rivers. As the low black-soil swamps fill the birds move to them to feed on aquatic grasses and the mature birds begin nest-building activities. As breeding finishes and the swamps dry out the geese begin once more to congregate on the permanent lagoons.

The rivers of the Northern Territory differ greatly hydrologically and these differences lead to fairly regular movements of the geese. The plains of the Mary and Adelaide rivers have large areas of low black soil which provide extensive breeding areas in the wet, but while the Mary has numerous lagoons that hold water in the dry, the Adelaide has very few. The East Alligator, West Alligator, and Wildman rivers have few swamps in the wet season and few billabongs in the dry. The South Alligator, however, forms very large swamps in its middle reaches that are fed by permanent streams and hold water in the dry season. In the dry season most of the geese between Darwin and Oenpelli gather on the South Alligator and, to a lesser extent, the Mary River. In the wet season they leave the South Alligator where the permanent swamps grow rush too dense for breeding (see page 55) and become most numerous on the Adelaide and Mary rivers, with smaller numbers on the other rivers.

The rivers to the west of Darwin show a similar movement pattern. The Daly River has much low black soil and many lagoons. Most of the birds of that region congregate there during the dry season and spread over the other rivers during the wet. Birds banded on the Adelaide River have been recovered on the Daly as well as on the Mary and South Alligator, so it is apparent that these three great dry-season refuges are likely to serve the whole of subcoastal Northern Territory.

Although most Magpie Geese are thus involved in only rather local movements, some more extensive movements occur, in some cases each year and in others at irregular intervals. From the north coast some geese move to some outlying islands in the wet and return to the mainland in the dry; this occurs on Melville Island and Croker but apparently not on Goulburn Island or Groote Eylandt. Birds from Cape York are regularly heard passing over Torres Strait, presumably to New Guinea, and the late Bishop Davies reported that natives regularly speared birds in passage on Sabai Island, a few miles off the New Guinea coast. Although many Magpie Geese breed in southern New Guinea it is thought that their numbers are greatly increased by birds from Australia each year.

Quite extensive movements occur inland in the dry season where there is no breeding. The birds leave the drying coastal swamps and become distributed over the inland lagoons with decreasing regularity as the distance from the coast increases. The limit of the inland movement cannot be defined but is rarely more than two hundred miles. Occasionally, however, when very dry conditions occur in the north, irruptions occur and geese find their way to the southern States; on at least two occasions a few have reached Tasmania. Fifteen such irruptions to southern Australia have been recorded since 1888, each following a drought in the Northern Territory.

Feeding

The Magpie Goose manipulates its food almost entirely with its bill. The feet are only used to bend down tall grasses so that the seedheads are within reach. They feed by grazing and filtering, that is, straining beakfuls of mud through the bill to secure food items in it, and by digging in the soil with the strong hooked bill for the underground bulbs of spike-rush. These birds often up-end to feed in water up to two feet deep and at times move far from water to graze young grass on the river levees or to dig in and turn over the hard sunbaked soil of the plains during the dry season.

The stomachs of 800 geese, mainly from the Adelaide River, Northern Territory, showed the birds to be completely herbivorous throughout their life.[48] The only animal food found were a few small caterpillars probably eaten accidentally. The most important food plants, those accounting for seventy per cent of the food, were grass-blades, the bulbs of spike-rush *Eleocharis,* and the seeds of wild rice *Oryza,* millet *Echinochloa, Paspalum,* and couch *Cynodon.* They also ate numerous other, less important, seeds, which included a wide variety of grasses, sedges, and flowering plants.

The annual food cycle begins in September and October when the first storms lead to a growth of green grass on the high black soil and river levees. At this time the geese are concentrated on the few remaining lagoons and promptly begin flighting to graze on the grass-blades. By November the swamps have begun to fill and *Paspalum* seed is ripening in them and forms the main food, in addition to bulbs of spike-rush dug from the bottom of shallow swamps. In December and January millet seed is added to the diet and in April the wild rice ripens, and seeds of grasses are almost the exclusive diet of this period.

As the dry season intensifies from May onwards, and as the crop of grass-seed is exhausted and the level of the swamps decline, the geese pay more attention to the edges, where their main diet becomes the underground bulbs of spike-rushes which are dug from the mud. As the swamps recede they retreat with the edges to the most permanent parts until, in the depth of the dry season, the swamps are reduced to small bare mud pools and the bulbs can only be secured easily in the narrow muddy verge. As the pools recede many geese begin the very much more difficult task of digging in the bare, hard, sunbaked mud of the plains for these bulbs, which are the only abundant food available to them for a period of several weeks.

The food of the goslings is mainly the seeds of swamp grasses *Oryza, Paspalum,* and *Panicum,* and the water plantain, *Sesbania,* and although arthropods are found in the stomachs quite frequently they are primarily herbivorous, even at that early stage of life. The adults assist the young to find food both by bending down seedheads until they are within reach and by bringing food up from water too deep for them.

Breeding

Nesting colonies are practically confined to the low black-soil swamps and, although nests are built in all kinds of vegetation and water depths, for practical purposes they are confined to moderately dense stands of spike-rush and wild rice growing in water one to three feet deep. The swamp vegetation may be too thick or too thin and the water may be too deep or too shallow for a goose colony to develop. On the Adelaide River 77 per cent of nests were in places where spike-rush, *Eleocharis,* was dominant, 19 per cent where wild rice was dominant, 4 per cent among knife-grass, *Scleria,* and the remainder among a wide variety of herbs, sedges, and grasses. An analysis of the sites of a large number of nests in the Northern Territory has shown that most are found in places where the water depth ranges from 10 to 36 inches, where the density of the vegetation is between 1000 and 1600 shoots to a square yard, and where the vegetation is less than 48 inches tall. All three factors are important and interact.[48]

The density and composition of the swamp vegetation is determined by the depth of water, which in turn is determined by the distribution of high and low black soil as well as the rainfall and flooding regime in that year. Because of these requirements for nesting the location of breeding colonies and the time of the breeding season are controlled ultimately by the water conditions in the swamps. In a very early and extensive wet season suitable nesting conditions may develop early in the season and over wide areas, but in a wet season with low rainfall suitable water depths may be achieved in only a few places; in a late wet season nesting will be delayed, owing to late development of the nesting habitat.

The exact location of the colonies, as well as their size and the density of the nests within them, varies from year to year, according to the water depth and swamp vegetation density, and the density of nests varies greatly among colonies, in the same colony in different years and in different parts of the colony in the one year, for the same reasons. It is not possible to determine an average density of nests in goose colonies but as an example of density one typical colony contained 135 nests per 100 acres in one year. Colonies vary from a few acres to several square miles in extent.

Because of the strict nesting habitat requirements the distribution of breeding colonies of Magpie Geese is very closely controlled by the hydrology of the different rivers, and colonies are most numerous where low black-soil swamps of suitable depth and density occur most extensively and frequently.

Key to Plate II

SWAN, GEESE, AND SHELDUCKS

1. Black Swan.
2. Magpie Goose, male.
3. Magpie Goose, female.
4. Mountain Duck, female.
5. Mountain Duck, male.
6. Burdekin Duck.
7. Cape Barren Goose.

The Black Swan and Magpie Goose are larger, in comparison to the other birds, than they are shown here.

B.T.W. 1965

In the Northern Territory the colonies are most numerous and extensive on the Mary River and least extensive on the South and West Alligator rivers. The extent of breeding swamps is intermediate on the Adelaide and East Alligator rivers. West of Darwin most rivers have small flood-plains with few low black-soil swamps. There are only a few small colonies on the Finniss, Moyle, Fitzmaurice, and Ord rivers, but there is one very large colony on the Daly River that covers about sixteen square miles and is the largest single colony in the Northern Territory.

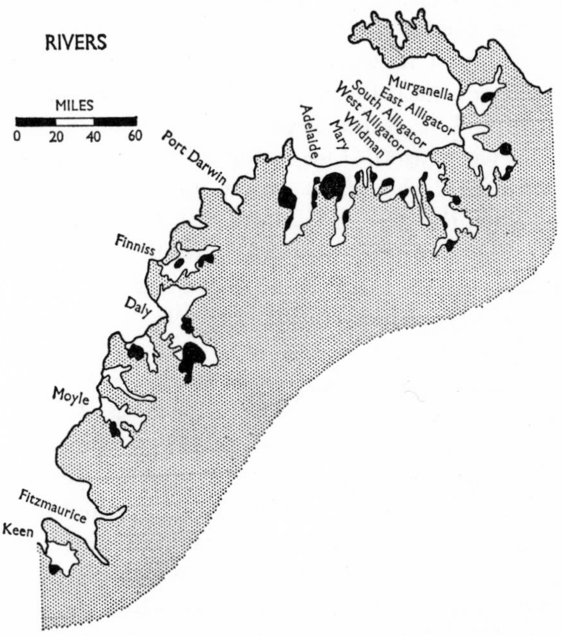

Map showing location and relative size of breeding colonies of the Magpie Goose in north-west Australia. The stippled areas are land other than the river plains.

In some years the rainfall is sufficiently high for more inland rivers and lakes to flood to a suitable depth and for a long enough period to allow nesting habitat to develop, and on these occasions the areas are colonized by geese from the subcoastal plains and some breeding occurs as far inland as Elliott. Frequently, however, the young perish, owing to premature disappearance of the water.

Magpie Geese apparently mate for life as mated pairs, and

family parties are seen at all times of the year. The male may have one female, but it is more common for him to have two. All three share in nest-building, incubation and the care of the young. Both females lay in the same nest, one usually beginning a day before the other. Breeding begins at the end of the wet season, usually in March or April, but the date can vary greatly owing to annual differences in the depth of the water and the density of the swamp vegetation. Eggs can sometimes be found as early as February or as late as July.

The sexual cycle begins with the first storms of the wet season, in October or November, but nest-building and egg-laying are delayed until the required conditions of water depth and vegetation density are developed in each swamp. This may lead to differences in egg-laying dates in different swamps and in different parts of the same swamp. The water depth and vegetation density change throughout the wet season. The water usually rises rapidly until the end of the rains and then falls slowly, and the vegetation changes are associated with the rate of rise and fall. Cyclones, however, often disrupt this cycle and the subsequent flooding destroys the nests. Renesting often occurs after these disasters, provided the correct water-level and vegetation conditions return, but this is by no means certain.

A breeding season timed to begin at the end of the wet season helps to ensure that the nests can only be flooded by an unpredictable cyclone, and not by the steady rains of the monsoon, but it also means that the young hatch into a swamp where the water is declining and so they run the risk of being stranded in a dry swamp. They and their parents move from place to place in the swamp following the water, but sometimes the water all goes before they are fledged and they perish. In some years, when the swamps are not well filled and dry early, very few, if any, young survive to fly. It is obviously an advantage to the geese to begin breeding as soon as the main rains end, so long as the other requirements of water depth and density of vegetation are met.

The Flock

Magpie Geese are usually found in flocks that can contain up to several thousand birds. The flock is an aggregation of family groups; in each group the male is dominant over the other members and defends an individual distance from other geese not belonging to the family.[23] The distance he defends includes his mate or mates and offspring, and the area defended is not fixed, but varies from

Upper: Trio of Magpie Geese digging in soft mud for bulbs of spike-rush.

Photo by Ederic Slater

Lower: Magpie Geese on a drying low black-soil swamp. This swamp, Tommy Policeman Plain on the Adelaide River, N.T., is the site of a large breeding colony. In the wet season nests are built mainly in the area beyond the egrets.

Photo by author

Upper: Dry-season camp of Magpie Geese on the well-grazed edge of a lagoon.
Photo by Ederic Slater

Lower: Dry-season concentration of Magpie Geese, Lake Finniss, N.T.
Photo by author

time to time and place to place, for reasons that are not yet fully understood. In the breeding season he defends about half an acre round the nest.

The composition of the flock varies in different places and seasonally. A sample of nearly two thousand birds shot or trapped suggested that over all the sex ratio in the goose population was unity, but in a breeding area it contained about seventy per cent females as the mated geese first took up station ready for the breeding season. The percentage of females in the colony varied throughout the wet season, as non-mated geese came into or left the colony to feed, in response to the changing availability of food in the swamps and on the plains, for example, when they moved to graze on the high black-soil plains and the mated groups were obliged to remain in their breeding area. In a feeding area where mainly non-breeding birds were congregated the sex composition was quite different. There was never any preponderance of females and at times they constituted only forty per cent of the population.

Colour banding has shown that flocks of Magpie Geese are not stable. Birds trapped and marked in one flock are often trapped or seen again a few days later in another flock. They tend to move about in family groups, rather than flocks, and a concentration of geese has a very strong attraction to groups flying over. Thus groups flying out from their roosting place to feed tend to be attracted to any concentration that they fly over *en route*. In the same way when large concentrations break up and go to roost they move in small groups and may disperse to several widely separated roosting places. A group may follow any other group to a different roost each night. Whilst a flock of Magpie Geese may appear at the same locality each day, it is probably composed of different birds. In general the flock behaviour of Magpie Geese is similar to that of more typically Anserine geese.[19, 32]

Nest

The nest is a large mound of floating vegetation trampled down and pulled up by the geese. There is a deep cup on the top of woven spike-rush or other material, but this is unlined and no down is used. Each nest is surrounded by an area of clear water, owing to the birds' pulling up and trampling down the vegetation during nest-building.

The building of the nest itself is the climax of a long period during which the geese construct numbers of platforms or stages in the swamps.[22] In building these stages the bird grasps a shoot of spike-rush near its top with the bill and pulls it down until it can be grasped by the foot and then trampled; where several shoots are dealt with at once the bird pulls them down by encircling the clump with its neck until they can be reached with the foot, trampling the whole into a fairly solid, tough, buoyant mass. The geese visit the breeding swamps long before the nests are built and eggs laid. In January, as the swamps begin to fill and the vegetation to emerge, they begin to build platforms or stages by bending down and trampling clumps of spike-rush. As the season proceeds these platforms become more elaborate and complex and involve several clumps of spike-rush woven into a substantial platform. The building of the platform is begun by the male, who also does the greater share of the work. Each platform is used only once; as soon as it has been used the geese move on and build a new one next time they stop in the swamp, and on it rest and court.

Shortly before egg-laying the construction of the stages become more elaborate and begins to include the uprooting or breaking off of shoots of spike-rush to add to the trampled-down clumps; the number of these increase until a substantial pile is formed. Even so, each stage is used only once until, finally, an egg is laid and the clutch is begun. This platform now becomes the nest and daily more material is uprooted and added to it to form a thick, deep cup.

Eggs

The eggs are uniform ovals, creamy white though usually nest-stained. The shell is coarse and slightly lustrous. The measurements of 692 eggs from 132 nests varied in length from 64 mm. to 80 mm. (mean 72 mm.) and in breadth from 46 mm. to 63 mm. (mean 53 mm.).

Clutch Size

The clutch size is hard to determine because two females lay in most nests and in addition many eggs are destroyed as they are laid by eagles, crows, snakes, and goannas. On the average seventy per cent of eggs laid are destroyed.

In 17 nests in which it was reasonably certain one female had laid and there was no predation the average clutch size was 8·6 eggs, and in 22 nests in which two females laid the clutch was only 9·4—not twice as many, as might have been expected. Perhaps when two females lay each limits the number of eggs it lays.

In the field from 1 to 16 eggs are found in Magpie Goose nests.

The numbers of eggs in 168 nests in which laying had ceased was distributed as below.

Number of eggs:	1	2	3	4	5	6	7	8	9	10	11	12	13	14	15	16
Number of nests:	3	2	10	10	15	28	15	25	15	20	16	8	0	1	1	1

Incubation

Incubation duties are shared by all birds of the trio, or pair, and consists more of standing over the eggs to shade them from the tropical sun than of warming them. The incubation time is 24 or 25 days.

Development of Young

After hatching the young remain in the nest for a day and are then led away by the pair or trio; the young utter a high-pitched, peeping contact call continuously. By the time the young hatch the spike-rush has usually lodged, and progression is not by swimming but by clambering over and through the dense growth. At night stages are built on which to rest.

The colour of the soft parts of the young quickly changes, and in three to five days the claret bill and legs have faded to yellow and by fourteen days to grey. The tail appears early, and is an inch long after the first week. Thereafter it grows about half an inch a week until it is three inches long, when growth becomes slower. The first down to be lost falls from the sides of the head between four and five weeks. Scapulars and wing coverts appear at four to five weeks and the secondary wing quills burst about the same time. The primary wing quills burst in the sixth or seventh week, or occasionally later, by which time the rest of the young goose is well feathered. The primaries are sufficiently grown for the young to fly at eleven weeks of age and the family then joins other family parties in the developing dry season flocks.

Status

Some idea of the former abundance of Magpie Geese in Victoria can be had from Broinowski's *Birds and Mammals of Australia.*[10] In 1965 I caught some geese in the Northern Territory to provide a stock for an attempt by the Victorian authorities to re-establish the species in that State, but in 1885 Broinowski described very different conditions when travelling from Hamilton to Ararat. "On our journey we encountered hundreds of nests of the Wild Goose, some of them in clusters, separated only by a few feet from each other and judging from actual observation these nests must have been in that locality in incalculable numbers."

Nearer civilization, however, the local populations were under assault by man.

> In the rainy seasons when the Gippsland lakes and rivers are high and the extensive flats in the vicinity of Sale are submerged, the surface waters are literally covered with Wild Geese and Black Swans, who seem to be on terms of perfect amity. The destruction of these birds carried on by means of swivel guns, which generally wound twice the number they secure, and by nets which drown great numbers that are never recovered, besides those which fall to the more legitimate sportsman is simply wholesale, but so far from diminishing their numbers seem to be greater each year. . . .

This happy state did not continue but "as the advance of the white man with his steam whistles and other barbarous noises of civilization became not a paradoxical but a veritable wild goose chase, the latter has betaken itself to the lagoons and rivers that empty themselves in Torres Straits, where these birds are to be seen in myriads".

In 1965 these "myriads" had been sadly reduced, though the bird is still numerous there. In the north it has always been an important item of food to aborigines, and this situation remains where they occur together. The birds are skilfully knocked out of the sky by throwing sticks and the eggs are collected in great numbers.

In the Northern Territory it is an important game bird. It is not, however, a good game bird, being slow on the wing, low-flying, very easily "ambushed", and of indifferent flavour and texture. In the Northern Territory there is an open season for Magpie Geese, but elsewhere it is fully protected, except from aborigines who exercise ancestral hunting rights.

In most of its range the Magpie Goose has no effect on agriculture, but attempts to cultivate rice on the flood-plains of the Northern Territory rivers and in southern New Guinea have led to invasion of these crops and damage to them by geese. Sometimes the damage is quite severe, though it is usually far outweighed by other agronomic factors. There is no efficient method of scaring geese from crops, but, from what is known of their ecology, it is apparent that damage to a developing industry will only occur in the pioneer phase and, as the crops become established and the water-levels in the breeding swamps controlled for irrigation purposes, geese will be eradicated from the rice-growing districts.

Although the Magpie Goose is still very numerous and widespread in the tropics, its range has been greatly reduced in Australia, owing to the elimination of the southern colonies. Despite its present abundance there is no room for complacency. It is now known to have a very specialized diet and breeding habitat and these must be upset by the advance of agriculture into the subcoastal plains of the Northern Territory, where the greatest numbers remain. Agriculture can be expected to lead to destruction of swamp vegetation by grazing stock and alteration of water-levels, thus disrupting the breeding habitat, as well as the destruction of the birds that will undoubtedly invade the crops.

The controlling authorities are aware of the dangers and have been able to retain very large areas in the Northern Territory for the conservation of geese, and at present the species seems reasonably secure. The unique place of the bird in the waterfowl family, however, as well as its position as the bird that typifies the Australian tropics to most people, demands that its future be assured beyond all doubt.

Water Whistle-duck

Dendrocygna arcuata (Horsfield)

References

Dendrocygna Swainson, Class. Birds, 2, p. 365, 1837.
Anas arcuata Horsfield, Zool. Research, Java, 1837. (Java.)

Other Names:

Wandering Tree-duck, Water Whistler, Whistle-duck, Red Whistle-duck, Wandering Whistle-duck, Wandering Whistling Duck, Whistler, Black-legged Whistler, Whistling Tree-duck.

There are no generally accepted vernacular names for the two Australian Dendrocygnini. In standard works they are usually referred to as the Plumed Whistling Duck, *D. eytoni*, and the Wandering Whistling Duck, *D. arcuata*, but both are "plumed" and *eytoni* "wanders" far more than *arcuata*. In southern Australia, where the birds are rarely seen, they are usually referred to by the artificial names in the Australian Checklist, Whistling Tree-duck, *arcuata*, and Plumed Tree-duck, *eytoni*, but both whistle and neither has much association with trees. In north Queensland, where they are numerous but are not considered prime game birds, they are often known as Whistlers, with various descriptive adjectives. In the Northern Territory, where they are an important game bird, they are usually called Whistle-ducks.

Lavery has tried to bring some order and has suggested Whistler, with adjectives to describe the habitat; Water Whistler for *arcuata*, and Grass Whistler for *eytoni*. It does not seem wise, however, to encourage the name Whistler, which is already occupied by a large group of song-birds, *Pachycephala*, so I have preferred to adopt the Northern Territory name, Whistle-duck, and to use Lavery's terms to differentiate the species on the basis of their usual habitat.

Description

ADULT MALE. General colour above brownish black; the feathers and the back and scapulars bordered with rich chestnut; primaries and outer wing coverts black, inner wing coverts deep chestnut; tail black; central tail coverts black but outer ones white; crown brownish black, a line extends down back of neck; face light brown; foreneck and breast rufous with occasional black spots; abdomen chestnut; undertail white; plumes on flanks are lengthened and are white with broad chestnut edges; bill black; legs and feet black; iris red-brown.

ADULT FEMALE. As for male.

IMMATURE. Immatures are similar to, but duller in colour than, adults.

DUCKLING. Crown, neck, back and tail, dark brown; throat, breast and abdomen, light brown; foreneck dark brown; face light brown with dark-brown stripe below eye extending from back of neck almost to bill.

Size

	Weight gm.	*Length mm.*	*Wingspread mm.*	*Wing mm.*	*Bill mm.*
Adult Male					
Maximum	948	609	890	230	52
Minimum	866	550	812	196	39
Average	741	582	847	214	48
Number measured	*287*	*78*	*86*	*82*	*24*
Adult Female					
Maximum	976	573	896	231	50
Minimum	453	550	800	201	39
Average	732	568	838	214	47
Number measured	*293*	*46*	*74*	*86*	*47*

Voice

The voice is a shrill, high-pitched whistle uttered as a single note or as a multisyllabic twitter. To the human ear the sounds are very similar to those of the Grass Whistle-duck, but unfortunately sound spectographs are not available to permit comparison.

Routine

Water Whistle-ducks are nearly always in dense flocks, either on the water or roosting on the bank, and the individuals are tightly packed together. The flocks are usually in constant movement with birds running swiftly from place to place and sparring with their neighbours. During the heat of the day, however, they may be quiet and still. They always have the observer under observation first and are usually seen with heads and necks erect, a forest of necks, poised to take off. When disturbed the flock swims together into a very tight group, jumps together, and flies to another part of the swamp in a very dense flock. The flight is heavy and slow with a distinctive whistle from the slowly beating wings.

On the water they swim actively and dive constantly; once, in chest-deep water in a recently flooded creek on the Adelaide River, Northern Territory, I was approached by a flock of two to three thousand birds, and by standing quietly beside a paperbark-tree allowed them to pass by, a few feet on each side. The flock was tightly packed and moved forward at about five miles an hour, the foremost birds dived continuously and each emerged hurriedly swallowing a piece of submerged grass or herbage, the rearmost ranks continually flew forward to the front and dived immediately on alighting, so that the flock seemed to be rolling forward. With the constant diving and surfacing and the constant skidding in of the alighting birds the water boiled and the air was alive with the constant twittering and whistling.

Field Recognition

Whistle-ducks would be unmistakable, even if the air around them at rest, or in flight, did not usually quiver with incessant shrill whistling.

The posture of the two species on land is quite different: the Grass Whistle-duck holds its neck and body very erect at all times, the Water Whistle-duck keeps its head and neck less erect and its body is held nearly horizontal. On the water the dense flock and erect necks quickly distinguish Whistle-ducks. The neck of the Grass Whistle-duck is extended, that of the Water Whistle-duck usually is not, and the Water Whistle-duck floats lower than the Grass Whistle-ducks, but at a distance it is difficult to distinguish the species with certainty. At closer range the Water Whistle-duck is smaller, darker, and lacks the very prominent plumes over the back of the Grass Whistle-duck. Its plumes show as a white line at water-level.

In flight also Whistle-ducks are unmistakable. The wings are short and rounded, unlike any other duck's, and beat more slowly; the long neck is extended and the head depressed, giving the shoulders a hunched appearance, and the long legs trail out behind. When alighting both species lower the legs and depress the neck long before they reach the water. The Grass Whistle-duck has more pointed wings than the Water Whistle-duck, but the latter is more easily distinguished by its very much darker colour, chestnut shoulders and light throat, contrasting with the darker body.

Flying away from the observer, both species show the white rump patch, but it is very much more obvious on the Water Whistle-duck. Once seen the difference can be easily appreciated and is an excellent field mark.

Relationships

Whistle-ducks are small birds with long necks and legs and rounded wings. There is no plumage difference between the sexes and the tarsus is always reticulate in front as in the Swans, Geese, and Freckled Duck. They are very different to other waterfowl and until recently were considered a separate subfamily. They are now, however, considered to be a tribe, Dendrocygnini, of the subfamily Anserinae, associated with the Swans and Geese.

The tribe consists of a single genus of eight strikingly similar species that are distributed through the tropical regions of all continents and oceans. There are three representatives in the Australasian region. *Dendrocygna guttata* is widely distributed in Indonesia and New Guinea, but has not yet been seen in Australia; *D. arcuata* is widely distributed in Indonesia, New Guinea, and Northern Australia, and *D. eytoni* is restricted to Australia, with occasional stragglers to southern New Guinea.

Three races of the Water Whistle-duck have been recognized on the basis of their size. *D. a. australis* is the largest and is found in Australia and New Guinea. *D. a. arcuata,* the nominate race, is intermediate in size and ranges from the Philippines through Indonesia. *D. a. pygmaea,* the smallest race, is restricted to New Britain.

Habitat

Water Whistle-ducks secure nearly all of their food in water and much of it by diving; they might almost be considered the ecological equivalent of the Hardhead. They favour the deepest and most permanent water areas where aquatic plants and bottom fauna are most highly developed, though they do use whatever other waters are available at times.

Distribution and Movements

The species extends from the Philippines through Indonesia, New

Britain, and New Guinea to Australia. The population that formerly existed in New Caledonia is now presumed extinct. Although it has been thought that the Fiji populations were extinct also, having been eradicated by the introduced mongoose, it was seen there in 1959.[79] In the Philippines it is common throughout the islands as a breeding species,[30] but, according to Smythies,[90] there are only two records from Borneo, both in the south, where it is presumably resident. It is common throughout Java and at least some islands of the Celebes and Moluccas; it has been recorded in Timor.

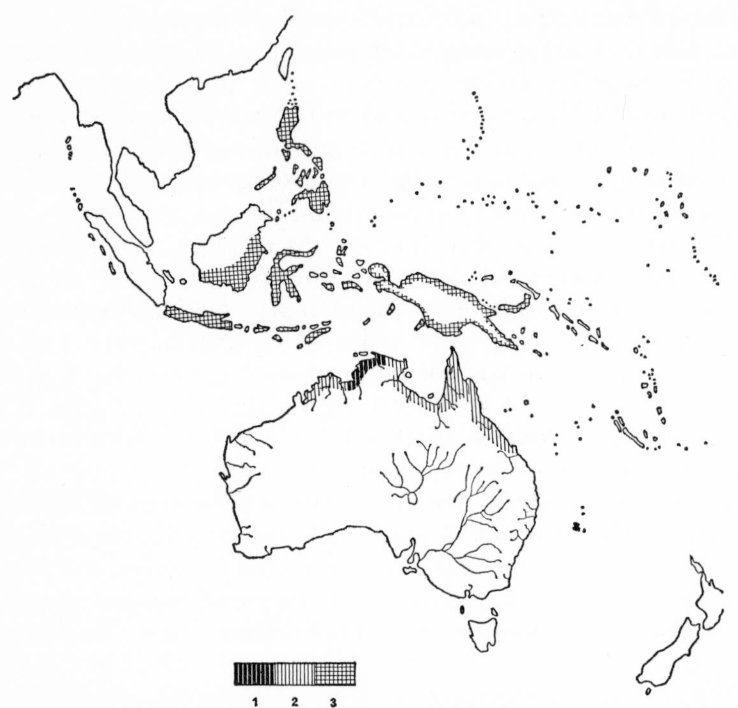

DISTRIBUTION OF THE WATER WHISTLE-DUCK

The vertical hatching shows the range of *D. a. australis*, the darker (No. 1) showing the greatest density, and the lighter a lesser density. Square hatching shows the range of *D. a. arcuata* and *D. a. pygmaea*; *pygmaea* is thought to be restricted to New Britain at present.

In New Guinea it is widely distributed in the lowland rivers and swamps, particularly in the Fly and Sepik regions. There are occasional occurrences in the Wahgi valley in the highlands, but no record of its breeding or permanently residing there. Until recently it was believed that, in New Guinea, it was largely a winter visitor from Australia, but Hoogerwerf has shown that large numbers are present near Merauke, both in summer and winter, and that 192 of 355 examined in January to March were in breeding condition.[60] Rand[85] found three birds on the Fly River in breeding condition, and four that I examined at Lake Balimo in the same region were also in breeding condition in November 1964. It has not yet been established if Water Whistle-ducks do move between New Guinea and Australia, but this is suggested by the frequent sighting of flocks flying over the Torres Islands. It is also now well established that large numbers are present in New Guinea throughout the year and breed there.

In Australia the range of the species is in the tropics, but it was a more frequent visitor to the south in the past. Thus in 1909 Hall[53] recorded that it was rare on the Murray River, and he had only seen one flock in eight to nine years, but that thirty years before it had been numerous. Today it is only seen on the Murray River as an extremely rare vagrant. Mathews records that it was formerly shot by market gunners in the Clarence River district of north-east New South Wales, but it no longer occurs there. The bird is at present restricted to the tropical regions between the Kimberley Ranges in the west and about Rockhampton in the east, though vagrants are sometimes recorded farther south; one reached Perth, Western Australia, in 1899 and I have seen odd ones at Griffith, New South Wales. It occasionally appears in South Australia.

Its distribution in the tropics is determined by the abundance of its preferred habitat, extensive freshwater lagoons and swamps. The greatest numbers known to me are on the plains of the sub-coastal rivers of the Northern Territory between Darwin and the South Alligator where very many thousands are present at all times; west of Darwin the numbers are less, owing to smaller flood-plains, except for the Daly River, which has a very large flood-plain where the numbers are very high. Quantitative figures are not available, but in the 1964 dry season there were at least 30,000 on the Mary River and 40,000 on the Daly, and smaller but nevertheless impressive numbers on the other rivers of the region. In Queensland it is widely distributed but is only really numerous in the most favoured part, between Ingham and Bowen. It can be locally abundant on the small coastal plains of Cape York and, in the wet season, is thinly distributed throughout the Cape. The bird is said to be common on the west coast of Cape York, but this region has not been surveyed; it is, however, remarkable that Thomson[93] failed to see it there during extensive travels in the area.

The main movements of the Water Whistle-duck are local concentrations and dispersal following the changing availability of their aquatic feeding habitat and are controlled ultimately by rainfall. This conclusion is based on observational data only, air surveys in the Northern Territory subcoastal regions and detailed counts in a small area in north Queensland by Lavery.[69] The observations in both areas lead to the same general conclusions, but in the absence of data from individually marked birds the scale of more extensive movements cannot be explored. That Water Whistle-ducks do, occasionally at least, move far from their normal range is shown by the occasional occurrence of specimens in South Australia, for example. A pair were trapped, and held in the author's collection, near Griffith, New South Wales, in 1957, an abnormally dry year, and a group of seventeen were associated with large numbers of Black Ducks on Tombullen Swamp in the same district in January 1952, an abnormally wet year, and two were collected. In 1951 and 1952 also some reached South Australia. It is probable that these were all vagrant birds associated with wandering groups of more mobile species, but the full scale of movements in the species' true tropical range has not yet been explored.

In the Northern Territory changes in the distribution of Whistle-ducks throughout the year suggest that their movements are quite local within the subcoastal plains and similar to those of the Magpie Goose. In the wet season the birds are widely dispersed throughout the area, located mainly on the edges of the large black-soil swamps, on river banks, and throughout the forests near the billabongs and pools of surface water, breeding. As these waters dry successively from about May onwards, at different annual rates, according to the date of ending of the wet season, the birds move and gradually congregate into larger and larger flocks on the more permanent water areas until at the end of the dry season immense congregations occur.

As with the Magpie Goose, there is a good deal of inter-river movement, the great numbers of birds congregating on the rivers where suitable dry-season habitat is most extensively developed. The preferred dry-season habitats are deep lagoons that carry dense growth of sedges on the edges and some water-lilies and other aquatics in the deeper parts, but where these are not available bare, open, muddy creeks and pools on the scorched plains are acceptable, provided there is submerged vegetation. Because of these needs the dry-season populations on the Adelaide River are not great and do not number more than a few thousand birds, and the numbers are similar on the Wildman, South Alligator, and East Alligator rivers, where dry-season habitat is not extensively developed.

The greatest dry-season concentrations occur on the extensive lagoons of the mid regions of the South Alligator River, and on the plains of the Mary and Daly rivers. These river plains are extensive and are crossed by numerous winding creeks and lagoons, and great numbers of birds congregate here. Congregations of one to two thousand birds are found very widely distributed over very large areas.

Soon after the beginning of the wet season, and as the water-level rises in the black-soil swamps and the lagoons fill, these flocks disperse and spread throughout the subcoastal plains again. At this time the numbers of birds in the Adelaide River district increases greatly as immigrant flocks arrive and locate themselves on many lagoons, later to disperse more widely in individual pairs as the wet season continues. In the Northern Territory the main movements are in east-west directions along the subcoastal plains following the changing distribution of habitat, but there is also some extension of range inland in the wet season as the more inland swamps fill.

Feeding

In each area where Water Whistle-ducks have been watched—that is, in southern New Guinea, the Northern Territory, and north-east Queensland—their feeding habitat has been similar. They are nearly always found feeding in lagoons, billabongs, or flooded meadows, and occasionally on the edges of creeks and rivers. In the Northern Territory feeding on the edges of rivers, which in that region are usually muddy and mangrove-fringed, is less usual than in north Queensland, where it is common, and in New Guinea where they are found on the banks of most streams, even in rain-forests. They seldom feed in swamps in north Queensland, but in the Northern Territory do so consistently and regularly.

Feeding is entirely in water and many of the birds' actions are quaintly reminiscent of Coots, Hardheads, and Blue-bills. They feed by dabbling in shallow edges, stripping the seeds and inflorescences from plants growing in water, or by diving. They dive constantly and expertly in water up to ten feet deep and presumably reach its bottom. The bird springs forward and enters the water head first and emerges swimming rapidly. Frequently whole flocks move forward, feeding as they go.

Water Whistle-ducks prefer to locate themselves at the food source and usually camp on the edge of the lagoon on which they are feeding, entering the water in small numbers throughout the day and night to feed. Where the water areas are large, however, feeding movements of several miles sometimes occur, the birds flying to another part of the swamp or to another lagoon in whistling groups just after dark. They return at first light, each incoming flock being greeted by a loud outburst of whistling. The returning birds usually alight on the water, swim rapidly to the shore and run up the bank to the camp.

In 260 gizzards collected on the Adelaide River, Northern Territory, water-lilies and aquatic grasses were the most important foods. Water-lilies were found in more than half the birds examined and the seeds, buds, and parts of the leaves of these plants comprised 30 per cent of the total volume of the food. Grasses were found in 70 per cent of the birds and comprised 42 per cent of the total food; the grasses eaten were all aquatic types, characteristic of lagoons, *Paspalum,* wild rice *Oryza,* couch *Cynodon,* and barnyard-grass *Echinochloa.* Various sedges were the only other group of over-all importance and contributed 17 per cent of the food. The remainder was made up of a wide variety of emergent and submergent aquatic plants.

A more extensive study of the food eaten was carried out near Townsville, north Queensland, in which over a thousand stomachs were examined.[69] Vegetable materials were found in every stomach and accounted for 99 per cent of the total volume of food. Of these plants, Gentianaceae was the most important food, being found in 49 per cent of the birds and comprising 22 per cent of the total volume of food. Grasses were almost equally important and accounted for 22 per cent of the volume of food, the most important were barnyard-grass *E. colonum,* mud-grass *Pseudoraphis spinescens,* and Para grass *Brachiara.* The other important groups of plants were water-lilies and sedges, which accounted for 15 per cent and 20 per cent of the total food and were present in 26 per cent and 63 per cent of the birds respectively. The remainder of the food comprised a very wide variety of aquatic plants and submerged swamp plants and included smartweeds *Polygonum,* water-snowflake *Nymphoides,* pondweed *Potamogeton,* nardoo *Marsilea,* duckweed *Lemna,* and many others.

There were considerable locality differences in the food eaten, as might be expected in a bird of local habits that feeds in large groups. Thus at Bowen, in a large swamp where the water had been stabilized artificially to a greater extent than existed in some other local habitats, and was dominated by coastal club rush, *Scirpus littoralis*, in 287 birds this plant accounted for 85 per cent of the diet. In more natural lagoons in the same district the rushes accounted for only 17 per cent of the food, and water-lilies for 20 per cent, smartweeds for 14 per cent and grasses for 17 per cent. Similarly in the Northern Territory gizzards collected in the dry season on the Adelaide River contained mainly water-lilies and spike-rush, abundant plants, but on the Mary River these were not found in the gizzards, which contained a very wide variety of aquatic plants belonging to several other families.

There is a fairly regular annual variation in the food related to the amounts of the different habitats made available to the birds by the changing rainfall regime. Thus on the coastal plains of north Queensland, when the first rains of the wet season flood the meadows and grasslands, the birds feed there on recently submerged grasses, particularly barnyard-grass, *E. colonum*, but as these extensive water areas recede the birds gradually retreat to the deeper, more permanent parts where aquatic plants have had time to develop and eat less grass but more water-lilies, snowflake, and sedges; finally, as even the centres become unattractive, the birds may move out to a few large concentration areas with permanent water, and subsist on a wide variety of less favoured foods. Annual differences in this routine can easily occur with variations in rainfall; in dry years the meadows may not flood extensively nor may water-lilies develop, so the birds subsist mainly on other plants, but in wet years the favoured habitat may be extensive and the birds have the grasses and water-lilies available for a longer period.

Breeding

The courtship displays of Whistle-ducks are known to be similar, in many respects, to those of the Swans and Geese, but there seems to be no full and satisfactory description of any species. Although it is not yet proved for Water Whistle-ducks, Whistle-ducks in general usually mate for life; flocks of Water Whistle-ducks, however, at all times clearly include many mated birds, so there is little doubt that they do conform to the rest of the genus in this way. The selection of the nest site, incubation duties, and care of the young are shared by both male and female. The parents remain with the young at least until they are fully fledged. It is not uncommon to see large rafts of young, as the broods amalgamate, with very few or no adults. Whether some parents desert their broods on amalgamation, or whether the absence of parents is accidental, is not known.

In the Northern Territory sexual activity, shown by courtship displays and increased fighting among males, begins very soon after the first rains of the wet season, usually in November, when large concentrations begin to break up into smaller flocks that then disperse to other newly replenished lagoons and swamps. The earliest nest examined was on 10th January and the latest on 25th July. These data are consistent with those collected by Hoogerwerf in New Guinea, where the birds were sexually active in the wet season, December to May, and in north Queensland, where the breeding season is generally in the period December to April but varies according to the rainfall.

The difference in duration that can be caused by differences in the rainfall is well shown by Lavery's work in north Queensland.[69] In 1961, a year of severe drought, sexual activity began as usual with the first rains, but what little breeding occurred was restricted to the period 4th January to 17th February. It ceased when the water-level in the lagoons and the vegetation failed to develop, owing to inadequate rain. Many flocks did not even disperse to breed and most males dissected were not in breeding condition. Clearly, in addition to the short breeding season, a great part of the population failed to nest at all.

Conditions in 1962-3 provided a contrast; rain was very heavy and widespread and the breeding season was very extensive, both in the numbers of birds involved, the proportion of the population, and the period in which clutches were begun. Every adult collected was in breeding condition, very many more breeding birds were present than usual, and broods were later common along the coast. The breeding season itself extended from 21st December 1962 to April 1963 at least.

Clearly individuals of the Water Whistle-duck, like many other waterfowl, both in the tropics and the dry interior, vary in the rate of their response to the factors that initiate breeding, so that the numbers of birds that breed is related to the ability of the habitat to support the young. In unfavourable years only a few birds are triggered to breed, but in exceptionally favourable ones the whole population, including a mobile element, participates. A very similar pattern of behaviour is followed by the Black Duck in the inland.

Upper: Under-water photograph of a Water Whistle-duck. Although it secures much of its food under water, its movements and swimming are clumsy.

Photo by Ederic Slater

Lower: Water Whistle-ducks rising from a Northern Territory lagoon. Note characteristic flight silhouette of Whistle-ducks.

Photo by author

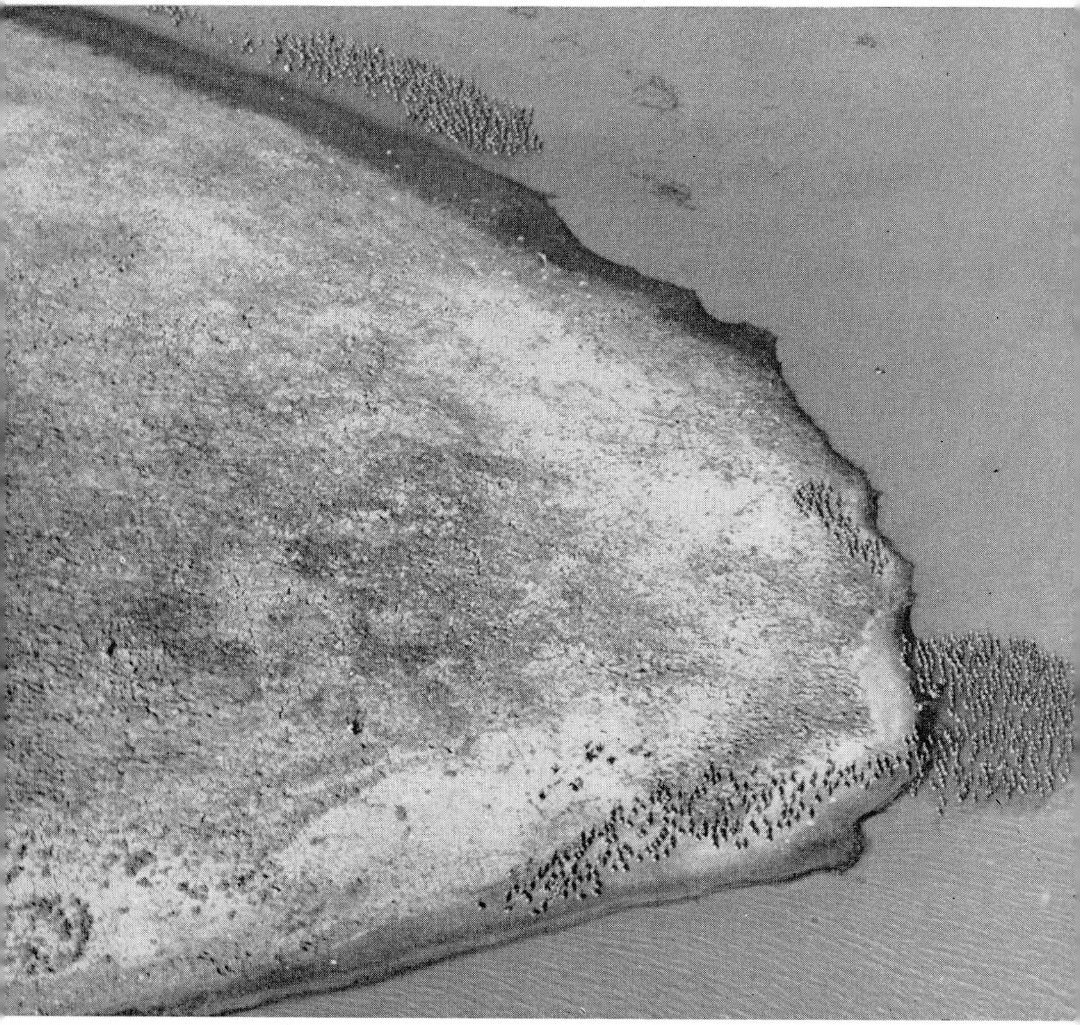

Upper: Water Whistle-ducks in daytime camp on the edge of a dry-season lagoon near Darwin, N.T. *Photo by Ederic Slater*

Lower: Dry-season camps of Water Whistle-ducks on a Mary River lagoon, N.T. *Photo by author*

The breeding season is related to the water-level, the growth of nesting cover, and also the amount of food available. Measurements of all these simultaneously on the one lagoon in 1962-3 showed that the volume of the testes, an indication of sexual activity in the male, and the amount of food, as measured by the density of seedheads of barnyard-grass, the most important food of the ducklings, closely parallel the water-level as it rises and falls. Clutches were begun well before the peak water-level was reached, a perfectly safe procedure for a species that nests on land and is in no great danger from flooding, and ceases as the water begins to decline. Broods are abroad from just before the peak water-level is achieved until it is strongly declining. In chronology with the supply of barnyard-millet seed this means that birds, young and parents, are most numerous when the seeds are most abundant and that broods have ceased hatching in plenty of time for the young to be flying before the breeding lagoons become too low in level to be unsuitable habitat and the food is exhausted.

There is some sexual activity induced by rainfall outside the normal breeding season. This has been reported by Lavery, who found some active testes among birds in flocks, following unseasonal rain in August and October. There was, however, little breeding behaviour seen and the females were apparently unaffected either by the rain or the males' activities. Apparently no breeding resulted. Hoogerwerf also collected an occasional male with enlarged gonads in September in New Guinea.

Nest

The nest is a scrape in the ground, usually sheltered by a bush or long grass. It is sometimes close to the water but more commonly far from it, often in quite short grass with very little cover. There is usually a layer of grass under the eggs but no down.

Eggs

The eggs are hard and vitreous in appearance and cream in colour. They are rather pointed in shape; 114 eggs from 15 nests measured in length 47-53 mm. (average 51 mm.) and in breadth 35-39 mm. (average 37 mm.).

Clutch Size

There are no quantitative data on clutch size. According to Delacour[26] it varies from 6 to 15 eggs.

Incubation

The incubation period is 28 to 30 days.

Development of Young

In the wild the ducklings are led to the water by both parents within a few hours of the last young hatching and begin to feed immediately. Young reared in captivity are about 20 grammes in weight on hatching and the first feathers to appear are on the face at about 40 days of age. They are fully feathered by 10 weeks, but the primaries are not fully developed and they are unable to fly until 12 to 13 weeks of age.[69]

It is possible that this very lengthy period of development was associated with cage conditions and could be very much shorter in the wild, owing to different nutrition, exercise, and general living conditions. If, however, the development period is something of the order described it forms a remarkable contrast to the development time of some of the opportunist breeding species of inland Australia, for example, the Grey Teal, that fledges in 6 to 8 weeks. Presumably these birds must become mobile more quickly because of their erratic habitat than do the Whistle-ducks in the more reliable tropics.

Status

Although they are shot along with other ducks wherever they occur, Whistle-ducks are not held in high regard as game birds. Most shooters prefer the greater size and palatability of Black Ducks, as well as the need to exercise more skill in hunting them. In north Queensland, where Black Ducks are abundant, Water Whistle-ducks comprise only 5·4 per cent of the total bag.[69] In the Northern Territory, also, Black Ducks are much more appreciated by the shooter, but, because of their general scarcity, Whistle-ducks are considered an acceptable substitute. They have had no serious effects on agriculture yet, but development of crops most likely to attract them, such as rice, has not been extensive within their range. Where rice has been cultivated in the Ord River district, Western Australia, Adelaide River, Northern Territory, and near Merauke, New Guinea, they have caused some damage to newly sown and germinating crops.

Water Whistle-ducks are still very numerous in the tropics, but their distribution is not extensive and their preferred habitat, whilst quite widespread, is localized and vulnerable to agricultural and urban development. The most extensive areas of habitat and the greatest populations of the birds are on the subcoastal plains of the Northern Territory, an area that, whilst not utilized by agricultural and grazing industries, has been seriously threatened in the past and, no doubt, will be developed in the future. Should this happen Water Whistle-ducks will decline in numbers, and there is no cause for complacency at present.

Grass Whistle-duck

Dendrocygna eytoni (Eyton)

References

Dendrocygna Swainson, Class. Birds, 2, p. 365, 1837.
Leptotarsis eytoni Eyton, Monogr. Anat., p. 111, 1838. (North-west Australia.)

Other Names

Grass Whistler, Whistle-duck, Plumed Whistling Duck, Plumed Tree-duck, Eyton's Tree-duck, Monkey Duck, Grey Whistler, Red-legged Whistler, Whistler.

The general unsuitability of the vernacular names usually given to this species have been described under the Water Whistle-duck.

Description

ADULT MALE. General colour above brown, with yellow margins on feathers of upper back; upper tail coverts buff, each feather with a dark spot and tip; rump and tail dark brown; crown pale brown; face and neck very pale brown; throat almost white; wing above brown, below pale brown; breast chestnut barred transversely with conspicuous black bars; abdomen pale buff, long lanceolate plumes arise from the flank, each is buff with a broad black margin; bill pink, more or less mottled with black; legs and feet pink; iris yellow.

ADULT FEMALE. As for male.

IMMATURE. The immatures resemble the adults but are paler in colour and the breast marking is not so distinct.

DUCKLING. Topside dark brown with a chestnut suffusion; there is a longitudinal grey-brown stripe on each side of back; throat, foreneck and underside generally light brown, the breast has chestnut suffusion; face light brown with a dark-brown stripe through and surrounding the eye and a less distinct broader brown line below the eye. The duckling is distinguished from that of *arcuata* by the black stripes and generally more reddish colour.

Size

	Weight gm.	*Length* mm.	*Wingspread* mm.	*Wing* mm.	*Bill* mm.
Adult Male					
Maximum	930	616	915	242	48
Minimum	600	437	750	222	37
Average	788	501	859	232	40
Number measured	*63*	*66*	*65*	*59*	*65*
Adult Female					
Maximum	1400	559	903	245	49
Minimum	580	413	802	215	37
Average	792	496	856	228	43
Number measured	*65*	*65*	*58*	*57*	*65*

Voice

The voice is a shrill, high-pitched whistle in both sexes. It can be a single note or a multisyllabic twitter. At rest, as in flight, from the flock there is usually a continuous twitter interspersed with periodic shrill whistles. The wings also whistle in flight.

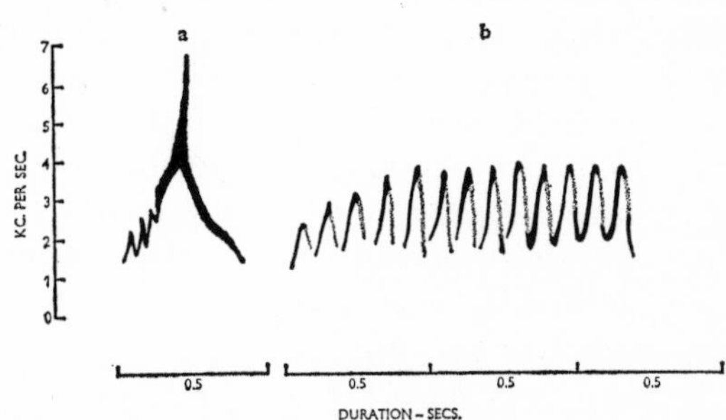

Sonogram of the calls of the Grass Whistle-duck, showing (*a*) the shrill whistle and (*b*) the twitter.

Routine

Although Grass Whistle-ducks are seen in small groups and, occasionally, as individuals in flocks of Water Whistle-ducks, they are more commonly grouped in very large flocks. They are found in dense clusters on the ground on the edge of dams, lagoons, rivers or swamps during the day—a forest of heads watches as one approaches. In late afternoon they stream out in successive groups to feed elsewhere throughout the night. On return the birds spiral down to the water, but immediately swim to the shore and rapidly run up the bank to the communal roosting place.

They walk long distances gracefully, but swim slowly and awkwardly. The flight is slow and the wings flap slowly with the characteristic whistling sound. On alighting the long legs are dropped and the neck depressed long before landing. They perch awkwardly and, in the wild, very rarely indeed. They can dive, but rarely do so except when wounded.

Field Recognition

The field recognition of Whistle-ducks in general and the distinguishing marks of the two Australian species have been described in the life history of the Water Whistle-duck.

Relationships

The relationships of the Grass Whistle-duck within the family have been described in the life history of the Water Whistle-duck.

Habitat

The Grass Whistle-duck is the typical duck of the tropical grasslands in much the same way as the Wood Duck is the typical duck of the temperate grasslands. In the north, where it is most common, in the dry season it congregates in large camps or roosts; each camp is located on a bare edge of a lagoon, swamp, or river, or even on a stock tank. It feeds on the lagoon edges, meadows, and widely across the short-grass plains. Because it does not feed in the water the condition of this is not important and it may be merely a small muddy pool. The Water Whistle-duck, which secures all of its food from the water, often selects camp sites near lagoons with plentiful vegetation. It is more important for the Grass Whistle-duck to find a site with a bare open bank and short grass near by. In the wet season, when the grass may be several feet tall, it is widely distributed, breeding throughout these grasslands and feeding on the more open areas, particularly on the edges of pools or swamps. It occupies similar habitat in southern New South Wales and is found camping on swamps or tanks on bare, open grass plains.

Distribution and Movements

The Grass Whistle-duck is confined to the Australian mainland, but there have been occasional vagrants in Tasmania. These records were uncommon even when there were considerable populations on the Murray River, but since these populations have declined there has been no recent Tasmanian record. It has also occasionally straggled to New Zealand and to New Guinea.

The occurrence in New Guinea is limited to Daru, where de Vis collected one in 1896,[97] and to Kombe, near Merauke, in West New Guinea, where Hoogerwerf collected nineteen specimens in 1959 and 1961.[59] It is significant that there had been other collectors in the area in the intervening years, but none had recorded the species, and that each New Guinea record (as well as the New Zealand one) followed severe droughts in Northern Australia. The birds were probably vagrants. The fact that some New Guinea birds in 1959 had "medium sized testes (about 15 mm.)" is not of great significance, since this size does not indicate a very high level of sexual activity. In Australia the Grass Whistle-duck has an extensive range, and breeds throughout it, from the Kimberleys in the west to as far south as the Murray River in the east. Distribution at all seasons has not been studied in detail, but it seems to be best considered in the three zones shown in the map.

The main breeding range extends from the Gwydir River in northern New South Wales in a great arc across the inland Mitchell-grass plains of Queensland, the Northern Territory, and Western Australia. Within this range the species is very widely distributed and numerous wherever there is grass with suitable sites for camps. It avoids the scrublands, the rocky escarpments of Arnhem Land, the forests of the north-east Queensland coast, and the muddy estuaries and mangrove swamps of the coast generally. It usually does not breed near the coast, advancing inland during the wet season to the renewed grasslands and lagoons; in exceptionally wet seasons, however, considerable numbers remain and breed in coastal districts. There are no quantitative data available on the populations, except that it is more numerous by far in the open grasslands of western Queensland and the Barkly Tableland than elsewhere. Near Townsville it is the commoner of the two Whistle-ducks and outnumbers the Water Whistle-duck in the dry season tenfold. In subcoastal areas of the Northern Territory the reverse is true, and the Water Whistle-duck outnumbers the Grass Whistle-duck at least a hundred-fold. The difference is most likely to be due to the availability of grasslands. Grasslands are widespread in the eastern half of the bird's range but are very poorly developed in the Northern Territory; the flood-plains are bare mud in the dry season and swamp in the wet, and inland the country is covered with dense *Eucalyptus* forest.

In the more southern parts of its range it was formerly very much more numerous than it is now. Until about 1920 it was very common in north-western New South Wales, but this region must now be included in its zone of scattered and unusual occurrence. Most of inland New South Wales south to the Murray River, south-west Queensland, and the fringe of the monsoon zone in the Northern Territory is characterized by scattered breeding colonies of Grass Whistle-ducks, more numerous in the better watered regions

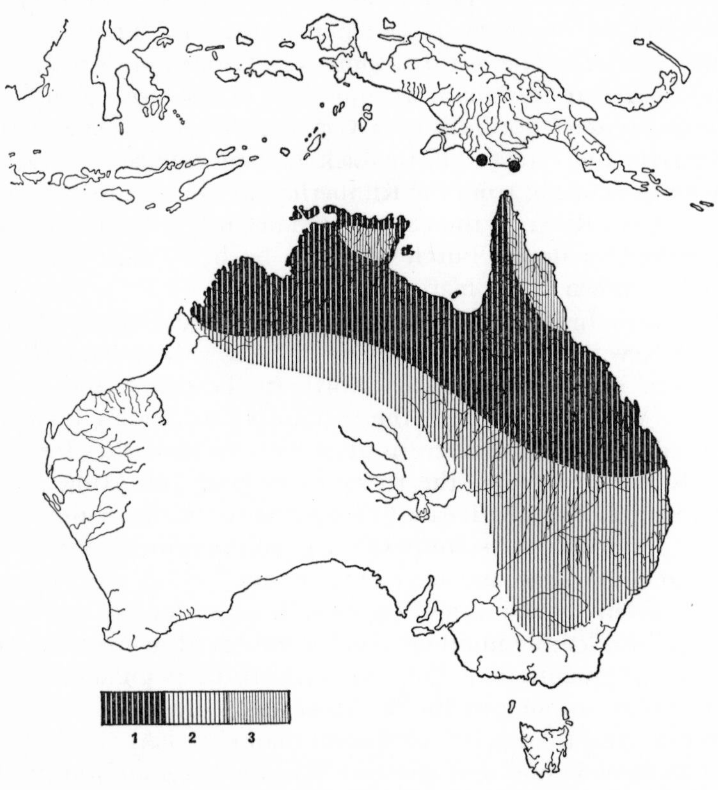

DISTRIBUTION OF THE GRASS WHISTLE-DUCK

The main breeding range is shown by the darkest shading (No. 1); the species also breeds, though in smaller numbers, in the area shaded No. 2, which is characterized by very widely scattered isolated groups. There is little or no breeding in the areas marked No. 3, and elsewhere in Australia the bird is unknown. The spots indicate extra-continental records.

than elsewhere. Although, in the north, dry-season flocks can number several thousands, in the inland they are seldom greater than two hundred and more commonly number about fifty birds. There is some evidence that some of the most southern colonies are of very recent origin and might not prove permanent.

In some places localized breeding colonies exist, but the numbers of birds south of the tropical coastal regions vary greatly according to seasonal conditions. In dry seasons in tropical Australia the numbers in the south increase greatly and vagrant flocks become very common, but do not usually survive to form breeding colonies. In years of abnormally high rainfall in southern Australia numbers of birds also arrive in the flooded districts and breed; some of these invasions have resulted in small breeding colonies in the Riverina, which have survived since the 1950 floods.

The main movement pattern of the species in the tropics is a concentration towards the coast, or other better watered regions, in the dry season and a dispersal during the wet season. During the dry season the birds are gregarious and are found in large camps from which they make local foraging flights. The sites of these camps are traditional and the most favourable are occupied by a flock each year, but smaller camps may develop in what are apparently less favourable situations and be abandoned after a year or two.

Whether the same birds return to the same major camp in successive years is not known, but it seems likely that they do. Certainly birds banded during the dry season remain in the general area to breed in the wet.[69] It is known also that at least occasionally a banded bird is found in the camp in several successive years, though others are found elsewhere, but the degree of permanence of the flocks' composition is not known.

Lavery watched one large camp near Townsville throughout five years and found its members in the dry season were usually round about three thousand, but there was a good deal of fluctuation as flocks joined it and others left. Returns of banded birds, however, suggested that, over all, the composition of the flock was quite stable throughout the dry season. This is unlike the situation that will be described for the Grey Teal, where very few birds remain in a concentration for very long; there is constant change in individuals in it, though the total numbers may remain fairly constant for long periods. On dispersal from the camp, in the wet season, it was clear from banded birds that the movement was multi-directional over the coastal plains and inland—a few birds even moved as far as the Murray River, 1200 miles away. Clearly the movements of the species from breeding areas to concentration areas can be extensive, but the complete scale has not been studied.

Feeding

Unlike the Water Whistle-duck, which is liable to feed in the water alongside its camp and accordingly prefers the richest water habitat available, the Grass Whistle-duck feeds mainly on land, and the type of water is immaterial in its choice of camp site. They are often found located on small, muddy, or brackish pools, far out on the dry plains. Doubtless factors other than food are more important in determining the site.

The birds fly out at night to feed on the plains or along the edges of swamps. The feeding movement is not simultaneous. Small groups leave successively from late afternoon until early evening, the rate of departure increasing greatly after dark. The groups may move considerable distances to feed; a flock near Townsville was utilizing 21 sites, some of them 17 miles away.[69] The feeding behaviour is similar to that of the Wood Duck in southern Australia. An area of attractive food is selected and visited nightly until it is exhausted or becomes unattractive, perhaps by a change in maturity. The group then changes its location and feeds elsewhere. Some feeding sites are only visited for a night or two, but others continue to attract birds for some weeks. On the feeding area the birds, in compact groups, move constantly and keep up an incessant whistling. The whistling can attract other passing flocks and undoubtedly leads to the merging of groups from several camps. While feeding they are very alert and difficult to stalk.

The food eaten in the Northern Territory was examined in 102 stomachs collected in the dry season and 34 in the wet, in the Adelaide River valley. This small sample was enough to show that the food was entirely vegetable. In the wet season it consisted almost entirely of grasses (96 per cent) and a wide variety of legumes, herbs, and sedges. The most important grasses were barnyard millets *Echinochloa*, couch *Cynodon*, *Paspalum*, and a small amount of wild rice *Oryza*. In the dry season, when the plains were bare, dry, and dusty, the birds fed on the edges of lagoons and swamps and were eating mainly spike-rushes *Eleocharis*, and sedges Cyperaceae.

A more adequate sample of 350 birds examined by Lavery in north Queensland showed very similar food habits.[69] Near the coast grasses were the dominant food plant, they were found in 93 per cent of the birds and accounted for 68 per cent of the total volume of food eaten. Of the grasses, barnyard-grass *E. colonum* was found in 84 per cent of the stomachs and made up 47 per cent of the total food. It remained a very important food throughout the whole year. Apart from the grasses, the only other important group of plants were the sedges, which accounted for 14 per cent of the volume and had been eaten by 60 per cent of the birds. The remainder of the food was made up of legumes, nardoo and a very wide variety of herbaceous plants. Farther inland where grasses were less abundant their relative importance to the birds was less and sedges were the most important group of plants, being found in 93 per cent of the birds and providing 51 per cent of the food. One genus of sedge, *Fimbristylis,* alone provided 42 per cent of the total food. Grasses were commonly eaten, being in 86 per cent of the birds, but provided only 19 per cent of the total food; again barnyard millet was the grass most important to the birds.

The seasonal sequence of food is similar in the two regions. Grasses are the dominant food throughout the wet season, but especially so at its end when practically nothing else is eaten. In the dry season when few grasses grow and there is virtually no seed available the birds feed in the moister places on sedges and whatever else is available.

Very few stomachs have been examined from birds in the southern colonies. The feeding behaviour is exactly the same as that of the large flocks of the north, but I have only seen six stomachs, all from Griffith, New South Wales. Of these, four were entirely filled with wheat seed and the other two with rice seed and barnyard-grass —presumably stubble feeding is important.

Breeding

Grass Whistle-ducks remain mated for long periods, probably for life. The flocks are clearly composed of mated pairs at all times. Fighting between males is more or less constant in the flocks, but becomes more intense with the beginning of the wet season. With the first rains the flocks become more mobile and display and posturing are more frequent among the males, in which signs of increasing sexual activity can be found within a couple of weeks of the first rains while the flocks are still congregated. Within a few days of the beginning of steady rain the birds move onto the water and disperse to breed near the shallow-water areas that have become abundant throughout the grasslands.

In subcoastal regions of the Northern Territory the dry season congregations of Grass Whistle-ducks are on the edges of lagoons and billabongs on the plains, and during the breeding season the birds disperse to the higher land near by, which does not suffer flooding, and breed in the grasslands. The young are led to pools and lagoons on hatching. The total scale of movement is unknown, but although there is some movement farther inland, as the more distant lagoons are replenished, many birds are also found throughout the wet season breeding quite close to the dry-season concentration places, sometimes in the same lagoon.

In north-east Queensland movements between the dry-season camps and breeding places are more extensive.[69] Here the shallow swamps and meadows needed for breeding habitat are not well developed near the coast and most occur west of the Dividing Range, a hundred miles or more inland. Usually there is no breeding on the coastal plain; the birds move inland some distance as the lagoons fill. In years of drought, however, many birds remain on the coast and some breeding occurs on the coastal plains. Presumably the dry weather inland prevents suitable breeding conditions and some birds accept the closest approach to the desired breeding habitat that is available on the coastal plains.

Clutches are begun in both Queensland and the Northern Territory in the period February to April, but February and March are the months of greatest activity. There is evidence that the extent of the breeding season is affected by the rainfall. In exceptionally wet years breeding may begin early and extend into May, and in very late or poor wet seasons it may be delayed or involve only part of the population, but there are not enough data available yet to fully explore the effects of weather on the breeding season.

There is little information available on the breeding of the southern populations of Grass Whistle-ducks. One group of eighty birds, located on an earth dam in the Riverina, breeds in September and October.[58] Another group of about thirty lives near Griffith, New South Wales, and can be found there in most months of the year. Two birds were collected there in October and both were in breeding condition, but two others shot in March were not. Another group of fifty lived on a large lagoon on the Murrumbidgee River until 1955 when it was drained; prior to that they could be found there throughout the year and seven shot in August 1952 were in breeding condition. Grass Whistle-ducks were found breeding on the Macquarie Marshes in September 1893. From Moree in northern New South Wales Morse recorded that the birds were "very numerous in spring and summer. Nests are often found out on the plains a mile or two from water. Usually breeds in October but I have just heard of a nest of 17 eggs found in January."[81] What evidence there is suggests that these southern inland groups usually breed in the spring, August to October.

On hatching, the male and female, both of which have been involved in the incubation of the eggs, lead the young to water, often for a mile or more across the grasslands and remain with them as they mature. D'Ombrain has described how remarkably fearless the birds often are when with young.[29] A brood of newly hatched ducklings was herded for half a mile to a fowl-yard and driven inside. The male and female remained in company with them and were easily secured in the same yard.

Nest

The nest is merely a scrape in the ground, under long grass or a bush, lined with a few pieces of grass or lignum.

Eggs

The eggs are pure white and vitreous in appearance, they are oval and distinctly pointed. In 14 nests 112 eggs varied in length from 44 mm. to 51 mm. (average 48 mm.) and in breadth from 33 mm. to 38 mm. (average 36 mm.).

Clutch Size

There are no quantitative data, but according to North the clutch is 10 to 12. Nine clutches I have measured, however, varied from 8 to 14 eggs.

Incubation

The incubation period is 28 days.

Status

Species with nearly identical needs normally cannot coexist permanently because one must always have a slight "edge" on the other and in time, owing to natural selection will replace it. It is a source of interest to see the two Whistle-ducks, very closely related and of similar habits and appearance, living together in large numbers. Obviously they must have rather different living needs, despite their general similarity, and from the life history of the Grass Whistle-duck *eytoni*, described here, and that of the Water Whistle-duck *arcuata*, in the previous section, the main points of difference in their ecology can be summarized. *Eytoni* completely overlaps *arcuata* in range and although they separate in some places during the breeding season they do not in others. However, there are marked differences in local numbers; where *eytoni* occurs in great numbers, for example, in north Queensland, *arcuata* is much less common, and vice versa, for example, in the Northern Territory.

Both species are quite capable of undertaking long movements when necessary, as is shown by the occasional appearance of *arcuata* in south-western New South Wales, a thousand miles south of its normal range, but, on the whole, one species is rather sedentary and the other more nomadic, so that competition usually does not arise. When necessary one species moves away. *Arcuata* is fairly sedentary and normally undertakes only local movements from congregation areas to near-by breeding lagoons. *Eytoni,* on the other hand, is strongly nomadic and can move widely in adverse conditions; in fact, it moves quite widely in each year between breeding and concentration areas. The two species live side by side in the same lagoons for much of the year and sometimes throughout the whole year, especially in the Northern Territory, and mixed flocks are not uncommon. The two species are quite sharply separated, however, by the location of their feeding places and the food actually eaten. The food they eat is quite different. While both may live on the same lagoon, *arcuata* depends on the aquatic plants of the lagoon itself, and *eytoni* leaves it to feed on distant grasslands. These are some of the main differences in the two birds' living needs; no doubt there are many others that have not yet been determined.

The Grass Whistle-duck is seldom shot as game in north Queensland, presumably because other "better" ducks are common there. In the Northern Territory it is shot along with all other waterfowl, but shooting pressure in this region at present is not heavy except close to the one large town, Darwin. Elsewhere in its range there is a very sparse human population, except in the extreme south. In the south any birds that appear among other ducks are liable to be shot as curiosities, despite legal protection, unless protected by the landholder on whose property they occur. When attempts have been made to cultivate cereal crops in the tropics the Grass Whistle-duck has been known to graze on the young growth, causing some damage, but these occasions have been very rare and the damage slight.

The Grass Whistle-duck is one of the few species of Australian waterfowl that may have benefited from settlement. Its needs are simple, lagoon or dam edges to camp on and short pasture to graze and feed on. It seems likely that it has not been seriously hindered by the grazing of cattle throughout its range, but rather may have benefited from some practices of the industry, such as the provision of numerous ground tanks and the effect of grazing in maintaining short grass cover for longer periods of the year than occurs under primitive conditions, thus making suitable food more abundant and widespread.

Certainly it is very numerous in places and very widely distributed; it is not disturbed much by sportsmen or greatly opposed by agriculture, and perhaps is assisted by grazing pursuits. There seems no immediate problem in the conservation of Grass Whistle-ducks in northern Australia.

Black Swan

Cygnus atratus (Latham)

References

Cygnus Bechstein, Orn. Taschenb., part 2, 1803, p. 404.
Anas atrata Latham, Index Orn., 2, p. 834, 1790. (N.S.W.)

Other Names

None.

Description

ADULT MALE. General colour of all plumage black, often with a brownish tinge; breast and abdomen paler than rest of body; feathers on back often have a greyish border; wing black with white tips, the amount of white being variable (usually the first 10 primaries, all primary coverts, last two feathers of adula, and the first 3 to 6 secondaries are entirely white, the remaining secondaries, secondary coverts, and the first two feathers of adula have some white, remainder of feathers on wing black); bill varies from orange to dark red, there is a white bar distally and the nail is off-white; iris varies from white to red and seems affected by the sexual cycle; legs dark grey.

ADULT FEMALE. As for male, but bill and iris are generally lighter in colour.

IMMATURE. Before the first moult all plumage is dull grey-brown and mottled; after the first moult it is black; before the first moult the wing feathers that are white in adults are black-tipped; after this moult in some birds full adult plumage is achieved, but in others some primaries remain marked with black or dark grey until at least three years of age.

Portrait of a Grass Whistle-duck. *Photo by Ederic Slater*

Upper: Daytime camp of Grass Whistle-ducks on the well-grazed edge of a lagoon, Townsville.

Lower: Grass Whistle-ducks in camp. *Photos by Ederic Slater*

CYGNET. The downy young are light grey; bill, dark grey-black with light-grey tip; legs and feet, dark grey; iris, grey-brown.

Size

	Weight *gm.*	*Length* *mm.*	*Wingspread* *mm.*	*Wing* *mm.*	*Bill* *mm.*	*Neck* *mm.*
Adult Male						
Maximum	8750	1423	2055	543	79	880
Minimum	4600	1175	1700	434	57	702
Average	6270	1292	1898	489	69	782
Number measured	*247*	*244*	*185*	*240*	*247*	*194*
Adult Female						
Maximum	7200	1300	1910	499	72	765
Minimum	3700	1065	1610	416	56	572
Average	5100	1161	1769	461	63	675
Number measured	*219*	*219*	*144*	*215*	*219*	*103*

Voice

Black Swans have a high-pitched, musical bugle that takes many forms in different situations, but the details have not been studied.

Routine

Swans can be found nearly anywhere, in pairs, family parties, or very large flocks, and are one of the most familiar birds in southern Australia. They are usually seen scattered over large bodies of water but often come ashore and walk clumsily about, feeding.

They rise with difficulty, needing forty or fifty yards' take-off distance. In thick vegetation, among timber or in rough water, they cannot rise, and in these situations can be caught from boats or even sometimes on foot. In open water they can sometimes be driven downwind and, being unable to rise, caught. The flight is strong but slow, undulating and graceful. They fly in long skeins or Vs, unlike other Australian waterfowl. They fly about the lake during the day, but most movements from it are undertaken at night when the bugling of swans flying over to some other waterhole is a common sound in most places near water in southern Australia.

In moult the pinions are shed simultaneously and for a time the birds are flightless and very vulnerable; at this time they keep as far out in the lake as possible. Some swans can be found in moult throughout the whole year in any large concentration, but the greatest numbers are found following the main breeding season, in spring and early summer.

Relationships

The classification of the world's swans is still not settled. Until recently it was believed that they could not validly be separated from the geese and that the tribe Anserini included Swans, Geese, and *Coscoroba*, a peculiar short-necked bird that provides a link taxonomically between the geese and the swans. Recent studies of skeletons[101] and behaviour, however, leave little doubt that a valid tribe, Cygnini, exists that includes the swans and *Coscoroba* and separates them from the geese, Anserini.

Delacour[26] holds that the five species of swans belong to one genus, *Cygnus*; these are the Black Swan, the Black-necked Swan, *C. melanocoryphus* of South America, and three pure white Northern Hemisphere birds, *C. cygnus*, the Whooper and Trumpeter Swans, *C. columbianus*, Whistling Swans, and *C. olor*, the Mute Swan. Several authors, however, believe that two genera should be recognized, *Olor* and *Cygnus*. The Black Swan would belong in *Cygnus* together with the Mute Swan and the Black-necked Swan.

The Black Swan is uniform throughout its range and no races have been recognized.

Field Recognition

The large black shape, very long slender neck, and striking white pinions distinguish it from all other birds in flight. At rest the white feathers are normally not seen.

Males are larger than females and adults larger than juveniles; although these differences are not obvious in the field males can be distinguished from females by the experienced observer; in flight the neck of the males is quite noticeably longer in relation to the body than in females and when swimming the head of the male is held higher and the neck is more erect than in females; when near males can be seen also to have a longer head with a straighter upper mandible.

Habitat

Swans can be found in any habitat but are most numerous in large permanent lakes, which can be either fresh or brackish. The largest concentrations of swans in Australia are found in the Moulting Lagoon, Tasmania, and the Coorong, South Australia, both of which are brackish, but they are also very numerous in the freshwater lakes of western Victoria, the Southern Tablelands of New South Wales and elsewhere. They frequent inland billabongs and lagoons in small numbers and can be found at times in muddy floodwaters of the inland and even coastal rivers. The Black Swan is one of the most adaptable of waterfowl.

Although large expanses of water are preferred the depth is critical; the birds can secure food to only about three feet below the surface, so abundant aquatic vegetation growing up to this level is essential to support a permanent population.

Distribution and Movements

Swans are very strong flyers and vagrants might be found anywhere; they have been recorded throughout the continent, except on the tip of Cape York Peninsula, and this mainly because no ornithologist has happened to be in that remote area at the appropriate time. They are distributed as a breeding species from about Bowen, north Queensland, to North-west Cape, Western Australia, and smaller numbers are seen, and breeding regularly occurs, as far inland as indicated in the distribution map.

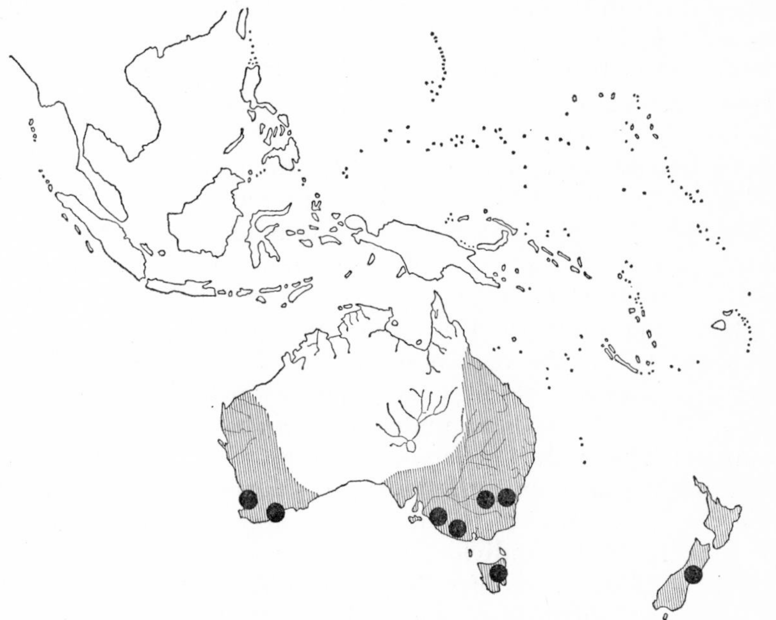

DISTRIBUTION OF THE BLACK SWAN

The shaded areas show the normal range of the Black Swan, and throughout this area breeding occurs whenever there is suitable habitat. The black spots indicate some especially favoured districts. In the unshaded area Black Swans are vagrants.

Despite this, however, the distribution is predominantly southern, and the great majority of Black Swans in eastern Australia are found in Tasmania and that part of the mainland south of a line between Sydney and Adelaide, and in Western Australia in the extreme south-west. In these regions swans are abundant at all times but actual counts are few. Our aerial counts in south-eastern New South Wales show that at present Lake George supports up to 5,000 birds and the New South Wales South Coast a further 5,000. Many large lakes in the inland, like Lakes Cowal and Brewster, Fletchers Lake, and Yanga Lake, support up to 15,000 birds at times. In 1957 I estimated 50,000 swans on the Coorong, and there were similar numbers on Lake Albert, but in normal years the numbers there are not so great.

The Black Swan was introduced to New Zealand in the early 1860s, partly in the hope that it would control waterweeds, and also for game and for its ornamental potential.[100] The introduction was very "successful" and the bird is now very numerous in New Zealand. It is distributed throughout both islands, but the greatest numbers occur in Waitato lakes in the North Island and in the Otago lakes and Lake Ellesmere in the south. At Lake Ellesmere there are an estimated 60,000-80,000 swans and there is regular exploitation of eggs for food both commercially and by local people; this is encouraged to keep the numbers in check.

It is usually thought that the Black Swan is sedentary and, as described by Sharland,[89] "does not move from its traditional breeding areas, nor does it appear to migrate, for numbers perish from starvation in times of shortage". Our studies do not support this idea at all. The work is based on regular counting of swans from low-flying aircraft on the Southern Tablelands and adjacent South Coast of New South Wales, the regular inspection of inland lakes, and the marking of swans with leg-bands and distinctive coloured neck collars. The work has been under way for three years and is continuing, but a preliminary analysis is possible.

Although some swans are found in following years in the lake where they were marked, many are not and move long distances very quickly. Some individuals have been caught moulting in different lakes hundreds of miles apart in successive years. Clearly there is, at least, a mobile element in the population.

There is a regular annual fluctuation in numbers of swans on the large clear lakes of the Southern Tablelands. The numbers increase each summer to many times the winter breeding population; these fluctuations are too great to be explained by breeding or local concentrations and, in any case, birds appear in the concentrations wearing collars that were placed on them in the inland. There are similar summer concentrations and dispersal in many of the inland lakes, along the Murray River and in the Coorong, and doubtless elsewhere that large areas of water occur.

Although significant numbers of moulting swans can be found at any time of the year, most moult during the summer concentration period. There seems little doubt that the concentrations are due not only to the general decrease in numbers and extent of small water areas during the summer, but also to movement by the birds to moult on larger and therefore safer waters. The decrease in numbers in the tablelands concentrations is associated with increasing water areas and the beginning of breeding inland; many birds marked in the summer on the tablelands are seen in the winter inland.

Concentrations of swans are not static in composition and there is considerable change in the individuals comprising them, even though the size might remain constant. The rate of turnover in a concentration is suggested by some of our work in inland New South Wales. As one example, in a concentration of 1,200 swans on Lake Brewster 381 were marked with collars, about one in three; three months later there were 1,800 swans present, but no more than 20 were marked. Clearly the population had completely turned over; if it could be assumed that the dilution of the marked population had been a continuous process, then as many as 10,000 birds might have passed through. There are several similar examples in our work.

When marked swans move from an area they do so in all compass directions, at all seasons, though in our present study, undertaken during a drought, there has been a marked bias towards the better-watered coastal districts, which might have been expected. The population on the New South Wales South Coast has increased from 1,000 to 5,000 in the three years, but even these birds are not stationary, and there is constant movement among them. The full scale of movements is not yet known, but swans from Lake George have dispersed all over south-eastern Australia to as far south as Moulting Lagoon, Tasmania, and from the New South Wales coast to the Coorong, South Australia.

The general summary of swan movements on present knowledge must be that, although suitable habitat supports a small resident population, most birds are nomadic and move erratically and widely according to the weather and distribution of habitat.

Food and Feeding

Standard texts usually credit Black Swans with feeding on aquatic plants and animals; our experience is that animals are not part of their diet and that they are completely vegetarian.

The Black Swan feeds mainly in water, reaching to the bottom or towards it with the long neck to collect algae or to uproot growing plants; in deep water it up-ends, reaching food over three feet below the surface. Surface dabbling to collect duckweed and other floating plants is common. Occasionally it stands in shallow water at the edge of the swamp, but more commonly remains where it can float. It frequently leaves the water to graze on green herbage on the bank and freely visits flooded or irrigated pastures, preferably if water remains on them at the time. It sometimes flies to isolated pastures and depressions, but prefers to secure its food in or very near the swamp, if possible.

In salt-water environments it leaves the water to drink at fresh-water soaks. This occurs extensively in the Coorong, where very large numbers of swans congregate at some soaks, having walked a hundred yards or more across the mud. At these times, as they can only rise from the land with great difficulty, if at all, they are extremely wary.

The food eaten in Barrenbox Swamp, a large cumbungi swamp near Griffith, New South Wales, has been examined in some detail by the examination of the contents of 617 stomachs. They were collected each month throughout two years. The food was entirely of vegetable origin; the vegetative parts of the plants were eaten and there was no preference for seedheads. The animals, which provided no significant volume of food, included a few molluscs, spiders, and insects, mainly larvae, probably collected accidentally along with the plants being eaten at the time.

The plants most frequently eaten were cumbungi *Typha angustifolia,* which was found in 37 per cent of the birds and comprised 19 per cent of the total volume of food, and algae Chlorophyceae that were found in 31 per cent of the birds and comprised 20 per cent of the volume. *Valisneria* (9 per cent of the volume) and pondweeds, *Potamogeton* spp. (12 per cent), were also of considerable importance. Other individual plants that provided more than 4 per cent of the food by volume included water-couch *Paspalum distichum,* water-milfoil *Myriophyllum,* duckweed *Azolla,* and barley-grass *Hordeum.*

Although the swans in this area were seen feeding all over

the swamp and particularly near the edge, most food was secured from relatively deep water. Forty per cent of the volume came from plants that grow in water more than 18 inches deep (*Typha, Najas, Valisneria, Potamogeton, Phragmites*), 33 per cent from water less than 18 inches deep (Characeae, Chlorophyceae, *Paspalum, Myriophyllum*), and 3 per cent from plants that grow on the boggy edges (Polygonaceae, Cyperaceae, *Juncus*), and 10 per cent from pasture plants only available periodically following flooding and inundation of the edges.

The water-level of Barrenbox Swamp is mainly controlled by drainage of excess irrigation water from the Murrumbidgee Irrigation Area as well as rainfall on the unusually large catchment area provided by the close reticulation of drains throughout this large area and directed to the swamp. The composition of the diet was related to the changes in water-level in the swamp as this made different feeding areas and thus plants available, rather than to an annual cycle of plant growth or food preference.

The usual cycle of water-level is that the level rises abruptly in May or June with the discharge of irrigation water prior to the rice harvest and remains full until midsummer when it declines. The level reached and fluctuations during the year are caused by rainfall. During the three years so far studied, in 1963 the swamp was overfull and flooded surrounding pastures, the water remained high during 1964, but fell to a very low level in autumn of 1965 and rose again during the winter.

Throughout this whole period the swans ate floating plants and plants characteristic of the edges in small quantities, in more or less constant amounts from month to month, but there were major annual differences in the utilization of other plant groups. In the summer of 1963, when the edge was flooded, the birds ate mainly pasture plants, up to 90 per cent of the total food; the deep-water plants, now of course, in very deep water, and the plants characteristic of shallow water, but now in deep water, were presumably less easy to secure or less attractive than the pasture. At the same season, in 1964 and 1965, when the swamp was two feet shallower, the main foods were the shallow-water plants and the deep-water plants; of the two groups the shallow-water plants were the more attractive.

In 1963 and 1965, when the swamp was very full, only small quantities of cumbungi were eaten, and the situation was similar in the spring of 1964 until declining levels made conditions suitable for a great growth of two annual pondweeds, *Potamogeton ochreatus* and *P. crispus*, which were then eaten to the exclusion of everything else. Following the bloom of these plants and the continued decline of the swamp to a very low level, cumbungi became almost the only food available and made up to 90 per cent of the diet in some months; the stems were uprooted and the softer basal portions and leaf sheaths eaten.

The food eaten at another study site, Lake George, near Canberra, has not been studied quantitatively, but as it is an open lake the swans can be closely watched and clearly the food preferences are similar and follow changes in the availability of pastures due to water-level changes, algae blooms, and the availability of pondweeds and submerged aquatics in different parts of the lake at different water-levels.

In a smaller study on the tropical coast, Lavery[69] found that in 60 stomachs the food was similar in type though, of course, quite different in species composition. Sixty per cent of the volume of food eaten was pondweed *Potamogeton*, 24 per cent sedges, and 15 per cent submerged aquatics; the sedges were mainly species that grow in water 12 to 30 inches deep. Pasture plants, however, were not utilized by swans in this district, a surprising result in a district where heavy rainfall frequently inundates pastures and grasslands.

According to stomach analyses the food of cygnets at Griffith, New South Wales, is very similar to that of the adults, though owing to their smaller size and shorter neck they are unable to secure food from such deep water as the adults. The principal foods are the hydrophytes growing in shallow water, the edge plants, and pasture when it is flooded. When living in deeper water they largely depend on their parents to uproot the bottom-growing plants, especially pondweeds.

Breeding

Swans generally mate for life; although the point has not yet been proved for Black Swans in the wild, their constant association in pairs or family parties suggests that it does hold with this species. The age at first breeding has not been determined in the field, though this work is now in progress, but we have collected a few birds whose testes contained sperms at the age of about 14 months. It seems that the birds may achieve sexual maturity at one year of age, but do not, of course, necessarily breed then. All concentrations of swans in the breeding season contain a very large number of non-breeding birds, but their condition cannot be determined until more information is available on the age at first breeding in the wild. As one example, in 1963 there were 2,000-3,000 swans in Lake George, but only 400 clutches were begun; the non-breeders probably included those that were immature and a very large number that were unable to breed because of a shortage of nesting sites.

The timing of the breeding season varies from place to place and is greatly influenced by the availability of suitable habitat. Thus in north-east Queensland, with a summer wet season, breeding occurs in reedbeds and on islands in salt-pans and on samphire flats that are dry during the winter but are usually flooded in December or January. If rainfall is sufficient to flood the area to a suitable depth eggs are laid in the period February to May. In years of unsatisfactory rain, however, when the salt-pans do not flood, or only partly, few swans breed, many nests are deserted, and many of the broods that do hatch perish, owing to the premature disappearance of the water.[69] In contrast, in the south, at Benger, Western Australia, flooding of the swamp occurs at the reverse season, the region having predominantly winter rainfall. Normally the swamp is full in June. Eggs are laid in June, July, and August.

In the more temporary habitats of the arid and semi-arid inland—lagoons, billabongs, and lignum swamps—breeding is erratic, and so swans breed whenever there is rainfall or flood to satisfy their breeding habitat requirements. Thus M. Schraeder, in south-west Queensland, has found nests in Bullawarra Lake in February, following its replenishment that summer, and he found nests in April around Cunnamulla, following heavy local rain in 1956. On the plains and in the lignum creeks and swamps west of Booligal, New South Wales, I have found nests of swans in January, February, June, July, August, September, and December in different years, each time following heavy local rain or a river fresh to fill a creek or depression. The most striking case I have seen was a group of three nests in a half-acre depression in an arid saltbush plain near Ivanhoe, New South Wales, that had been filled by a local storm in January, 1960. The water was only twenty inches deep and in the high evaporation rate of that district could not have remained for more than six weeks; nevertheless the swans attempted to nest.

In the same district, however, in permanent swamps, the breeding season is rather regular. Although some male swans may be found producing sperm in any month of the year in Barrenbox Swamp, generally testis rehabilitation in the population is complete in March, and significant numbers of males first produce sperms in April. The maximum numbers producing sperm are in June or July; thereafter the numbers decline. The rate of decline is determined to some extent by the condition of the swamp. In 1964, when it was very full, 25 per cent of the males were producing sperm in December, but in 1965, when it was very low, sperm production ceased in September. The sexual cycle of the female is similar but occurs later. Each year from 1963 to 1965 there was an increase in the size of the oocytes in the winter, the maximum size being achieved in July in 1963 and August in 1964 and 1965; after these months it rapidly declined, egg-laying being completed. In 1964 there was an additional burst of sexual activity in December; there was no obvious reason for this in the weather, but one unusual event was the massive growth of the annual *Potamogeton* species, which were eaten to the exclusion of all other food. The event suggested that the sexual activity could have been associated with improved nutrition of the birds.

There was a similar event in Lake George, confirming the ability of swans to breed at any time of the year that conditions are suitable; breeding was continuous from December 1962 to February 1964. Considerable numbers of nests were begun in each month in this period, but particularly from December 1962 to February 1963 when many more clutches were begun than in the "normal" breeding season, April to August. The reasons for the unusually extended breeding season in Lake George in 1962-4 could not be determined, but again it was associated with an unusually great food supply; in this case an alga bloom of quite unprecedented magnitude.

The tentative conclusion, at present, must be that the swan has a regular breeding season which is probably controlled by fixed annual factors, but that it has the capacity to breed at any time conditions become suitable. The availability of a firm nest foundation is very important, as will be described below. There is a possibility that increased food supply is also an important factor in timing the breeding season, though, of course, the increased food supply could just as logically have been caused by the unknown factor that "caused" the breeding season in the first place.

Nest

The nest may be built on land or among swamp vegetation; where both sites are available the ground seems to be preferred, since the greater part of the local population then breeds there. Nests are also found on the tops of flooded stumps, in the bases of trees, and in floating masses of debris.

Littler[70] mentions the edge of swamps as nest sites and does not specify islands, but my experience and that of all other authors suggests that ground nests are only built on islands. On small islands dense colonies develop, a situation rare among swans, each bird maintaining a peck distance of about five feet from its neighbours. The earliest nests are usually begun on banks of water-swept algae in the shallows or at the water's edge; later breeders are obliged to move inland until the whole island is occupied. The ground nest is built of whatever material is available, including sedges, wind-swept algae, grass, wheat in flooded wheatfields, or twigs up to an inch or more thick in flooded billabongs. Usually the first egg is laid as soon as a small amount of material is gathered and the birds continue construction during incubation by uprooting all vegetation within reach or by pilfering from neighbours' nests. The completed nests are 2 to 3 feet in diameter and up to one foot in height.

In water the nests are built in dense vegetation, the ideal site in New South Wales being scattered dense clumps of cumbungi. The cumbungi provides abundant, easily collected bulk. The nest is a large buoyant heap of vegetation up to 5 feet in diameter and 3 to 4 feet deep, one foot protruding above water. It is usually anchored by rooted plants but often breaks loose and drifts about as the birds brood.

The distribution of nests in a bed of cane-grass, *Eragrostis australasica,* on Lake George was analysed to determine the factors influencing the distribution of nests and hence of nesting colonies. Of 188 nests, 135 were used once, 33 were used twice, 19 were used three times, and one four times. In fifty acres of cane-grass the swans had the choice of uniform stands one to two acres in extent, solid beds dissected by occasional channels and open areas, a patchwork of open water and clumps 3 to 5 feet in diameter, isolated clumps up to 20 feet in diameter, or isolated small clumps 3 to 5 feet in diameter. There was a very heavy preference for isolated clumps between 5 and 20 feet in diameter; presumably smaller clumps provided inadequate nest material or were subject to wave action, whereas larger clumps were undesirable, perhaps because of difficulty of access to the nest or the restriction of escape possibilities. When disturbed swans prefer to slip off the nest and swim quietly away with the head held very low.

Cane-grass grows in shallow water; its density decreases with increasing depth of water, but its height is not affected directly. The distribution of nests was also examined with respect to these two characteristics of the cane-grass as well as the water depth. Most nests (109 out of 134) were in water between 16 and 24 inches deep; at this depth the density of the cane-grass varied from about 500 to 3000 stems per square yard and varied in height from 50 to 58 inches. Clearly reeds of this height and density provided adequate nest material and support for the massive nest and sufficient protection, with the associated water depth, from ground predators. Nest construction over deeper water would give even more protection from predators but less, probably insufficient, nest material and support; nesting in shallower water would give better support and a better supply of nest material but less protection from predators.

If these are, in fact, the important considerations in the selection of a nest site for swans, then the nesting situations in other areas are easily explained; on islands abundant nest material is not important, since solid ground supports the clutch and the surrounding water gives protection from ground predators. In cumbungi swamps the very dense clumps of the cumbungi provide abundant nest material, in all water depths in which it grows, so with nest material abundant everywhere most swan nests are as far from the shore as possible.

Eggs

The eggs are elliptical and pale green when fresh, though they quickly become nest-stained. The shell is coarse grained and slightly lustrous; 353 eggs from 63 clutches varied in length from 96 to 115 mm. (average 104 mm.) and in breadth from 60 to 73 mm. (average 67 mm.).

Clutch

The size of the clutch laid in 407 nests on lakes near Canberra varied from 4 to 10 eggs (average 5·5). The distribution of clutch size was as below.

Number of eggs:	3	4	5	6	7	8	9	10
Number of clutches:	0	67	132	145	57	4	1	1

The nest containing 10 eggs had eggs of two very distinct sizes and shapes, so they may have been laid by two females. These nests were visited regularly during egg-laying and incubation, so can be accepted as true clutch size. Even so, brooding swans skilfully retrieve eggs that roll from the nest and just as skilfully retrieve eggs laid by other females to begin a clutch within bill range. The frequent appearance of fresh eggs in heavily incubated clutches is probably due to this.

The only other substantial clutch-size data I have seen refer to the eggs in 187 nests near Townsville, Queensland.[69] Here the number of eggs varied from 1 to 8, with an average of 4·5, and the commonest number was 3 to 6 eggs. The clutches were apparently complete when found, so predators could have already removed some eggs. If this was not the case a latitudinal variation in clutch size is shown.

Standard texts give the clutch size as 4 to 8 (Delacour) and "usually 4 to 6" (Cayley).

Incubation

Both parents participate in incubation and relieve one another with elaborate ceremony. Incubation begins after the third egg is laid in clutches of 4 and 5, after the fourth egg in clutches of 6, and after the fifth egg in clutches of 7 or more. Hatching of the brood extends over 24 to 48 hours, and frequently the first young leave the nest with one parent while the other broods the remaining eggs. Often with large clutches the last egg is deserted before it hatches.

The mean incubation period in 44 clutches, that is, from the beginning of brooding to the hatching of the last egg, varied from 35 to 45 days (average 39·7 days). The commonest period was 39 to 41 days.

Development of Young

The mean clutch size is 5·5 eggs; from these an average of 4·1 cygnets hatch and by the time of fledging 2·7 survive. That, after fledging, juveniles suffer a heavier mortality rate than adults is suggested by the observation that of 81 carcasses found on the shores of Lake George 52 were of juvenile birds.

On hatching the cygnets are covered with grey down; the retrices appear at 20-30 days of age and there is some feathering round the eyes at 30-35 days. The first feathers on the scapulars appear at about 55 days and on the lower neck and upper tail coverts at about 65 days. Between 75 and 95 days of age the young are fully feathered, except for some down on the lower back and wings. The primaries and secondaries are fully grown between 140 and 180 days, by which time the back is usually fully feathered.

The colour of the soft parts also changes with age. At hatching the iris is grey-brown and changes to brown between 60 and 80 days and to red-brown between 135 and 170 days. The dark-grey bill of the newly hatched cygnet changes to red between 85 and 120 days of age.

At hatching cygnets weigh from 125-215 gm. (average 171), the wing measurements are 39-50 mm. (average 44 mm.) and the bill

19-24 mm. (average 22 mm.). From the recapture of cygnets, toe-punched at hatching and therefore of known age, it has been seen that the range of weight and bill measurements respectively is: at 30 days 380-590 gm., 32-39 mm., at 90 days 1600-3200 gm., 52-61 mm., and at 180 days, when they may begin to fly, 4000-5000 gm., 58-68 mm.

Status

The statements in Delacour,[26] apparently gleaned from old literature, concerning the abundance of the Black Swan, give a completely false idea of the status of the Black Swan in Australia. For example, "Today the birds are still numerous in many places, mostly in Sanctuaries"; "They often congregate in hundreds and unless too mercilessly persecuted, they hold their own easily"; "In Western Australia great quantities of eggs are gathered by the natives who also kill a lot of flightless birds."

The Black Swan is abundant throughout most of its ancestral range and has recently extended its breeding range into tropical Queensland where man's activity has created new areas of habitat. It is abundant in most suitable districts, be they sanctuaries or not. The birds gather in thousands, not hundreds. The swan is not mercilessly persecuted, but rather is one of the few Australian birds that, in addition to being protected by law, is heavily protected by public sentiment, so that the biologist who would collect swans for scientific purposes treads warily when near country people and duck-shooters, and when State authorities have needed to reduce local over-population there have been sustained public outcries. Aborigines have not destroyed many swans' eggs for fifty years or more.

A few sections of the community, however, do not admire swans; these include fishermen, who, in some districts, feel that large concentrations in coastal lagoons may deplete fish populations by feeding on aquatic vegetation and thus destroying their food and cover. This point has not yet been studied, though such depletion certainly does seem possible when several thousand swans sit on a small lagoon, but no action has been permitted against swans on these grounds. In the Wimmera district of Victoria enormous concentrations of swans occur and invade pastures and cereal crops, undoubtedly damaging some. The true extent of agricultural damage is not known, but the Government has found it expedient in a few recent years to allow short controlled shooting seasons, locally, to reduce the numbers of swans and to make the remainder more susceptible to scaring methods. In some districts of Tasmania, where swans are very numerous indeed, similar shooting seasons have been held for ostensibly similar reasons, though it seems possible that an ancient tradition of swan shooting has also been involved in that State's decisions to reduce swan numbers.

One would wish all waterfowl in Australia were as secure as Black Swans and that their conservation presented so few problems.

Source of Data

The biology of the Black Swan is now under study by the C.S.I.R.O. Division of Wildlife Research and this account is based on the preliminary results of that study.

Mute Swan

Cygnus olor (Gmelin)

References

Cygnus Bechstein, Orn. Taschenb., part 2, 1803, p. 404.
Anas olor Gmelin, Syst. Nat., 1, part 2, 1789. (Russia.)

Description

As the Mute Swan is the only white swan in or, under existing quarantine laws, likely to be in Australia, little description is needed. The plumage is entirely white and the bill is orange with a black knob at the base. The bird is considerably larger than the Black Swan.

Juveniles have greyish plumage and grey bills. The bill colour changes to orange during the first year of life. The grey plumage is replaced during the first winter, but some grey feathers may be retained until the second winter.

Size

ADULT MALE. Wing 560-622 mm.; tarsus 98-120 mm.; bill 70-85 mm.; length 1270-1560 mm.

ADULT FEMALE. Wing 535-570 mm.; bill 73-90 mm.; length as male.

Distribution

The Mute Swan has a wide distribution in Europe and Asia, including Great Britain, southern Sweden, Denmark, northern Germany, Poland, Rumania, central Asia, Mongolia, and Dauria. It has been widely spread by man since Roman times, so that today it is hard to know what populations are truly native and what are the result of introductions.

It is not certain whether Mute Swans are native to Great Britain

Upper: Black Swans in flight; note several wearing the identifying neckbands of the C.S.I.R.O *Photo by Ederic Slater*

Lower: Black Swans coming ashore and grouped to drink at a freshwater soak, Coorong, S.A. *Photo by author*

Upper: Portion of a nesting colony of Black Swans on an island in Lake George, N.S.W.

Lower: Nest relief ceremony; the incoming bird is greeted and returns the greeting.

Photos by Ederic Slater

or the result of an early introduction; opinion at present favours the view that they were originally indigenous in parts of England but that the wild population was brought into a semi-domesticated state during the twelfth century. In England it enjoyed the special status of being a royal bird; although swans could be kept on private waters under licence, all others were the property of the Crown.[94] Royal licences were issued to communities, companies, and some individuals to keep swans in domestic or semi-domestic state, provided that they were marked with a distinctive and registered brand. Colourful ceremonies developed, and in some places persist, round the annual catching and marking of the young with the owner's brand.

Australian Occurrence

Despite its colourful past in England our main interest in the Mute Swan in Australia must be its possible relationship with the native Black Swan. Introduced as an ornamental bird to ponds and lakes, mainly in gardens and parks in capital cities, it has occasionally been released on more natural waters in northern Tasmania and south-west Western Australia. In these situations the species has become established, but has shown no inclination to extend its range or to increase greatly in numbers. The Australian experience to date, as well as that in New Zealand, suggests that the Mute Swan is unlikely to expand its range greatly in these countries, particularly in the presence of populations of the Black Swan.

In New Zealand the Mute Swan was deliberately introduced in 1866 and the Black Swan in 1864. Today the Mute Swan is restricted to ornamental ponds and a few small colonies in the Canterbury, Otago, Hawke's Bay and Wairarapa districts, but the Black Swan is one of the most abundant waterfowl in New Zealand. It is completely acclimatized to the wild and there are breeding colonies of many thousands of birds.[83]

Mute Swans are beautiful birds and undoubtedly ornamental on artificial waters in Europe. It was, however, disappointing to hear newspaper correspondents recently advocate their acclimatization on Lake Burley Griffin, in the centre of Canberra, the National Capital, to "add character to it". This lake, as well as all other lakes in the district, supports large populations of Black Swans and some of their major breeding colonies occur near by. Mute Swans could only live in competition with this attractive species.

The author has seen two Mute Swans flying along the Lachlan River near Booligal, New South Wales, in an apparently wild state, so the possibility of its ultimately establishing itself in the wild in Australia cannot be ignored.

Relationships

The position of the Mute Swan in the waterfowl family has been described in the life history of the Black Swan.

Life History

In Europe most wild birds inhabit lakes and lagoons and in winter congregate in bays and estuaries, but semi-domesticated birds can be found anywhere at all. Their movements are mainly local, but there is some migration from northern Europe to southern Europe and the Middle East in winter. Apart from the one record quoted of birds in the field, in Australia they seem to be entirely sedentary and seldom, if ever, leave the pond on which they live.

Watching Mute Swans feed in small rivers and water meadows in Europe one is constantly reminded of the feeding behaviour of Black Swans. The food has not been studied in detail, but in England the Mute Swan seems to eat mainly waterweeds and sometimes grazes on land. It has been reported to occasionally eat small fish and amphibia and to attack and drown ducklings and young coots and moorhens, traits that have not yet been seen in Black Swans.

Mute Swans pair for life. Females do not nest until they are two or three years old. The nests are usually on small islands or in vegetation in shallow water. Unlike the Black Swan, which often nests in colonies, they are very pugnacious and solitary in the breeding season. Nest construction and incubation are by the female only, but the male savagely defends the area. The nest itself is a very large and sturdy heap of whatever vegetation is available. In Australia the breeding season is in late winter and spring, but in parks, where the birds are sheltered and continually fed by tourists, it can occur at any time.

According to Kortright the clutch is 3 to 5 eggs in the first year of breeding, but up to 7 in the second year, and later it is 9 to 11 eggs.[67] The incubation period is 35 days. The eggs are dull greenish white with a very coarse shell and usually a thin coating of lime. They are very similar in appearance to the eggs of the Black Swan, but considerably larger. Eggs of Mute Swans vary in length from 112 to 124 mm. and in width from 71 to 89 mm.

Freckled Duck

Stictonetta naevosa (Gould)

References

Stictonetta Reichenbach, Nat. Sys. Vog., 9, 1852.

Anas naevosa Gould, P.Z.S., p. 177, 1840. (Western Australia.)

Other Names

Oatmeal Duck, Monkey Duck, Diamantina Duck, Speckled Duck.

Description

ADULT MALE. General colour above dark brown to almost black, the colour darkening with age, uniformly freckled with irregular oblong spots or freckles usually 2-3 mm. in length and 1-2 mm. wide, off-white or buff, the freckles smaller on the head and neck than elsewhere; underside, throat and foreneck, as back but lighter, owing to more extensive freckling; breast dark brown with freckles as back; remainder of underside, including undertail, pale brown freckled with white and rarely buff; wing, topside of primaries, dark brown; wing coverts, as back; underside of primaries light brown; wing lining white, variably blotched at front, merging into brown blotched with white at rear; iris brown; legs and feet slate grey; bill slate grey, the bill distinctly dished above and heavy at the base, typical measurements of exposed culmen are length 5·6 cm., height at base 2·2 cm. In the breeding season the base of the bill is orange-red in colour.

ADULT FEMALE. As for male, but generally lighter in colour; ground colour of the topside, throat, and foreneck dark brown but never black; freckles buff or, less commonly, white, with less contrast between ground colour and freckles than in the male; iris brown; legs and feet slate grey; bill slate grey.

IMMATURE. Similar to female, but very much lighter in colour. The ground colour is light brown and the freckles deep buff.

DUCKLING. Topside uniform light grey with brown suffusion; upper side of wings the same; underside, lower abdomen light grey, almost white; throat light grey, darker towards base; underwing pale grey with darker trailing edge; head, crown dark grey, above eye inconspicuously freckled with darker grey, paler grey below than above eye; the down on the head has a black base, creamy grey centre and dark grey tip, on the body the down is uniformly grey; bill blue-grey, pink spot on nail; legs and feet blue-grey; webs buff; claws brown.

Size

	Weight *gm.*	*Length* *mm.*	*Wingspread* *mm.*	*Wing* *mm.*	*Bill* *mm.*
Adult Male					
Maximum	1130	591	867	258	59
Minimum	747	519	714	186	50
Average	969	556	822	232	54
Number measured	*63*	*57*	*42*	*62*	*63*
Adult Female					
Maximum	985	533	850	236	53
Minimum	691	480	732	205	46
Average	842	508	784	224	52
Number measured	*31*	*31*	*19*	*31*	*29*

Voice

Freckled Ducks are rarely heard to make much sound in the wild, and this has led to some colourful descriptions of their voice, which is quite unlike that of other ducks—"Its voice is likened to the grunt of a Berkshire pig", "between a sniff and a snort", and "like a belch backwards". Although the function of most of the sounds is not yet understood, at least they have now been recorded and are shown in the following figure. It is gratifying to find that expensive modern tape recorders and sound spectrographs show that the early descriptions of the voice were very apt.

The contact call of the downy ducklings is a shrill chirrup, uttered continuously (*a*); it is not unlike the rapid chirping of a cricket. The ducklings, a few weeks old, also possess the flute-like alarm call of the adults, the development of the call is from a chicken-like "cheep".

The alarm call is delivered with head and neck erect and the bill extended vertically. The sound is a soft, flute-like pipe, "whee-yu" (*b*). The posture and the sound itself are similar to those of the Black Swan. The identity call of adults is a soft, melodious, multisyllabic piping, often consisting of both short and long syllables as shown (*c*), but also sometimes only the single long note is used. Both the contact and identity calls are very soft and are inaudible from twenty yards' range. The alarm call has been recorded from both sexes, but the contact call has only been recorded, with certainty, so far from males.

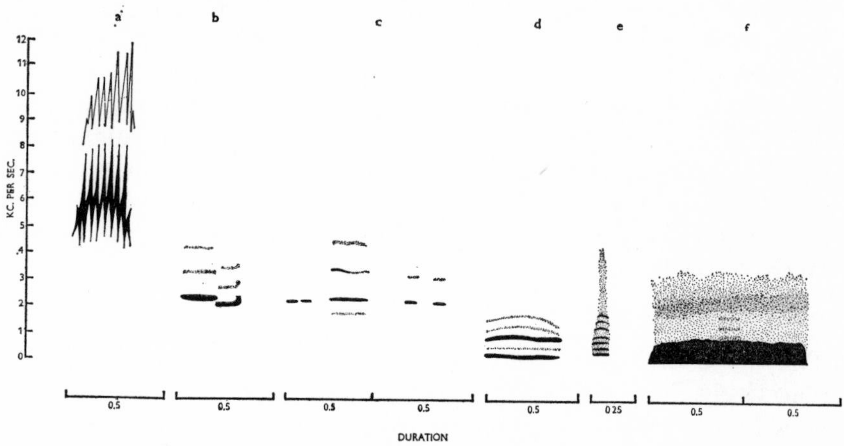

Diagram of sonograms of sounds made by Freckled Ducks.

Sounds believed to be the threat call have been induced by introducing an extra male to a pen containing a mated pair. Fighting follows between both members of the pair and the intruder. The resident female at this time utters a loud discordant quack (*d*) and the resident male a short, raucous roar (*e*), that is literally "between a sniff and a snort". Holding an adult male in the hand produces what is probably the distress call, a very loud, discordant bray (*f*); the example shown has $1\frac{1}{2}$ seconds duration, but examples continuing for 3-4 seconds have been recorded.

Routine

Although in dry seasons concentrations of several hundred Freckled Ducks occur, they are more usually found in family parties of five or six birds; a flock of more than twenty is unusual. Freckled Ducks are usually associated with other ducks, particularly Black Ducks, and there is no tendency to separate from them in flight; a few Freckled Ducks flying with Black Ducks can be very inconspicuous. They fly swiftly, at times, in open situations, but at other times are slow on the wing.

During the day Freckled Ducks rest in dense cover and are usually inconspicuous. Captive birds held in enclosures planted with cumbungi beat down the centres of the clumps and form roosting platforms, in a manner similar to that reported for the Magpie Goose. In open water, when no cover is available, they have a very characteristic habit of roosting on the tops of fence-posts and stumps protruding a few inches from the water, one bird to each post. In 1958 I saw a line of nearly two hundred Freckled Ducks sitting on a line of fence-posts, a remarkable sight.

Roosting by day in deep water, at dusk they fly to the shore to feed, cruising the shallows, and remain throughout the night. The flight at these times is slow and silent and just above the water. On large swamps they fly to the edge, but, when sheltered by box swamps on the plains, sometimes move a mile or more to lignum creeks or pools.

Field Recognition

The shape in flight is very characteristic, but difficult to describe objectively. The wings are smaller in proportion to the body size than those of a Black Duck, sharper, the neck is shorter and much thicker, and the head larger. The neck is depressed slightly in flight, giving the bird a hunched appearance. In flight, as the colour is uniform, the bird gives the impression of being much darker than it really is.

Overhead the common species are easily separated from the Freckled Duck by the underwing pattern. It lacks the white under-wings and light throat of the Black Duck, the apparently translucent wings of the Hardhead, and the light throat of the Grey Teal. It appears as a very dark bird in which the abdomen and proximal parts of the wings are much lighter than the remainder of the plumage.

On the water it must be distinguished from other ducks by subjective judgment, if the watcher is too distant to see that it lacks the white throat of the Grey Teal and the face pattern of the Black Duck. It is larger than the other common ducks, floats higher, and the head is noticeably heavier. The general impression is of a very dark, almost black, duck with a large pointed head.

Relationships

The relationship of the Freckled Duck to other waterfowl is not finally settled and recently has been the subject of much discussion.

John Gould first pointed out in 1838 that although in general appearance and habits it was like a dabbling duck it had a reticulate tarsus and no speculum and that the sexes had the same plumage, all characteristics of geese;[50] in 1899 Campbell showed a further similarity in its trachea, which was simple and had no bulla.[11] Delacour and Mayr recognized these peculiarities, but as they had no information at all on its life history or downy plumage, preferred to consider it tentatively an aberrant dabbling duck.[27] Verheyen later showed that it had some skeletal features that resembled geese and swans, particularly the number of vertebrae, and considered that it could be a separate subfamily of waterfowl, closely related to the geese and swans.[96] Later authors with no new information have considered that it might be Anserine after all.[62] It is probably not possible to settle the Freckled Ducks' relationships to everyone's satisfaction, since it combines features that, by one author or another, are considered characteristic of each subfamily. The most significant of these are summarized below.

Anseranatinae. In older male Freckled Ducks the trachea is coiled outside the sternum. Although the relative length of the coil is less than in *Anseranas,* where it extends beyond the breastbone, the situation is similar. The only other waterfowl with a similar elongated trachea are some of the swans, but in these it is inside the sternum. The Freckled Duck, however, is sharply distinguished from *Anseranas* by its skeletal characters, behaviour, colour pattern of young, moult, and most other biological characters.

Anserinae. It resembles the Anserinae in having a reticulate tarsus, simple syrinx without bulla, and simple plumage without speculum; sexual dimorphism is slight and there is probably a single annual moult. The colour pattern of the downy young is similar to that of the swans but quite unlike the Dendrocygnini or Cereopsini.[45, 46] Of the 14 skeletal characters listed by Woolfenden[101] to define the Anserinae it possesses six. Its whole deportment is swan-like—voice, feeding, walking, and swimming. Its life history, building elaborate nests at water-level and living in small family parties, is consistent with swans.

The behaviour is still under study, but its threat action of throwing the neck along the water and trumpeting, as well as its alarm reaction of throwing the head and bill vertical and calling in a flute-like whistle, are very reminiscent of swans. The very fact that little courtship display has been seen during close watches of many wild birds and of captives throughout the whole year suggests this is simple in nature as in the swans and geese.

Anatinae. Its shape and appearance are duck-like and its skeletal characters are predominantly those of the Anatinae. The downy duckling plumage has some similarity to those of the Oxyurini.

The study of the bird's biology, behaviour, and anatomy is continuing, but at present there seems no reason to consider its many Anserine features all to be the result of convergence. The simplest explanation is that the bird is Anserine, but not closely related to the Dendrocygnini or other tribes. I therefore place it as a separate mongeneric tribe of the Anserinae, the Stictonettini. Few would deny that the waterfowl family of today passed, in evolution, through duck-like ancestors before differentiating into swans, geese, and others. The Freckled Duck is probably the closest living waterfowl to that ancestor and is yet another of the several primitive survivals in Australia.

Habitat

The breeding habitat of the Freckled Duck is heavily vegetated areas of fresh water and these are also favoured at other times.[47] The water can be a permanent swamp or a freshly flooded creek. In inland New South Wales the greatest and most permanent populations are in the largest cumbungi swamps and the most permanent lignum swamps. In coastal districts the densest of the tea-tree swamps are the most favoured breeding habitats.

In the non-breeding season, and in dry weather generally, many Freckled Ducks remain in the cumbungi swamps; others move more widely and are found in lagoons, billabongs, and lakes, but I have never seen or heard of breeding in these situations, nor do the birds usually stay there very long. In flood also birds leave the cumbungi swamps, but avoid the areas of open floodwater; instead they disperse throughout the newly flooded lignum and cane-grass creeks and swamps. There is little doubt that the present distribution and numbers of Freckled Ducks are limited by the availability of permanent cumbungi and tea-tree swamps.

Distribution and Movements

There are records of Freckled Ducks from most parts of Australia, at one time or another, but there is little doubt that most of these birds were vagrants. They are only found regularly in a few parts of the Murray-Darling Basin in the south-east and in the extreme south-west of Western Australia. In Western Australia they breed regularly at Benger, south of Perth, and at Moora, north of that city, and occasionally elsewhere in the south-west. The regular range in Western Australia is very limited, but vagrants, and some breeding, probably occur more widely in good seasons than published records suggest. In New South Wales they are not uncommon throughout the Riverina district, including the Murrumbidgee and Lachlan rivers from Narrandera to Balranald. In this region there are two places where Freckled Ducks may always be found, and

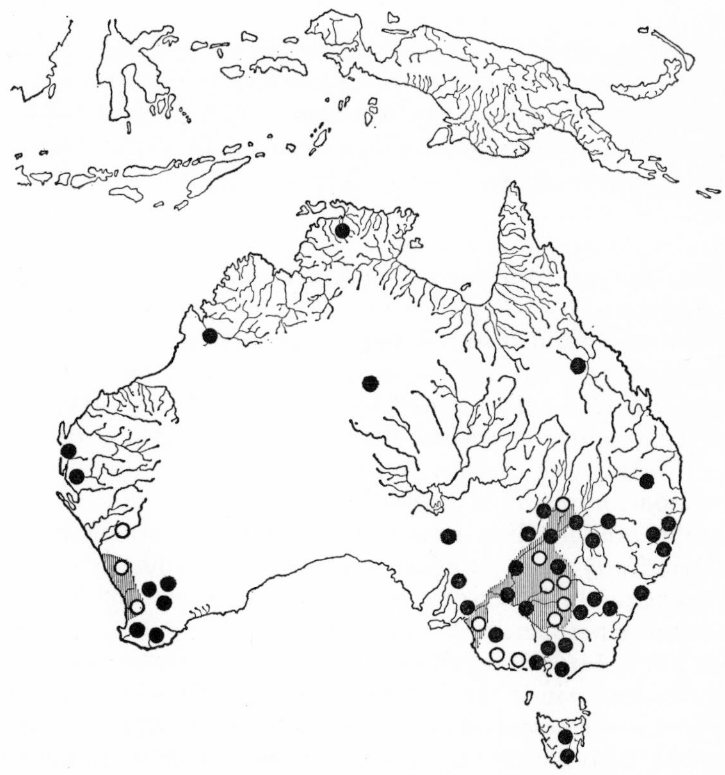

DISTRIBUTION OF THE FRECKLED DUCK

The spots indicate districts in which Freckled Ducks have been recorded; only one record for each district is shown. The open circles refer to breeding records. In the shaded area Freckled Ducks are found, even if in small numbers, at all times in most years.

some breeding occurs in most, and probably, all years. These are Barrenbox Swamp, a large permanent cumbungi swamp near Griffith, and the reedbeds, also largely cumbungi, at the junction of the Lachlan and Murrumbidgee rivers. Freckled Ducks are found in the lignum swamps and creeks of the two rivers whenever these contain water, but breeding only occurs there, and in the box clumps, following really extensive flooding. At these times, as in 1950, 1955, and 1956, there is widespread breeding throughout the lignum areas west of Booligal and Hillston on the Lachlan River, that is, in the complex of channels and swamps of Merrowie, Merungle, Merrimajeel, and Muggabah creeks, and along the Willandra creek. There is also widespread breeding in flood time in the temporary creeks and swamps on the plains south of the Murrumbidgee River.

Beyond these areas, in eastern Australia, breeding is known to occur regularly in the cumbungi swamps of the central and lower Murray River, the denser tea-tree swamps of south-east South Australia near Naracoorte and Keith, and in some of the lakes of the channel country of south-west Queensland, whenever these are flooded.

In the Australian Museum there is a specimen of a downy duckling derived from an egg hatched under a domestic fowl at West Maitland, New South Wales. It is not known if the egg was collected locally, but if so it is one of the very few records of coastal nesting in eastern Australia known to the author. Jackson collected one egg near Grafton in 1892.[61] In view of the birds' preference for permanent, dense swamps and the former abundance of this habitat on the North Coast of New South Wales, perhaps the species bred there in some numbers in the early days.

In the non-breeding season Freckled Ducks are nomadic and move erratically throughout the breeding range and beyond. At this time flocks might be encountered almost anywhere in inland Australia. Where permanent, heavily vegetated swamps occur small concentrations of birds develop, so that one can be reasonably certain of finding examples in the same area throughout the winter and spring. Elsewhere movements are less predictable and most records refer to nomadic groups that arrive in the area, remain a few days, and then disappear.

In dry seasons their movements are more extensive, in common with those of most other ducks of the inland. In 1957, a year of drought, as the surface water and small swamps in inland New South Wales dried, Freckled Ducks concentrated on the few larger, more permanent waters. One such group developed on Lake Merrimajeel near Booligal, where there were 200 birds present in January 1958. This number had increased to 600 by April 1958, associated with many thousands of Teal and Pink-eared Ducks, and by June 1958 they had dispersed. A similar concentration was reported by Hobbs near Wentworth and several other smaller groups were observed, for example, about 300 on Barrenbox Swamp near Griffith, 100 on Lake Ballyrogan near Hillston, and 150 on Lake Cowal. This total of over 1600 Freckled Ducks in these few areas in one part of their range makes the estimate of a total Australian population of 2000 to 3000 birds mentioned by Weller (in Delacour), from an unquoted source, seem a gross underestimate.

Following drought-induced dispersal of concentrations, extensive movements of Freckled Duck occur, and most of the records of the species in places distant from the normal breeding range occurred in years of drought. Thus the specimen from Botany Bay, New South Wales, was collected in 1889, the year following what was the greatest drought in history to that time. The next record in that area was in 1897, following the disastrous droughts in 1895 and 1896, and there were no further records until 1958, following the 1957 drought. Similarly the records at Ulmarra, 1897, and Armidale, New South Wales, 1892, the sole record from North-west Cape, Western Australia, 1884, and those from Tasmania and the Alligator River, Northern Territory, 1902, all followed years of inland drought. The record at Alice Springs in 1958 was in another drought year, as were the records for north Queensland.

It seems probable that the movement pattern of the Freckled Duck is similar to that of the Black Duck. That is, it is basically sedentary, normally having little need for extensive movement because of the permanent nature of its habitat, but it possesses the ability to move to exploit newly formed habitat and to move very widely to escape prolonged drought.

Feeding

Freckled Ducks in the wild have been watched filtering food from the surface of the water, up-ending and dabbling with other ducks and wading along the shore in shallow water, and the feeding actions have been watched with captive birds.[42]

Captive ducklings have been maintained, in an open-air pen, with a very liquid mash provided in a bowl and were first seen feeding when two days old. The action was a filtering one, with only the tip of the bill immersed, and a noticeable swirl was set up. By four days of age they paid much attention to sprouting bird seed in the enclosure, nibbling the green shoots, and were seen to nibble occasionally at the soil, presumably to secure grit. On the fourth day of age, when placed in a small pond covered with floating duckweed *Lemna,* they fed freely on it, swam slowly, and rapidly filtered the plants from the surface; occasionally the head was completely immersed. These feeding actions were continued until, at 74 days of age, they were released into a large pen with an earth floor and provided with a small running stream. The food provided in the pen was mash in a bowl, small seed on the ground, floating, and in water one to two inches deep, and floating duckweed. The birds forthwith abandoned the mash and from then on fed entirely by filtering seed and duckweed from the water's surface and from water one to two inches deep.

Adult captive birds, maintained on a pond two-thirds of an acre in extent, have three main feeding actions. Bottom filtering is by far the most common method of feeding; the birds wade slowly in shallow water, seldom more than two inches deep. The bill is immersed and is held immediately above the soil surface and a rapid filtering action is set up so that the fine particles of mud on the surface swirl up. It has been possible to watch this action at very close range (two feet) in perfectly clear water on several occasions. The bill has not yet been seen to enter the mud itself, but is maintained immediately above it—a true filtering, rather than a dabbling, action.

Filtering of surface water is the least frequently seen. The action is exactly similar to that of the Shoveler and numerous other dabbling ducks. The birds swim slowly, filtering and nibbling at surface particles. Captive birds spend a great deal of time running their bills along the edges of logs and posts and concrete walls in the water that have become encrusted with algae. The bill action is nibbling and they have been clearly seen to be feeding extensively on the algae.

Like many other ducks, Freckled Ducks up-end, but their action under water seems to be different. Captive birds, placed in a glass tank with two feet of water, up-ended freely, and again it was seen that filtering was confined to immediately above the surface of the soil on the bottom. The birds did not dabble in the mud, nor did they pay attention to plants and food items on the bottom. When freshly caught birds were released on the pond most of their time was spent up-ending, but this was soon abandoned in favour of bottom filtering. The pond already carried various dabbling ducks, so, presumably, food was only abundant where it was placed on and near the edge of the water, up-ending thus being unprofitable. Up-ending was practically confined to water about two feet deep; it was rarely attempted in deeper water and seldom in shallow. Two feet is about the depth in which a Freckled Duck can reach the bottom. Occasionally the birds have been seen to immerse their heads and necks only, but it has not been possible to determine the action of the bill under water.

There have been very few notes on the food of Freckled Ducks; Gould reported that gizzards contained "small fish and minute shells", and Hobbs watched a flock feeding on floating waterweed. The only quantitative data are from 27 gizzards that I collected between 1952 and 1964, mainly in lignum and cumbungi swamps near Griffith, New South Wales.

One of the most constant sources of food was algae, nearly every stomach examined contained some and it accounted for 30 per cent of the total volume; seeds of smartweeds and docks were also found in most stomachs and provided 22 per cent of the food. Various aquatic grasses, including barnyard-grass and water couch, which are important to most inland ducks, were also eaten by Freckled Ducks and were found in 60 per cent of the birds and accounted for 16 per cent of the food. Other plant food included the seeds of many aquatic plants, sedges, nardoo, clovers, and thistles; usually these were found in only one or two of the stomachs.

Most birds contained some insects, but these only provided 6 per cent of the total food, and although a few crustaceans and shells were found these were not important. The whole bulk of the animal food accounted for 11 per cent of the total food.

Breeding

Nothing has been recorded of the pairing behaviour of the Freckled Duck in the wild or in captivity. I have seen nothing beyond a few head-bobbings that could have been mating behaviour. Although the full story is not told yet, all my experience suggests that the displays are very simple indeed.

In the breeding season the males assume a red base to the bill, but little is known of the persistence of the red coloration or its exact relationship to the breeding season or sexual cycle. At all seasons the location of the red area can be recognized as a different coloured and textured area; it is generally lighter in colour than the rest of the bill, no doubt owing to a proliferation of blood-vessels beneath the surface. Captive males began to assume the red coloration at ten months of age. They required three weeks before it was fully developed and it was retained for at least five months. In their second year it remained for five months again, though there was no breeding. Males captured in November, when egg-laying had been finished for at least twelve weeks locally, judged from the numbers of juvenile birds in the flocks, retained the red bill for a further six weeks in captivity.

Many ducks of the inland have erratic breeding seasons strongly influenced by climatic factors, particularly the flooding of the rivers and billabongs.[40] Some species, for example, Grey Teal and Pink-eared Ducks, have breeding seasons that are almost completely controlled by changes in the water-level, whereas others, those more characteristic of deep permanent swamps, have more regular breeding, a part of the population breeding each year and at about the same time. These species, the Black Duck and probably the Hardhead, however, retain the capacity to breed also at any time of the year that exceptionally favourable conditions occur.

When there is a major flood all ducks breed and each species has a definite place in a time sequence of breeding related to the water conditions; some breed on a rising water-level and some on a declining one. It is more meaningful to refer to the position of a species' breeding season in that sequence than to allot it to a specific season or month. In this connection the generalized statements of the breeding season of the Freckled Duck that appear in standard textbooks, for example, September to November, are often misleading.

Most records of Freckled Duck's breeding refer to the period September to December. There are, however, two records that do not fit into this period. In April 1906 a clutch was taken in the Macquarie Marshes, New South Wales (Australian Museum Collection). Seven nests with eggs were seen by M. Schraeder in Bullawarra Lake, south-western Queensland, on 9th April 1955. Both these out-of-season records were associated with exceptionally heavy rainfall and flooding. In 1906 the average annual rainfall was exceeded twofold in central New South Wales and there was extensive flooding on the Macquarie River. In 1955 Bulloo Lake underwent one of its rare replenishments, owing to exceptional rain in south-west Queensland. Both events suggest that Freckled Ducks, like other inland species, can be stimulated to breed by excessive rain or flood, and observations made at Griffith, New South Wales, support this idea.

Freckled Duck nests or broods are rarely seen and populations are not large enough to permit regular sampling for examination of the birds' sexual state. It has been possible, however, to secure some data at Griffith on the breeding periods in most years between 1952 and 1963. Briefly, 1952, 1955, and 1956 were years of extensive flooding; 1954, 1957, and 1958 were years of low water-levels and mild drought; in the other years there was rain normal for the district and the rivers rose each spring to replenish the billabongs, but there was no significant flooding.

In the flood years 1952, 1955, and 1956 breeding of Freckled Duck was widespread and the breeding season extended. In 1952 a rise in level began in April on the Murrumbidgee and in May on the Lachlan, and by mid June many thousands of square miles were flooded. Grey Teal began breeding in early June, Black Duck in early July, and Pink-eared Duck in August.

The age of young ducks and the sexual state of adults collected showed that the Freckled Ducks began breeding in mid June and continued until at least mid September. At Booligal, ninety miles west of Griffith, I found two clutches, and the late Miss Turner, of Angora, several more; these, together with the dissection of birds collected, showed breeding here continued until at least the end of September.

In 1955 the Murrumbidgee River flooded in July, and breeding of Grey Teal began in late July and continued until the end of October; Black Ducks bred earlier than usual and the first clutch was begun on 21st July and the last on 29th August. Freckled Ducks examined in August were not in breeding condition, but those collected in September were, leaving no doubt the breeding had begun later than in the Black Duck.

Exceptionally severe floods began in March 1956. Breeding of Grey Teal began in late March and was still in progress on 10th January 1957. Black Ducks bred between 6th May and 10th August 1956. Freckled Ducks were present, but there was no evidence of breeding until 28th September, when a pre-flying juvenile was shot. This bird could only have hatched in early July. On the same day a brood about four weeks old was pursued, indicating that the eggs had been laid in mid August. Birds in breeding condition were collected in January. Clearly in this great flood Freckled Ducks had a very extended breeding season, from July 1956 to January 1957.

In each other year, until 1965, Freckled Ducks have been collected periodically, but birds in breeding condition have only been found in the period September to November.

Benger, Western Australia, is in the winter-rainfall belt, and Benger Swamp floods annually. The first rains begin in May and the swamp is usually full by the beginning of June. It declines in level during summer and is finally drained for agricultural purposes in December. When the swamps flood all local species of ducks colonize it and breed. Since 1958 Mr R. Taylor has regularly patrolled the swamp by canoe and searched for and recorded duck-nesting data. He has kindly allowed me to peruse his journals.

The duck-breeding season at Benger is quite regular and follows the regular seasonal flooding, with the slight variation of two or three weeks from year to year, according to the detail of the rainfall and flooding regime. Black Ducks breed between June and October, Hardheads in October and November, and Freckled Ducks between October and December. Clearly at Benger, as in New South Wales, the Freckled Duck breeds later in the season than the other species. It seems that the regulation of the breeding season is similar to that of the Black Duck and Hardhead and unlike the Grey Teal and Pink-eared Duck. The breeding season is basically regular, but at least some birds retain the ability to breed at other times of the year in order to exploit exceptionally favourable conditions when they occur.

Nest

I have only examined two authenticated nests; in each case they were well-constructed bowl-shaped structures of fine sticks of lignum, with some *Eleocharis*, placed in lignum bushes in 4 feet of water, at water-level. Seven nests examined by M. Schraeder in south-west Queensland were similar but placed one to two feet above water-level, in a declining swamp; probably they were built at an earlier water-level. R. Taylor records that he has not yet seen a nest of this description; those he has observed have been built in hollows among flood rubbish in the bases of trees and in artificial sites built by him for the birds' convenience.

The observation (Frith, in Delacour) that the down in Freckled Ducks' nests is used as a lining to the nest, whereas in those of other ducks it is distributed among the eggs, must be withdrawn. Since then I have seen ground nests of Chestnut Teal, Shovelers, and Black Ducks that have had a similar conformation of down, probably due to the mechanical effects of moving the eggs during incubation. A similar state of affairs probably exists for the Freckled Duck.

Clutch Size

The clutch size has been reported as 5 to 7. Clutch data collected by the author, R. Taylor, and M. Schraeder, when combined with

Upper: Freckled Duck; juvenile male in characteristic roosting posture on a submerged log.

Lower: Head of Freckled Duck, showing bill and head shape.

Photos by Ederic Slater

Cape Barren Geese, Kangaroo Island, S.A. *Photos by Ederic Slater*

data of clutches held by Australian Museums, show that the clutch varies from 5 to 14 eggs, with 7 as the commonest clutch and 7·4 as the mean clutch size. The distribution of size among 19 clutches was as below.

Number of eggs:	5	6	7	8	9	10	14
Number of clutches:	3	1	7	1	3	2	1

Eggs

The size of the eggs reported by Serventy and Whittel, 58 mm. by 42 mm., and adopted by Delacour, was possibly based on a clutch of eggs not properly authenticated and perhaps refers to the Hardhead.[88] Freckled Duck's eggs are normally larger, and 62 eggs measured in length 60-65 mm. (average 63 mm.) and in breadth 45-48 mm. (average 47 mm.).

One completely authenticated clutch, that is, with the female collected on the nest, was recorded at Bool Lagoon, South Australia, in 1946 (Hood pers. comm.); the eggs' measurements were as below: 64·4 mm. by 45·6 mm., 64·3 mm. by 47·0 mm., 64·0 mm. by 46·5 mm., 63·2 mm. by 46·5 mm., 60·0 mm. by 43·3 mm., 62·2 mm. by 47·5 mm.

The eggs examined by the author differ from those described by Delacour as "thick pale greenish white . . . resembling those of the Grey Duck". The eggs are cream or ivory in colour, glossy and smooth; the shell is thick and softer than other duck eggs. They are less pointed and more nearly oval than the eggs of the Black (Grey) Duck. The size and appearance of the eggs have been correctly described by North.[82]

Incubation

Incubation takes 26 to 28 days, according to R. Taylor.

Development of Ducklings

The only notes on young Freckled Ducks are those concerning a brood reared in captivity by Miss Nicholls of C.S.I.R.O. Division of Wildlife Research in Perth and later by myself in Canberra.[42]

One dead one-day-old duckling measured 180 mm. in length and weighed 43 grammes. Its bill was 20 mm. long, tarsus 23 mm., and wing 23 mm. At five days of age five other live ducklings weighed 60, 58, 52, 40 and 39 grammes.

At 14 days of age tail quills began to appear in the most advanced birds, and by 18 days the quills of the primaries and those of the secondaries were beginning to burst. At 23 days of age there were a few feathers on the flanks, back, and elsewhere. By the time the ducklings were 32 days old the breasts were almost completely feathered and the primaries were beginning to grow. The crown, nape of neck, back, and rump were still covered with down. The growth of the primaries and disappearance of remaining down continued steadily until the primaries were fully developed during the ninth week of age. At this time the birds were in complete juvenile plumage. This plumage was similar in both sexes, but differed from that of the adult plumage in being a much lighter brown and having much deeper buff marking.

This rate of plumage development is similar to that of Chestnut Teal and Black Duck reared in captivity. In the Chestnut Teal the first body feathers appeared at 20-29 days of age, the primaries were one inch long at 52-65 days and fully grown at 58-80 days. In the Black Duck these stages were reached at 21-29, 45-65, and 54-69 days respectively. At 37 weeks of age the Freckled Ducks underwent a complete moult and assumed the adult plumage that has been described. For the first time the sexes could be distinguished.

Status

The status of the Freckled Duck is anomalous; most birds breed in New South Wales and many wander to neighbouring States where there is less breeding but where useful drought refuges exist. In New South Wales its rarity is recognized and it is legally protected from shooting, but elsewhere it is considered a game bird and is shot. The efforts of New South Wales to conserve the bird can be jeopardized, especially in droughts when much of the inland population gathers in permanent waters in other States.

It is commonly associated with Black Ducks and other game species and, although it is very distinctive in flight, many shooters claim inability to recognize it, in defence of their legal but unethical act of shooting. A skilled shooter who knows his ducks and selects the bird he wishes to shoot in a flock never seems to secure Freckled Ducks. It is less attractive as food than the other common game ducks, but is quite acceptable.

Although the Freckled Duck is not so rare as is sometimes suggested, it is among the less common of all Australian ducks and one of the rarer waterfowl of the world. Although quite widely distributed, it is not numerous and its main populations are supported by a very small number of permanent swamps, mainly in inland New South Wales, the population being augmented by occasional flooding of suitable areas of the inland, which permits more extensive breeding.

The future of the main breeding swamps is by no means secure; many are merely storage areas for drainage water from the irrigation areas, this water being subsequently used for other purposes. It is not difficult to imagine that a change in policy of the controlling body, or an increased demand for this water, could eliminate the swamps as other similar ones have been recently eliminated.

The more natural breeding areas in the lignum creeks and swamps of the Lachlan and Murrumbidgee rivers are in serious jeopardy, as the present trend of water conservation and usage on these rivers is to decrease the frequency of flooding of the effluents and the replenishment of the swamps. The districts in which Freckled Ducks breed in the greatest numbers in South Australia and south-west Western Australia are the present locations of vigorous drainage programmes.

The Freckled Duck's position is insecure and it could decline rather rapidly with further destruction of its habitat. Work in progress suggests that it is a rather unique primitive species, perhaps closer to the original stock of the Family Anatidae than any other present-day species, and on these grounds alone urgent consideration should be given to positive measures for its conservation.

Source of Data

The ecology and behaviour of the Freckled Duck is now under study by C.S.I.R.O. Division of Wildlife Research. This account is based on preliminary results of this study.[42]

Cape Barren Goose

Cereopsis novaehollandiae Latham

References

Cereopsis Latham, Index Orn. Sup., p. 67, 1801.
Cereopsis novaehollandiae Latham, Index Orn. Sup., p. 67, 1801. (Bass Strait.)

Other Name

Pig Goose.

Description

ADULT MALE. General colour ash grey, head paler and having a white crown; short scapulars have a broad dark-grey subterminal bar and the longer ones an oval spot; wing coverts marked as scapulars; primaries grey, the terminal half being black; secondaries grey with black tips; upper tail coverts and upper side of tail black; underside grey, except for tail which is black; iris hazel brown; feet black; tarsus varies from pale pink to deep carmine, and black from feet extends upwards in variable distance; bill black; cere covers much of the bill and is greenish-yellow.

ADULT FEMALE. Similar to male.

DUCKLING. Very boldly marked; top of head, back of neck, and upper surface, dark brown, there is a broad light-grey stripe on each side of back; underside light grey; face grey with broad black-brown stripe extending through eye; wing black-brown with pale-grey leading edge; bill black with green cere; legs and feet grey-green; iris black.

Plumage

The Cape Barren Goose has one moult each year, after the breeding season. There is a legend that at this time it does not pass through a flightless period, moulting the primaries successively. This, however, is not so, the primaries are moulted simultaneously as in most other waterfowl, and for a period the birds are flightless.

Size

There are very few measurements available. For fourteen adult males collected in the 1965 open season the following were recorded: weight 3700-5100 grammes, length 750-910 mm., wingspread 1370-1620 mm., wing 450-490 mm., bill (including cere) 48-53 mm. According to Mathews, females are slightly smaller.

Voice

The females have a low-pitched grunt; males also grunt, but in addition have a fairly high-pitched, rapid multisyllabic honk or trumpet. On the ground they are usually quiet, except when alarmed or displaying, but in flight are very vocal.

Routine

Cape Barren Geese are most characteristic of small islands, where they favour beaches, rocky prominences, and grassed areas; they are seldom found in scrub except when breeding. They are occasionally found on the edge of lagoons and in grassy fields on the larger islands and occasionally on the mainland.

They are usually found in small groups, and flocks of non-breeding birds occur at all times of the year. The flocks are usually small but have been recorded as large as three hundred birds. It is not known if there is any social organization in the flock other than that within the families composing it, but field observations suggest that there is not.

They are grazing birds, are usually on land and seldom enter the water, except when wounded or when pursued with their young. In this last case young and adults readily enter the sea and swim strongly, but except where beaches exist have difficulty in regaining the shore. They fly strongly and are very wary and alert, being difficult to approach. When approached they walk away with heads erect, breaking into a lumbering run and taking wing to leave the area.

Field Identification

The bird cannot be confused with any other. On land it is a large, long-legged, grey goose-like bird, usually seen with head erect, watching the observer.

Flying away it is uniform grey in colour, except for the tail and wing-tips, which are black; from below the pattern is the same, grey body with black undertail and wing-tips. When close by the pink legs and prominent green cere are easily seen and diagnostic, if any special mark is needed.

Relationships

The Cape Barren Goose has confused taxonomists since its first discovery and its relationships are still not finally settled.

The first specimen to have reached European notice was caught by Jacques-Julien Houten de Labillardière in the Recherche Archipelago in 1792. He thought it a swan:

> . . . on the same island there was a numerous flock of swans, several of which allowed themselves to be taken by hand, but the rest, apprised of the danger, immediately flew away. This new species is somewhat smaller than our wild swan, and of an ash-coloured grey, a little lighter on the belly. The bill is blackish with a tumour of sulphur-yellow at its base.

It was dubbed *Cygne cendre.* The French zoologist Vieillot first thought the bird to be the young of the Black Swan, but later named it *Anser griseus,* that is, a true goose. Latham, however, had proposed the new genus *Cereopsis* and refrained from giving it the vernacular name "Goose"; he preferred to call it the New Holland *Cereopsis* and was obviously unsure of its exact relationships.

In shape and colour it is not unlike the true geese of the Northern Hemisphere, Anserini. It has a reticulate tarsus and syrinx without bulla, both characters suggesting ancient origin, but the colour pattern of the downy ducklings, as well as some aspects of its behaviour, suggest the South American Kelp Goose *Chloephaga.* Although still doubtful, Delacour and Mayr[27] placed it tentatively with the Tadornini, that is, as an aberrant Shelduck. It is widely held to be similar and related to the extinct New Zealand Goose *Cnemiornis,* and there has been a recent attempt to revive the idea that it is a true goose on the basis of some of its behaviour patterns.

There is no doubt that the bird is correctly placed in the subfamily Anserinae, and all that remains now is to determine its status in that subfamily. Although future anatomical and behavioural work may change the situation, the proposition of Woolfenden, from a comparative study of waterfowl skeletons, is the best compromise at present. He showed that the Cape Barren Goose had skeletal affinities with both the true geese and the shelducks, but were more similar to the geese, so proposed a separate tribe, the Cereopsini;[101] this suggestion is followed here.

Habitat

The Cape Barren Goose breeds on islands. Those of the Furneaux Group on which they breed vary in size from Isabella Island of 20 acres to Badger of 2,500 acres. Most of these islands are low-lying and vegetated with grass, *Poa* tussocks, and some scrub, and have rocky shores.

The two most important breeding islands are Chappell and Goose Islands and these differ ecologically.[52] Chappell is low-lying to the north but reaches a stony peak, which is avoided by the geese, at the southern end. The island is covered with scrub of barilla, *Atriplex cinerea*, box, *Rhagodia baccata*, and various other shrubs and small trees. Geese breed throughout the scrub. Goose Island is low-lying and the northern end, where most geese breed, is vegetated with *Poa* and short grasses, including barley-grass *Hordeum*, rye-grass *Lolium*, and some herbs. There is no scrub and only a few clumps of boxthorn. It would appear that the birds are fairly elastic in their requirements for breeding habitat.

During the summer many remain on the breeding islands, but others range over the larger Flinders and Cape Barren islands as well as coastal districts on the mainland, and are found in open grasslands and on the edges of lagoons and swamps, wherever green grazing is available.

Distribution and Movements

The birds are widely distributed on islands of the southern coast, from the Furneaux Group off the north-east coast of Tasmania in the east to the Recherche Archipelago off Western Australia, but the detailed distribution is known only in the Furneaux Group, there having been no comprehensive survey of other areas. It is usually assumed that the Furneaux Group is the "stronghold" of the species, but there are many birds elsewhere that perhaps contribute more to the over-all numbers than is generally realized.

The surveys and census of geese have been most thorough in the Furneaux Group, owing to the efforts of the Tasmanian Animals and Birds Protection Board, which has conducted air surveys of the area each year since 1957, during the breeding season.[51, 52] Of the 47 islands and reefs recognized by the workers geese have been seen, at least once, on 43 and breeding regularly on 19 of them.

The most important breeding islands in the Furneaux Group are

Chappell, which in 1964 had 85 breeding pairs, Goose with 25 breeding pairs, and Badger and Vansittart with 20 pairs each. Other breeding islands in the group include Kangaroo, Green, Woody, Little Woody, Long, Boxen, Tin Kettle, Little Dog, Big Dog, Little Green, Chalky, Wybalaena, Sentinel, and Killiecrankie. It is to be noted that there is no breeding on the two large islands of the group, Flinders and Cape Barren.

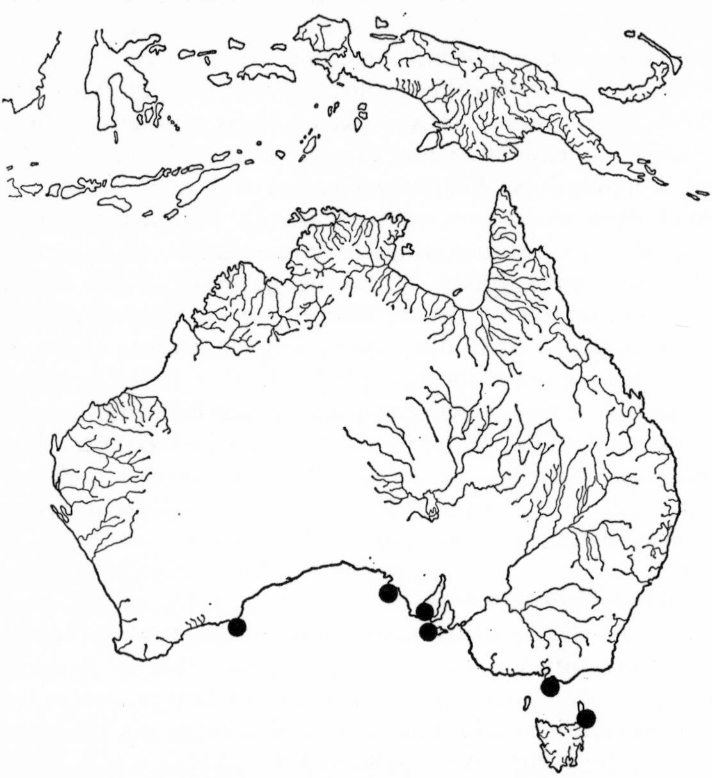

DISTRIBUTION OF THE CAPE BARREN GOOSE

The black spots show islands where breeding is known to occur. In summer scattered groups might be found on the mainland, and in north-east Tasmania, adjacent to these breeding areas.

It has long been known that geese formerly existed and bred in the Anser and Glennie groups of islands, off Wilson's Promontory, Victoria, but, strangely, it was not until 1964 that naturalists landed on those islands and confirmed the continued presence of geese there. Illegal shooters had apparently been landing there for years.

Geese were seen on Wattle, Anser, and Kanowna islands in the Anser Group and Great Glennie, Dannevig, Citadel, and McHugh islands in the Glennie Group, in numbers up to forty. Nests were found on Great Glennie Island, and the observers concluded that probably over one hundred pairs of birds were breeding in the area.[31]

Cape Barren Geese are also known to occur on the Kent and Hogan groups in Bass Strait. These groups, with the Furneaux and Anser and Glennie groups, form a chain of islands from the Tasmanian to the Victorian coast, so that from the air one is never out of sight of land.

In South Australia Cape Barren Geese are known to breed on Kangaroo Island, various islands in Spencer Gulf, in the Investigator Group, and in Nuyts Archipelago, but the data are fragmentary. In the Joseph Banks Group there were at least 120 geese in the winter of 1964, mainly on Winceby Island; breeding is reputed to occur in this group but has not been recently recorded. In the Investigator Group at least 30 geese and 14 broods of young were seen on Waldegrave Island in 1964. Geese are seen on islands of Nuyts Archipelago whenever it is visited; breeding has not been reported, though there seems little doubt that it occurs there. On Kangaroo Island an introduced colony thrives and usually numbers 200 to 250, and about 100 birds are fledged each year.

The data from the Archipelago of the Recherche, Western Australia, are even more fragmentary. The Archipelago extends for a hundred miles off the south coast of Western Australia. It was visited by a party from the Australian Geographical Society in November 1950, at which date most birds might have been expected to have left the breeding islands and most young to have been on the wing.[87] Small numbers of geese were seen on Figure of Eight, Boxer, Sandy Hook, Long, Hastings, Cliff, Termination, Round, Wedge, Combe, Douglas, Christmas, and Thomas islands. Clearly the birds are still very widespread in the Archipelago. A commentary was offered on the success of the protection laws locally: "Fresh cartridges were picked up on Thomas Island on the visit on March 1952. Also since many geese are openly kept in local fowlyards it is obvious that the law is being flouted with impunity."

Little is known of the movements of individual birds, since very few have yet been banded and there have been no detailed observations on the bird's distribution outside the breeding season. In the Furneaux Group, however, it is apparent that, following the breeding season, many birds quit the breeding islands and the population becomes more widely distributed throughout the group and on the more open parts and lagoons of Flinders Island. At the same time flocks appear in coastal districts of South Australia and Victoria. The numbers of these flocks are not great and their presence is often a closely guarded secret of the landholders on whose land they occur. Groups of 50 to 60 spend the summer on the mainland near Wilson's Promontory and at half a dozen localities in western Victoria and south-east South Australia. The largest summer concentrations known occur round Lake Alexandrina and Lake Albert in South Australia, where in summer as many as 500 birds occur.

It is commonly believed that these mainland flocks are derived from the Furneaux Group, but this has not been established. It might be significant that great numbers of birds remain in the Furneaux Group during the summer and that, despite its relative proximity to the group, few Cape Barren Geese visit north-east Tasmania. In view of the existence of breeding populations of unknown size on other island groups nearer the mainland, it seems probable that many of the mainland flocks are derived from near by, and their size suggests that the populations beyond the Furneaux Group may be larger than suspected. A recently established programme of marking the birds with coloured neck collars by the three eastern States will probably soon demonstrate the scale of movements of individual birds and the source of each mainland flock. Occasionally Cape Barren Geese wander farther afield, and there are reliable reports of their reaching the Riverina in 1956, a year of flood.

From the scattered references that remain it is difficult to form an accurate idea of the birds' former abundance on the mainland. It is generally assumed that this has declined very greatly during the last eighty years, but the evidence available is contradictory. According to correspondents of Mathews,[74] the goose at the turn of the century was "a common inhabitant of the western plains of Victoria" during the summer, and in 1906 Frank Smith reported that in one day "I counted two flocks, feeding on a bank in which there were 124 and 136 birds respectively. This was in February. In the summer (January) of 1906 I saw hundreds of the birds sprinkled (for over a mile) along a moist depression." Dennis[28] refers to them passing over the Western District of Victoria in considerable numbers. On the other hand, Campbell[12] recorded that "It occasionally visits the mainland or is driven thither through stress of weather" and finds cause for comment on an occasional small flock appearing near Melbourne. On balance, however, there seems to be no doubt that it formerly visited the mainland in greater numbers and in more localities than it does at present.

Feeding

The Cape Barren Goose feeds by grazing on land, the edge of lakes, and the seashore, but there has been no systematic or extensive study of its food preferences.

The only information on the food actually eaten comes from 44 stomachs that we collected during a short shooting season on Kangaroo, Badger, and Woody islands of the Furneaux Group in April 1965. The material was identified microscopically, since it was very finely divided.

The food in the stomachs was entirely vegetable and was predominantly grass-blades. Grasses were present in all stomachs and made up 65 per cent of the total bulk of food. The commonest grass was *Poa poaformis,* the common tussock of the islands; it was present in more than half of the stomachs. Other grasses included blades and a few seeds of the pasture-grass *Lolium perenne* (perennial rye), the cereal oats *Avena,* and the native spear-grass *Stipa,* wallaby-grass *Danthonia,* and barley-grass *Hordeum.* All the stomachs also contained various dicotyledonous leaves and seeds, including various clovers, medics, herbs, and succulents; 20 per cent of the sample contained some sedge, *Juncus.* Cape Barren Geese have also been seen on the seashore feeding on *Nitraria,* but this was not found in the small sample examined.

Breeding

Cape Barren Geese are found in pairs throughout the year and probably mate for life. Although they are at all times pugnacious and intolerant of others, courtship and fighting become more widespread and incessant with the approach of the breeding season. As early as February the pairs occupy their breeding territories and vigorously defend them.

The date of initiation of nest-building and laying varies from year to year, but the factors controlling it have not been studied; it has, however, been noted that when the summer and autumn are dry nest-building is delayed and restricted. It may occur as early as May, but June is more usual, and clutches are begun between May and August, though eggs have been as late as December. On the one island there is a very wide spread in time of egg-laying, some birds are still laying while other broods are fully fledged. Young goslings are usually found from early July, but the main hatching occurs in late July and mid August, which means that the main laying occurs in the period from late June to mid July.

The male assists with nest-building and fiercely defends the territory while the female is brooding. When the young leave the nest they are defended by both birds, who are very fierce and will attack any animal that approaches. They remain in their own territory until the young are about six weeks of age; the broods then amalgamate and are deserted by some of the parents. Groups of up to 50 young have been seen. As they fledge the young form nomadic flocks of up to 250 birds that quit their home island and wander throughout the group, with some older birds. In captivity they do not become sexually mature until three years of age.

Nest

There is a tendency for the nests to be built on the western side of the islands exposed to the prevailing winds. They are often on rocky prominences from which there is good visibility and beside tussocks, bushes, and rocks.[52] On some islands they are found throughout fairly dense scrub and occasionally in dense prickly boxthorn-trees or dense tea-trees 18 feet from the ground; the materials in these nests suggest that they have been carried up from the ground by the birds.

The nest is a heap of whatever material is at hand. The height ranges from 2 to 12 inches and the cup averages 3½ inches in depth and 8 inches in width. It is lined with grey down, and this material is used to cover the eggs when the female leaves the nest and the whole is obscured with nest material.

Nests are usually widely separated, owing to the birds' savage defence of their territory, but they have occasionally been found less than 20 yards apart. Nests are often found on the site of the previous season's nest or beside it, an observation that suggests that pairs may return to the same nest site.

Eggs

The eggs are elliptical, white in colour, with a layer of lime over the shell, which is coarse-textured and glossy; 123 eggs measured in length 73-92 mm. (average 83 mm.) and in breadth 44-59 mm. (average 56 mm.).[52]

Clutch

The number of eggs found in a nest varies from one to 7, with a mean of 4·1, although there are unconfirmed reports of up to 12 eggs in a nest. The number of eggs in 210 clutches was as below.[52]

Number of eggs:	1	2	3	4	5	6	7
Number of nests:	5	11	20	43	69	19	3

Incubation

Incubation time is 35 days.

Status

The status of the Cape Barren Goose has been in dispute for many years. Since its first discovery it has been considered an item of food to the local people and a bird prized by sportsmen, who feel that with proper management there is no reason why shooting cannot continue. Landholders in the breeding areas maintain that the birds consume forage, destroy newly sown pastures by trampling, and foul them with their droppings, so that domestic stock will not graze there; they seek permission to destroy birds in their pastures.

On the other hand, the Cape Barren Goose is one of the least numerous geese of the world, sharing this dubious distinction with Ross's Goose of far Northern Canada and the Ne-ne of Hawaii, which has verged on extinction. It is confined to Australia and is one of the unique species of waterfowl that are endemic to this continent and of extreme value for evolutionary study. It merits conservation on this basis. It is also an attractive bird that adds much to the beauty of the areas it graces, and for that reason alone has another very high claim to careful conservation.

Although effective conservation measures are now being introduced into its island haunts this has not always been so and the geese have suffered greatly at the hand of man in the past.

They have been persecuted and used for food since George Bass first noted them on islands off the Victorian coast in 1797. Following his exploratory voyage a sealing industry developed in Bass Strait, leading to great destruction of geese and their eggs. The final collapse of the sealing industry, with the virtual elimination of seals in the 1820s did not result in great relief for the geese, since by then many of the islands were populated by descendants of the sealers and aboriginal women, who continued to use them as food.

During the latter part of the nineteenth century settlers and their flocks occupied the islands, much land was cleared, and there were permanent residents on most of them. Geese were held in disfavour by settlers because of their grass-eating habits and alleged fouling of the pastures they did not eat. They were used for food and their numbers reduced by systematic egg-destruction. This last practice has now almost disappeared, but probably still occurs illegally sometimes.

Since 1946 there have been extensive land-clearing operations and pasture introduction on the large Flinders Island, and settlement has moved from the smaller islands. Although most are still leased for grazing purposes, none has permanent inhabitants, and unfavourable economic conditions are at present making grazing and farming there even less profitable.

At the same time as this decline in value of pastoral pursuits in the islands, which might have been expected to give the geese relief, increased transport facilities made them more available to mainland and Tasmanian sportsmen who could travel by air for a day's goose-shooting. Owing to the scattered nature of the islands, effective policing by the Tasmanian Government was virtually impossible. In 1959, however, the season was closed and it is now thought that illegal shooting has almost ceased. The other island groups on which Cape Barren Geese breed have had similar histories and have been the prey of sealers, fishermen, and mobile hunters until today, but although many of them have been declared sanctuaries none is policed in any way and illegal destruction still undoubtedly occurs.

In 1957 Dr E. R. Guiler of the Animals and Birds Protection Board of Tasmania began regular air surveys of many of the islands of the Furneaux Group to establish changes in numbers of the birds. In air surveys of this type usually all the birds are not seen, so the figures show the minimum populations, but when the same workers repeat the same route year after year relative changes in abundance can be measured approximately. In 1957 1616 geese were counted, and this number declined to 943 in 1960; at this time regular open seasons for Cape Barren Geese were discontinued and the numbers rose steadily to 2642 in 1964. In 1965 only 1605 geese were seen, but it was considered that owing to dry weather more geese than usual had remained on Flinders Island beyond the breeding areas. As geese require three years to come to breeding age, few of the birds reared since the increase began have yet begun to breed, so an accelerated increase in numbers may be expected in the next few years. There seems no doubt that a steady increase is already occurring in the Cape Barren Goose populations of the Furneaux Group, and this forecast is reassuring.

Elsewhere in eastern Australia the numbers of geese are no longer declining. The few small flocks that visit Victoria and the coastal parts of South Australia are increasing in size and numbers. It is possible that these increases are a reflection of the situation in the Furneaux Group, but it is more likely that it reflects increases in breeding populations on other, closer, island groups.

The increase in Cape Barren Geese in the Furneaux Group is

certainly due, in part, to the ending of legal shooting and more effective law enforcement in the area. However, other factors are involved and are perhaps of greater importance. Among these must be considered the decline in number of permanent inhabitants on the islands, with consequently less destruction and disturbance of the birds during the breeding season. Of unknown importance are the ecological changes wrought by utilization of the islands. According to brief accounts of the islands in the nineteenth century, most islands on which the geese now breed and feed were scrub- or tree-covered and had little grass. It could be argued that the feeding areas available to the birds have been very greatly increased by clearing; certainly any new pastures established are quickly visited by groups of geese and the numbers regularly using the farmland established on Flinders Island are rapidly increasing. Guiler[52] feels that these ecological factors have been important in the rehabilitation of the birds. He points to islands that support what must be considered dense populations; for example, Woody Island has an average of one goose to 1·8 acres throughout the year and a nest on each 1·3 acres in the breeding season; Kangaroo Island supports 30 pairs of breeding birds, that is, one nest to 1·1 acres, and has an average goose population of one bird to 1·5 acres. He suggests that these islands may be approaching their maximum carrying capacity. There seems to be a good deal to commend this view.

Although the Cape Barren Goose is not numerous and there are probably less than 5000-6000 birds in the wild, there is no reliable evidence of its former numbers to permit comparison; in any case it is probably more numerous today than it has been in the last fifty years, and with this revival occurring in an age of decreasing agricultural utilization of its breeding islands, as well as of increasing conservation awareness on the part of controlling authorities and the public generally, there seems no reason why the species should not survive throughout its former range, given reasonably effective protection from the illegal hunters, who will persist, as well as by the acquisition of further breeding islands as reserves.

Source of Data

I have had little experience in the field with Cape Barren Geese. This account is largely based on the unpublished data of Dr E. R. Guiler of the Tasmanian Animals and Birds Protection Board and the University of Tasmania.

Mountain Duck

Tadorna tadornoides (Jardine and Selby)

References

Tadorna Fleming, Phil. of Zool., 2, p. 260, 1822.

Anas tadornoides Jardine and Selby, Ill. Orn., 2, p. 62, 1828. (N.S.W.)

Other Names

Chestnut-breasted Shelduck, Sheldrake.

Description

ADULT MALE. Head and neck black, often with brown suffusion, tinged with glossy green; a white ring at base of neck; breast and mantle cinnamon brown; back and scapulars black with very fine transverse brown lines; rump and upper side of tail black; abdomen dark brown with fine light-brown vermiculations; under tail glossy black; upper wing coverts white, forming prominent white shoulders; primaries black; secondaries glossy green for half of length, black at base; tertiaries rich chestnut; iris dark brown; legs and feet dark grey; bill black.

MALE IN ECLIPSE. According to Blaauw,[9] in eclipse the breast is yellowish brown and neck ring is less clearly defined.

ADULT FEMALE. Distinguished from males by the breast being bright chestnut, and by having a ring of white round the base of the bill and a white patch round the eye—in some the two white areas are continuous.

IMMATURE. Similar to adults but duller in colour; the white shoulder patches are flecked with grey. Most juveniles have white flecks between the bill and the eye.

Upper: Mountain Ducks gathering to moult on Lake George, N.S.W. *Photo by Ederic Slater*

Centre: Mountain Ducks on the water. *Photo by author*

Lower: Grazing on sedges at the water's edge. *Photo by Ederic Slater*

Upper: Habitat of the Burdekin Duck, the mangrove-fringed reaches of the Adelaide River, N.T.

Lower: Burdekin Ducks feeding in shallow water and roosting in a paperbark swamp.

Photos by author

DUCKLING. The downy duckling is very boldly marked. Crown, neck, and upper back brown; lower back mottled brown and light brown; face brown above eye, pure white below eye; throat, foreneck, underside, generally pure white; wing brown with broad transverse white band at mid point; iris dark brown; bill, legs, and feet, blue-grey.

Size

	Weight *gm.*	*Length* *mm.*	*Wingspread* *mm.*	*Wing* *mm.*	*Bill* *mm.*
Adult Male					
Maximum	1980	720	1320	392	49
Minimum	990	590	963	318	41
Average	1559	673	1117	358	46
Number measured	*67*	*68*	*75*	*50*	*68*
Adult Female					
Maximum	1850	675	1160	355	45
Minimum	878	555	943	304	38
Average	1291	610	1086	331	42
Number measured	*185*	*183*	*56*	*144*	*184*

Plumage

The Mountain Duck has two moults in the year, a post-nuptial moult involving wings, tail, and body in February and a pre-nuptial moult in which only the body feathers are changed in the autumn. Blaauw watched captive birds and reported that, following the post-nuptial moult, there was a distinct eclipse plumage; it was distinguished from the breeding plumage by the breast becoming yellow brown and the neck collar less clearly defined and duller. In the wild, birds in breeding plumage vary greatly in breast colour and the size and clarity of the neck collar, and in any sample the full range of colours reported by Blaauw can be present. Because of this wide variation the occurrence of an eclipse plumage similar to, but duller than, the breeding plumage could only be determined by the examination of individually marked birds before and after the post-nuptial moult, so it is not surprising that it has not been detected in the wild.

Although the distribution of white on the head and neck is a general guide to sex and age, there is much overlap and certain identification by this means alone is not possible. In a sample of 200 birds all females, both adult and juvenile, had white at the base of the bill, but so did many of the males (11 out of 53). There are sometimes white feathers between the base of the bill and the eye spot; no males had this but many females did (9 out of 72 adults and 68 out of 73 juveniles); in juveniles it was a scattering of white feathers, in adults usually a solid white area sometimes joining the bill and the eye spot. Nearly all females, of all ages, had white eye rings, but no male did, this then being a reasonably reliable guide to sex. All birds, except three females and one juvenile male, had white neck rings. In males the ring was on the average twice as wide in adults as in juveniles, and the females' neck rings averaged about the same in width as those of juvenile males, but did not differ in width between adults and juveniles. Nearly all juvenile females had white flecks on the cheeks, but no male of any age had white in this area.

The only really reliable plumage guide to sex is the presence of white round the eye in the female, but the amount of white is not a very reliable guide to age.

Voice

Mountain Ducks are very vocal, especially in flight. The identity call of the male is a low-pitched honk, the sound covers a frequency range of 0-2 kilocycles per second; there are prominent harmonics, but the energy is fairly equally distributed throughout the range; each syllable occupies about 0·25 seconds. The syllables of the female are of similar length, or slightly longer, but the call is very high-pitched and occupies a frequency range of 0-9 kilocycles per second. There are numerous well-developed harmonics and those between 4 and 7 kilocycles are particularly strong, leading to the high pitch of the honk.

In display, threatening, and fighting the honk of the male differs from the identity call, it has a "wavering" quality in tone and is uttered rapidly in pairs of syllables, one long, 0·25 second, and one short, 0·10 second; the paired syllables are spaced one second or so apart.

Routine

Except in the breeding season, when the males are isolated and non-breeding birds are found in small groups, Mountain Ducks are nearly always found in flocks that can be large and commonly number more than one thousand birds. During the day they rest in loose congregations on the edges of large lakes or estuaries and in late afternoon fly out to feed elsewhere in large honking skeins. They are usually in or on the edge of water, but sometimes fly into stubble fields or green crops some distance away. They are very rarely seen in trees, but occasionally perch and do so well. They swim well, very high on the water, and walk strongly. They seldom dive except when pursued during the flightless moulting period.

They are very wary and alert and difficult to approach. When disturbed the whole flock rises together and moves off rapidly. Cayley's succinct comment, "when disturbed, it rises quickly, uttering a harsh cry resembling 'chank chank' and leaves the locality", is very apt.[14] If on a small lake they leave the area entirely, but if on a large lake they settle in the centre and remain there, in a large raft, for hours, usually later swimming slowly back to their former resting place.

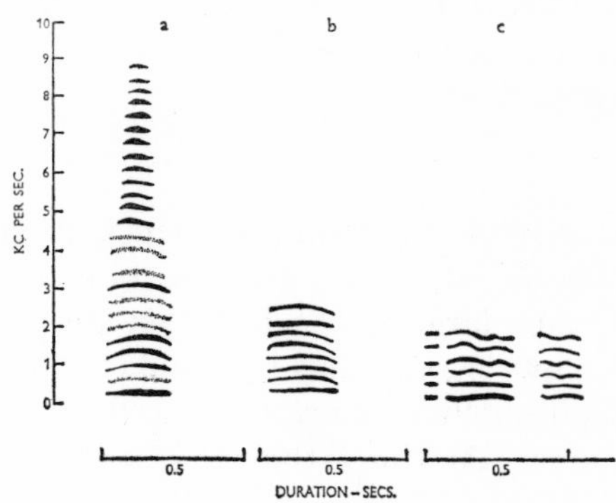

Diagram of sonogram of sounds made by Mountain Ducks, showing (*a*) the female contact call, (*b*) that of the male, and (*c*) the male in threat.

Field Identification

The size of the Mountain Duck and its heavy silhouette distinguish it at great distances from other ducks. On land it stands erect, and is usually alert, looking at the observer. The posture, which is more erect than that of a Black Duck but less than that of a Wood Duck, is very characteristic and is the best field mark, once it is learnt. Apart from this the very dark head and the white neck ring or white eye spot are reliable guides. On the water it floats very high and is very large. Its short neck, together with its size, prevents confusion with other ducks, even when the neck ring is not visible.

In flight it moves in long skeins or Vs, unlike any other waterfowl, except the Black Swan, from which it is immediately distinguished by its short neck. When it is flying away from the observer the large prominent wing patches contrasting with the very dark body are diagnostic, though in very poor light at long distance male Wood Ducks can superficially resemble Mountain Ducks.

When overhead, at great heights, the white underwings and dark body are very obvious, and although in this respect Mountain Ducks resemble Black Ducks, they are distinguished from them by having a dark throat, whereas the Black Duck has a light one. At lower altitudes the breast is seen to be lighter than the abdomen and the neck ring is visible.

Relationships

The Mountain Duck is a typical Shelduck and its relationship to this group and to waterfowl generally is described in the life history of the Burdekin Duck. Within the tribe Tadornini it is similar and closely related to the New Zealand Paradise Shelduck. No races can be recognized.

Habitat

The preferred habitat of the Mountain Duck is the muddy shoreline of large brackish lakes or estuaries, but it is by no means restricted to this, and large flocks form on deep clear freshwater lakes and in freshwater lagoons and billabongs. They frequent water areas on open plains, where they have a decided preference for lightly timbered areas. At times they frequent small claypans and ground tanks.

When living in salt water, the Mountain Duck apparently needs fresh water for drinking, and will leave the salt area periodically to drink. The most spectacular and best known movements to fresh water are in the Coorong, where freshwater soaks occur at the bases of the surrounding sandhills. These attract very large numbers of Mountain Ducks and other waterfowl. To drink at a soak may sometimes call for a walk of one or two hundred yards across open mud. Our observations suggest that few Mountain Ducks moult on the Coorong, the greatest numbers moving to the near-by freshwater lakes Albert and Alexandrina. Perhaps during the moult they are vulnerable and are not prepared to move from the water to the land for drinking water.

Distribution and Movements

The Mountain Duck is restricted to south-eastern and south-western Australia. In the distribution map the range is not shown to extend across the Great Australian Bight; this is perhaps due to an absence of observers rather than of Mountain Ducks, and it seems certain that they would occur on the coast there, at times anyway, in favoured places.

In Western Australia the greatest numbers are in the coastal lakes and estuaries and on offshore islands in the south-west, and the species is widely distributed in considerable numbers throughout the wheat-belt, where it lives on small swamps and ground tanks. In times of good rain it is quite common farther inland on flooded claypans and salt lakes. At times, in Western Australia, it wanders far from its normal range and has been recorded as far north as Cape Leveque.

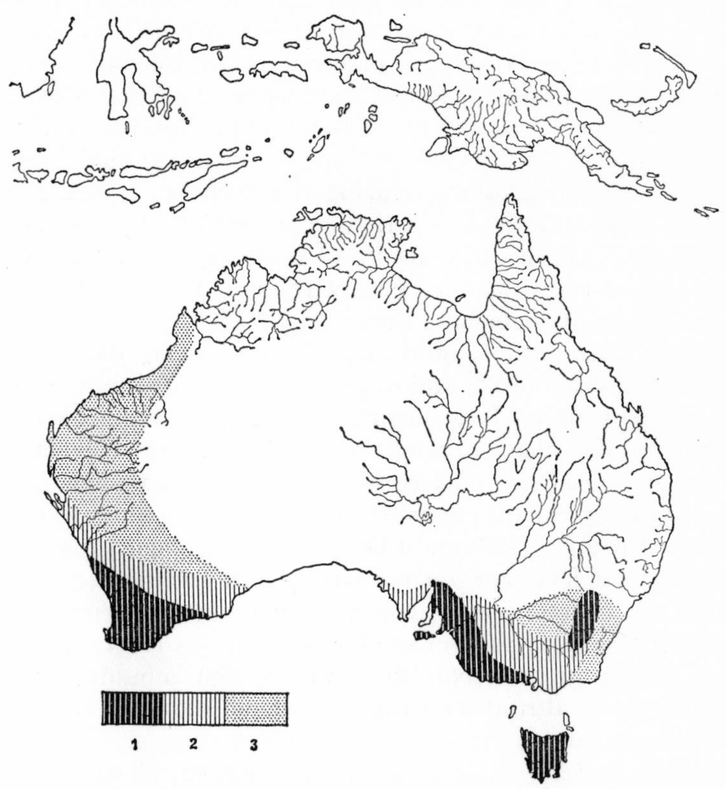

DISTRIBUTION OF THE MOUNTAIN DUCK

In the areas with the darkest shading (No. 1) the birds are numerous; the areas with intermediate shading (No. 2) carry sparse populations of scattered breeding colonies which may be more numerous in some years. In the areas with the lightest shading (No. 3) breeding is uncommon, but vagrants regularly occur.

In eastern Australia the main populations are in south-eastern South Australia and the western districts of Victoria, in Tasmania, and on the Southern Tablelands of New South Wales. In these districts it is abundant, widely spread as a breeding species, and in the summer numerous large concentrations form on the larger lakes. On the tablelands it extends to an altitude of at least 6000 feet.

Between the Victorian coastal districts and the Murray River it is widely distributed and quite abundant, but most birds leave the area during the summer to moult elsewhere. North of the Murray River there are very few Mountain Ducks, and only scattered breeding colonies occur in the winter and spring; these are most numerous between Wagga Wagga and Hay on the Murrumbidgee frontage. They leave this area in the summer. It is very uncommon on the New South Wales coast; there is only one record for the Sydney district, but they are more regularly seen along the South Coast.

It is widely distributed in Tasmania in the Midlands, east coastal districts, and the highland lakes. Tasmania annually receives an influx from the mainland during the summer and in drought years great concentrations occur. The source of these Tasmanian concentrations and the relationships of south-east Australian populations of Mountain Ducks have only recently been studied and a beginning made to understand them.

The movements of Mountain Ducks are quite regular, a concentration during the summer and dispersal to breed during the winter, with each pair of birds returning to a regular site. There is a persistent opinion that "during the breeding season they move to more elevated districts" (Delacour[26]). This is not true and is probably based on a piece of ingenious folklore manufactured to explain the common name of Mountain Duck applied to a bird that is most abundant at sea level and on the coast itself. During the breeding season birds from summer concentrations in estuaries disperse through the low-lying parts of south-east Australia. Most birds in the summer concentrations that do form in high mountain regions disperse to lower altitudes on the inland and coastal plains during the breeding season.

After the breeding season, during the summer, Mountain Ducks concentrate on lakes and estuaries, and wherever they have been watched systematically a regular pattern of concentration has been noted. It has only recently been learnt, and is reported here for the first time, that these are moulting concentrations. The development of a moult movement is of considerable interest, since it has only recently been established that the European Shelduck undertakes an extensive and regular moult migration.[18] The majority of the European population gathers in Heligoland, where 75,000 gather to moult; smaller concentrations occur in England and elsewhere. The Mountain Duck also moves long distances to moult, but it seems to differ from the European species in gathering in many smaller concentrations rather than a few very large ones. This is about the development one might expect in our unreliable climate and uncertainty of permanence of lakes. During the breeding season they are widely distributed, the isolated pairs breeding on small, often temporary, pools and lakes and ground tanks. It is suggested that these water areas are too small and uncertain for safety during the flightless period, so they move to the larger bodies of permanent water available for this purpose.

A typical moulting place for Mountain Ducks is Lake George, a large mountain lake near Canberra. Not more than 20-30 pairs breed there during the winter and early spring, but from November onwards the numbers increase until by January 1,000-2,000 are present, grouped into large rafts of flightless birds in full moult. The numbers decline during late summer and autumn and all except the few residents have dispersed by May.

Similar summer concentrations occur near Swansea, Tasmania, in the Coorong and lakes Alexandrina and Albert, South Australia, and in Lake Dumbleyung, Western Australia, and doubtless elsewhere. The situation in these areas has not been studied, but it is probable that all are the end result of moulting movements. Very similar patterns of concentration have been reported in southern Victoria, where the numbers of birds increase from November to January; they decline until, by August, very few remain.[80] There is no record of mass moulting in the area, but perhaps it occurs and has not been detected.

By watching birds, individually marked with coloured bands, Mr J. B. Hood has been able to show that, on return from the summer moult movement, many of the pairs return to the same waterhole and nest in the same tree-hole year after year. Some birds have returned annually for five years. With this in mind it is legitimate to assume that Mountain Ducks, caught and marked in the summer concentrations and later recovered in the winter breeding places, indicate the direction and distance of their original movement to moult just as effectively as the recovery of birds marked in the winter in the breeding areas and later recovered in a summer concentration elsewhere.

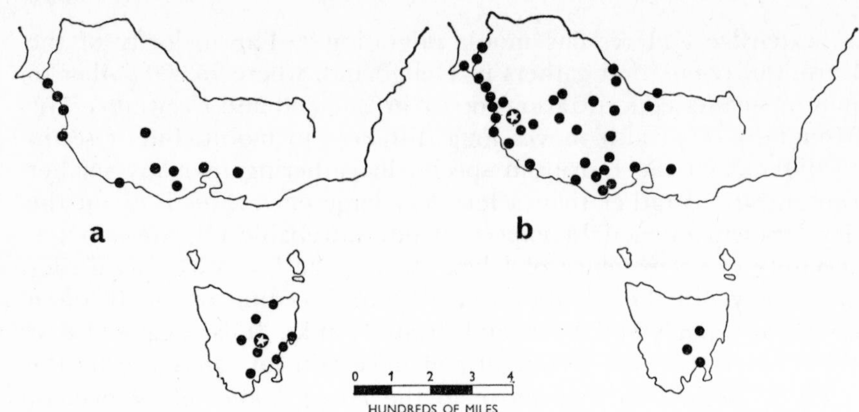

Places of recovery of Mountain Ducks banded during and just after the moult (*a*) in Tasmania and (*b*) in south-east South Australia. In each case the banding place is shown by a star. Note random nature of dispersal from each place.

After breeding near Naracoorte, South Australia, some Mountain Ducks remain locally, and many move throughout western Victoria and Tasmania, covering several hundreds of miles to the moulting place. Most, however, move to the Coorong and presumably moult there or on the near-by freshwater lakes. Most birds in the Tasmanian concentrations remain in that island, but some move to Victoria for the breeding season. Birds caught in summer moulting concentrations near Canberra later spread throughout the Southern Tablelands and as far west as western Victoria and South Australia (400 miles).

The pattern of movement is not fully understood yet, but it is clear that the birds in moulting concentrations are derived from very wide areas, and conversely birds that breed in that one district in the winter move widely in several directions during the summer. Those that breed at Naracoorte, for instance, are derived both from local birds and from visitors that come regularly from the Coorong and western Victoria, from as far east as Kerang, Canberra, and from Tasmania; some of the birds that regularly breed in Tasmania come from the mainland.

Feeding

There has been no study of the food or feeding habits of Mountain Ducks and there are very few references. According to Gould,[50] stomachs examined contained small fish, crustaceans, and molluscs;

according to Storr,[92] on Rottnest Island, Brine Shrimps are an important food; Hall[53] has recorded grass as a food. On the Coorong they clearly spend much time feeding on aquatic vegetation, the ducklings diving expertly to secure it. At Canberra they spend their feeding periods grazing emergent vegetation and aquatic plants in shallow water, as well as grazing in fields close to the water. In the inland, at Griffith, New South Wales, and in western Victoria they visit stubble fields and graze newly germinated pastures and crops.

A small sample of 30 stomachs has been examined, most were from Lake George, near Canberra, and the remainder from the Murray River near Shepparton. All except three contained both animal and vegetable items.

The commonest plants found were clover seeds and leaves, which were in 60 per cent of the birds, green algae Chlorophyceae, which were in 50 per cent, couch-grass *Cynodon* in 17 per cent, *Chara* in 13 per cent, and duckweed *Azolla* in 10 per cent. The rest of the plant food included medicks, grasses, sedges, pondweeds, and ribbonweeds. Clearly most of the plants were secured in water.

The animals in the birds were very varied. The commonest were insects: midge larvae and adults, Chironomidae, were in 40 per cent of the sample, water-boatmen *Corixa* in 40 per cent also, and water-fleas *Cladocera* in 17 per cent. The remainder of the animal food included dragonfly larvae, various beetles, mayflies, and mussel shells. All these animals are aquatic forms.

Breeding

Several pairs of Mountain Ducks, marked with coloured leg-bands, have been found in later years still together and, in some cases, breeding in the same tree-hole for several successive years. This, together with the common observation that Mountain Ducks are found in pairs of family parties throughout the year and that, even in large flocks, pairs are always together, is enough to show that they have a long pair bond, probably for life like some other Shelducks. According to Delacour, who has reared the species in captivity, they require three years to mature.

The pairs usually return from the summer concentrations to the breeding areas in March, but the date is greatly affected by the weather, especially at the edges of the range inland. Here in dry weather return is delayed sometimes for several weeks. In the breeding areas each group returns to the pool, billabong, or ground tank that it had occupied in the previous year. The pairs become more pugnacious towards one another during April and May and separate and move to occupy the breeding territory that they had occupied in the previous year. The breeding territory may be a small pool or tank or portion of the shoreline of a large lake and is vigorously defended by the male against other male Mountain Ducks. One male is capable of defending two hundred yards of shoreline of a large lake or a pool two or three acres in extent, at least.

The pair select the nest site together, flying into the trees and both looking in the hollows. Usually, with birds that have bred before, the same nest-hole that was used in the previous year is selected. This may be close to the male's territory but can be at least three miles away from it. During incubation the male maintains station in his territory, and is visited by the female when she leaves the nest to feed. On return to the nest the pair fly back together, usually the male in the lead; their flight might take them across other males' territories, but flying birds are not attacked by the owners. At the nest site the female lands in the tree and enters the nest-hole; the male may also pause, but more usually merely breaks his speed, then swings round and returns to his territory.

When the young are hatched the female leads them overland to the male's territory and the family is united there. When they are partly fledged the family parties move overland, if necessary, to larger bodies of water where the broods coalesce and are deserted by their parents. As summer continues the birds move out to the summer concentration areas and moulting begins.

On Rottnest Island, according to Storr,[92] after breeding the parties gather on the larger salt lakes and soon after or just before the young are fledged they are deserted by their parents. Flocks of immature birds develop in late September and are at their largest in November. These young birds shun the larger water areas and spend most time on the smaller lakes and disperse from the island during December. In Lake George, New South Wales, a very much larger lake than exists on Rottnest Island, this separation of the different age classes does not occur. The fledging of the young and their abandonment by their parents coincide with a continuous influx of birds from elsewhere and the beginning of moulting. The moulting flocks contain both local adult and local young of the year (not moulting, of course), as well as adults and young of the year from elsewhere.

There are little precise data on the timing and extent of the breeding season, but what there are suggest that the Mountain Duck has a regular breeding season throughout its range. In Western

Australia, on Rottnest Island, eggs are laid between mid June and late September, and the dates are similar in south-east South Australia and in the Deniliquin district, New South Wales, where J. Hobbs[58] has recorded that breeding always begins in July and in good seasons extends until November; farther north, at Griffith, the eggs are always laid in July and August, and the same dates seem to apply near Canberra, in the highlands. Littler records that in Tasmania eggs are laid in August and September.

Nest

The nest is usually in a tree-hole, often quite high. The tree can be green, growing far from water, or on the edge of a lagoon, or sometimes it is a dead tree standing in water. J. Hobbs has seen a nest 100 feet from the water, and I have seen several 60 to 70 feet high, as well as one in a grey box only 6 feet from the ground. On Rottnest Island they sometimes nest on the floor of small caves and are thought also to use limestone crevices for nesting sites. Nests have been found in rabbit-holes on treeless plains near Hay, New South Wales, and on the ground in thick grass in well-wooded areas near Canberra. Mellor (in Mathews) has described nests on the ground under overhanging fronds of blackboys, *Xanthorrhoea*.

Eggs

The eggs are typical for shelducks, oval, creamy white in colour, and have a close-grained lustrous shell; 94 eggs from 16 nests measured in length 62-74 mm. (average 68 mm.) and in breadth 45-51 mm. (average 49 mm.).

Clutch

The clutch is reported as usually 10 to 14, and occasionally as large as 22, but there are no published quantitative data. Clutches seen by the author have numbered 11, 5, 8, 14, 15, 11, 8, 8, 14.

According to Jones the eggs are laid at three-day intervals.

Incubation

Incubation takes 30 to 35 days (Jones in Delacour).

Status

The Mountain Duck is not considered a good game bird. It is very wary and difficult to stalk, but once on the wing is slow flying. It is practically inedible, though in some places a tradition of shooting Mountain Duck exists, and it is claimed that from the salt-water areas where this shooting is carried out its flavour is better. It is more regularly shot in the Coorong, South Australia, than elsewhere, and here a fine old sporting practice of firing from blinds into massed flocks drinking at soaks has persisted. Sometimes the soak is dug out to form a narrow gutter running away from the blind to afford a more efficient enfilade.

At times in western Victoria and elsewhere large flocks graze newly germinated pastures and wheat and pea crops and can cause severe damage to individual fields. In over-all assessment, however, the Mountain Duck is not of great economic importance.

The birds are very numerous and over their whole range not extensively hunted. Whilst large numbers frequent estuaries and salt-pans that are not liable to drainage and nest in tall trees away from feral foxes, there seems no reason why the Mountain Duck should not remain numerous or should present special conservation problems for some time.

Burdekin Duck

Tadorna radjah (Garnot)

References

Tadorna Fleming, Phil. of Zool., 2, 260, 1822.

Anas radjah Garnot, Voy. la Coquille, Zool. 8, 303, 1828. (Buru.)

Other Names

Radjah Shelduck, Whiteheaded Shelduck.

Description

ADULT MALE. Head, neck, breast, and abdomen, pure white, there is a chestnut band across the upper breast; upper back and scapulars rich chestnut with fine transverse black lines; back, rump, and tail, black; upper back brown crossed with inconspicuous fine white lines; undertail and flanks black; upper wing coverts white, crossed by fine black lines near tip of feathers; primaries black; speculum bright glossy green bordered above and below with black, outer and inner webs of the secondaries are white; bill, legs, and feet, pink or fleshy white; claws brown; iris white.

ADULT FEMALE. The plumage is similar to that of the adult male.

IMMATURE. In both sexes the plumage is similar to that of the adult, but the shoulders and other white parts are sometimes flecked with grey and brown, thus appearing duller.

DUCKLING. Crown chestnut; back of neck, back, and upper side of tail, dark brown; face, throat, foreneck, and underside, pure white; there is a broad dark-brown or black line from the bill through the eye to back of head; bill, legs, and feet, pink.

Size

	Weight gm.	*Length mm.*	*Wingspread mm.*	*Wing mm.*	*Bill mm.*
Adult Male					
Maximum	1101	555	991	268	54
Minimum	750	498	900	260	40
Average	934	541	949	276	46
Number measured	*46*	*46*	*39*	*42*	*47*
Adult Female					
Maximum	1130	610	985	298	55
Minimum	600	486	915	246	42
Average	839	528	945	268	48
Number measured	*49*	*49*	*44*	*39*	*49*

Voice

Burdekin Ducks are very vocal and call on water, land, and in flight. The female has a harsh rattling note and the male a hoarse whistle.

Routine

The Burdekin Duck is characteristic of shallow water and mudbanks. Sometimes, in the dry season, flocks of 200 or more congregate, but they are more usually found in pairs or groups of six to eight, apparently family parties. They are very rarely on the water and are usually wading on the edge of muddy pools or feeding on the land near by. I have never seen one more than 20 yards from water, and when feeding on the edges of lagoons they seldom go more than a few feet into the pandanus or timber fringe. On land they run about very swiftly and noisily challenge any newcomer at any season.

During the day they roost quietly on mudbanks, usually where there is some cover, or in flooded timber, moving out to feed in the late afternoon. They perch freely and well, usually, in the Northern Territory, in tall green paperbarks standing in water, and choose stout limbs on which they walk up and down easily and confidently. Before moving out to the feeding place there is a good deal of flying about, squabbling, and gathering in small groups in the trees near the edge of the cover. Where there are no trees they roost, in or under mangroves or on the edges of small muddy pools on the plains.

The flight is swift, considering the size of the duck, and they usually fly through the timber rather than over it. They are very vocal in flight, and the first sign of Burdekin Ducks is the harsh rattling call as they thread their way through the timber, low to the water.

Field Identification

At rest the Burdekin Duck can hardly be confused with any other bird. The pure white head and neck contrasting with the very dark wings and body are distinctive and diagnostic. The only other duck with a white head and neck is the White Pigmy Goose, with which there can be no confusion because of the difference in size alone.

In flight it is distinguished by the prominent white shoulder patches that contrast with the dark body. The only other duck with prominent white shoulder patches is the Mountain Duck, but the two do not overlap in range and in any case could be distinguished by the white head of the Burdekin Duck in contrast to the dark one of the Mountain Duck.

Overhead the bird is all white—head, neck, body, and the bases of the wings. Only the neck ring, tips of the wings, and the tail are dark, and identification is very simple.

Relationships

The tribe Tadornini of the subfamily Anatinae comprises 15 species of Shelducks and Sheldgeese, which are found mainly in South America and Africa, but there are two representatives in Europe and Asia and three in Australasia. The genus *Tadorna*, Shelducks, comprises seven species, of which six are found in temperate zones; the Burdekin Duck is the only tropical representative and is widely separated geographically from other Shelducks. Its closest relatives are the Mountain Duck *T. tadornoides* of southern Australia, and the Paradise Shelduck *T. variegata* of New Zealand.

The Burdekin Duck has been divided, on the basis of size, into two geographic races that intergrade in southern New Guinea. *T. r. radjah*, the small race, is found on Aru Island, the Moluccas, and New Guinea, and the mainland race, *T. r. rufitergum*, which is a little larger is confined to tropical Australia.

Habitat

The brief description of its habitat given by Philips,[84] that it is "a bird of rivers and freshwater lakes perhaps frequenting the coast during drought only", is very misleading. It is seldom seen on freshwater lakes, except in the dry season, when "freshwater" can hardly describe the muddy brackish pools that remain, and it is most numerous on the coast at all times, though, as will be explained, there is a tendency to move farther inland on some rivers during the dry season. The statement that it spends most of the year on inland rivers is not correct. Its preferred habitat is brackish water, mud-flats and mangroves near the coast.

The utilization of the habitat by the Burdekin Duck is similar throughout its range, but is best understood in subcoastal areas of the Northern Territory. Here a series of large senile rivers wander across their flood-plains and are separated from one another by slightly elevated forested country. Three major divisions are worth considering for Burdekin Ducks, the littoral, subcoastal plains, and high land (these correspond roughly to the Littoral Land System, the Subcoastal Plains Land System, and the forested Koolpinyah and Marrakai Land Systems of Christian and Stewart).[17]

The littoral extends along the coast in a strip up to a mile or so wide and near the mouths of the rivers occupies considerable areas. It consists of sand dunes, mangrove mud-flats and fringes to the rivers, salty mud-flats dissected by numerous creeks and stringers, mostly brackish and many under tidal influence, salt meadows and samphire flats; it neither floods nor supports herbage in the wet season. The subcoastal plains have been described as the main habitat of the Magpie Goose; they have extensive swamps and grass-lands in the wet season and scattered lagoons and dusty plains in the dry season; large paperbark swamps occur on the edges in places and remain wet at all seasons. The high land is bare, owing to burning in the dry season, and grows tall grass in the wet. There are many permanent lagoons.

In the dry season Burdekin Ducks are most numerous in the littoral, but many live in the paperbark swamps and small numbers occupy the lagoons on the plains and in the high land. In the wet season the littoral is less attractive, probably because of the absence of trees to provide nest sites, and most birds occupy the paperbark swamps, where they occur on the fringes of the low black-soil swamps of the plains and the mangrove fringes of the rivers. The local black-soil swamps, many of which form on the sites of lagoons that had supported Burdekin Ducks in the dry season, are unattractive, as are most lagoons on the high land.

In New Guinea the bird's habitat preferences are very similar; it is most common in mangrove and sago swamps and on the mud-banks and shoals of the large rivers and is also sparingly distributed throughout swampy rain-forest.

Distribution and Movements

Little is known of the Burdekin Duck's status in New Guinea, but according to Mayr[77] its range there is the "lowland rivers, particularly at the mouth". The only observations I have made of the bird in New Guinea confirm this distribution. A survey, mainly from low-flying aircraft and canoe, in 1964 showed the bird to be very sparingly distributed along the south coast near Port Moresby, the Fly River and Gulf of Papua; in the north only a few birds were seen, all on the Sepik River. The only Burdekin Ducks that were not within one mile of the seashore were six on the edge of Chambri Lake on the Sepik, fifty miles inland. The range of the Burdekin

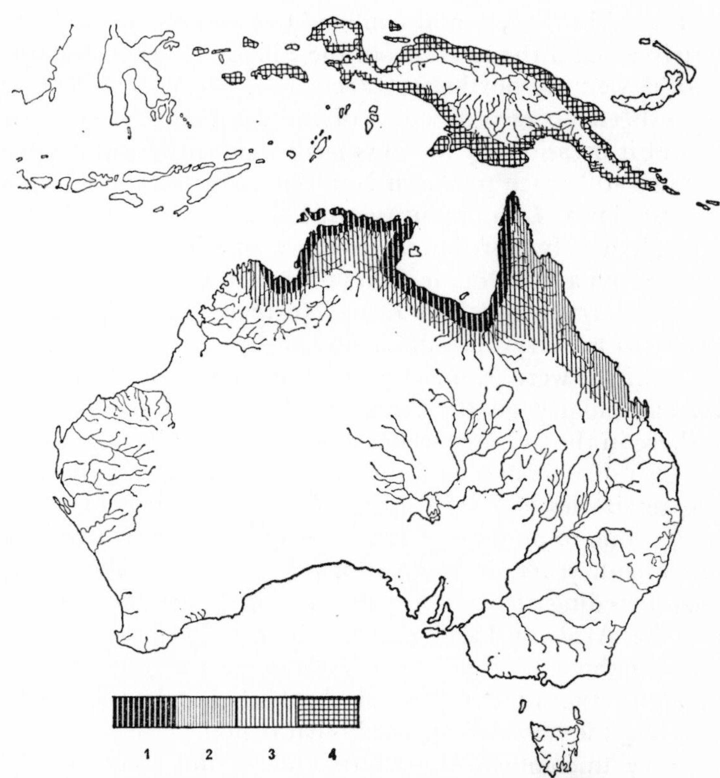

DISTRIBUTION OF THE BURDEKIN DUCK

The darkest shading (No. 1) shows the main breeding range; the birds also breed in the region marked No. 2, but in small numbers; inland (No. 3) vagrants occur. The square hatching (No. 4) shows the extra-continental range.

Duck in New Guinea is in regions where the diet of the indigenous people is notoriously low in animal protein. It is a conspicuous object and very easily hunted, so it seems highly probable that its rarity is due to hunting by the local people.

In Australia it is at present confined to the coastal tropics, but formerly it had a more extensive range and was found in coastal districts of northern New South Wales, including the lower Richmond and Clarence rivers. There were also occasional records in inland New South Wales; North saw a flock of fifteen near Moree in 1901 and had accounts of others as far south as Narromine. None of these southern populations have survived. For that matter, the species has virtually gone from the whole of the east coast of Australia.

The Burdekin Duck is now confined to a narrow coastal and subcoastal strip around the north from the Fitzroy River, Western Australia, to Bowen in northern Queensland. In Western Australia there have been no records south of the Kimberley region, but in Queensland it occasionally wanders farther down the coast and very rare vagrants still reach northern New South Wales, the most recent being reported near Lismore in August 1965.

Although widely distributed in the north it is nowhere really numerous. From a series of air surveys between Darwin and Oenpelli and between Darwin and Port Keats, Northern Territory, in 1956-9 it was seen to be very uncommon in the western area, where only occasional birds were seen. The greatest densities were east of Darwin, particularly on the Adelaide, Mary, and South Alligator rivers, where in the dry seasons flocks of 20 were frequent and groups of 50 to 60 not uncommon. In 1956 the number of pairs holding breeding territories along 70 miles of the Adelaide River was, on the average, one to about one and three-quarter miles. In the same, and subsequent, years air observations suggested that this was quite a normal breeding density for this region generally. The rivers draining the Arnhem Land plateau do not form such extensive plains as do those to the west of Oenpelli, and ground and air surveys along the north coast of Arnhem Land show that the Burdekin Duck is very rare indeed in that region.

It is very uncommon in eastern Queensland south of Cairns, and a land and air survey of the east coast of Cape York Peninsula in 1964 showed it was rare there also. According to Thomson,[93] it is more numerous on the western coast of Cape York Peninsula. His description says "abundant, especially in tidal estuaries, sandbanks and mudflats of Gulf rivers, and on the sea coast, but was not seen far inland". I have not been able to work on the Gulf coast, but examination of air photos shows that suitable habitat for Burdekin Ducks is extensively developed there, though it is not nearly so extensive as on the subcoastal rivers of the Northern Territory. This area must be considered the stronghold of the species today.

Burdekin Ducks are quite local in habits and move only in response to changing food supply. During the day they roost in tall green trees or mangrove swamps and at dusk or late afternoon fly a short distance to the edge of the swamp to feed throughout the night, returning to cover soon after dawn.

The seasonal movement pattern of the population in the Northern Territory is very similar to that described for the Magpie Goose. During the wet season the birds are widely distributed over the subcoastal plains wherever a creek, swamp, river bank, or buffalo wallow provides muddy water, and at the end of the wet season each pair becomes located on its breeding territory. As the dry season continues and surface waters dry, Burdekin Ducks concentrate on those few water areas that remain. This results in a concentration from the plains themselves to the rivers and permanent lagoons and a movement towards the mangrove swamps at the mouths of the rivers. At the same time part of the population on each river moves more widely to those rivers where dry-season swamps are most extensive. This movement results in a concentration on the South Alligator and Mary rivers where paperbark swamps and lagoons are most numerous. At the height of the dry season, however, the numbers of Burdekins on these rivers are little more than twice what could be accounted for by concentration of the wet-season population, with its young. The observations suggest that only a small part of the population is involved in the inter-river movements.

The greatest movements occur within the different river valleys and differ in scale and direction according to the hydrology of the river. On the Adelaide River the concentration is towards the mangroves and salt-pans of the mouth. On the Mary River the concentrations occur to the immense paperbark swamps on the plain. On the South Alligator River the lagoons in the upper reaches, at the confluence of Naurlangie and Jim Jim creeks, are the main concentration places. The plains of the Alligator, West Alligator, and Wildman rivers are quite small and contain very little dry-season habitat for Burdekin Ducks; the birds almost completely vacate these river valleys, except for the small coastal mangrove swamps, in the dry season and presumably join the flocks on the South Alligator.

Feeding

Burdekin Ducks feed entirely on land or in shallow water one or two inches deep. In shallow water they walk quickly, dabbling the bill from side to side rapidly. On land they confine their attention to wet or boggy ground and again keep moving, dabbling at the ground and sometimes clearly grazing. I have never seen, in the wild, the behaviour described by Jones[65] of captive birds repeatedly marking time to cause worms to break through the surface.

Each bird, or pair, has a feeding territory to which it resorts each morning and evening. This may be a small pool or a stretch of the edge of a larger lagoon. It is not obviously defended, but Burdekin Ducks show little inclination to feed in one another's territories. The roosting place can be several miles from the feeding territory. On one occasion whilst photographing Green Pigmy Geese I noted that Burdekin Ducks came to the lagoon edge from four different directions each afternoon at 4 p.m. and each morning soon after dawn; six pairs were involved. Of these, one pair was roosting in a large tree on the edge of the lagoon, but the others came from far away through the forest. One pair was ultimately followed and found to be roosting in a paperbark swamp four miles away.

There has been no study of the food eaten. Twenty-one stomachs collected in the dry season on the Adelaide River contained both animal and vegetable food. Animal food predominated and was found in all birds, comprising 95 per cent of the total bulk. The animals were nearly all molluscs of several species, but six stomachs also contained some large insects. Eight stomachs contained small quantities of algae and one was half full of sedge, in addition to some algae and molluscs.

Breeding

Flocks of Burdekin Ducks, at all seasons, consist of aggregations of birds that are obviously mated, suggesting that the pair bond is permanent, as in many other Shelducks.

The sexual cycle and breeding season appear regular, as in most tropical waterfowl. The sexual cycle begins prior to the wet season and testes examined before the first storms have been found to show some sexual activity. With the first rains of the wet season sexual activity rapidly increases and the males, which are never very tolerant of others, become very pugnacious. A male will attack any other Burdekin Duck of either sex that comes near him or his mate; sometimes he may attack his own mate. The groups at this season are in constant ferment with the males running round and rushing at one another.

As the wet season progresses during January and February the pairs take up breeding territories—a small pool, lagoon, or piece of river bank—and defend them. Intruding males are challenged by the male, which rushes forward with neck outstretched and feathers erect. During such encounters the female often participates, trumpeting and rushing at the males. With the related Mountain Duck the nest is often some distance from the territory defended by the male, but, although the observations are not complete, this does not seem to be so with the Burdekin Duck; the nest is usually near by.

The selection of the nest site is made by the pair together, and I have seen both birds flying up and looking into likely tree hollows. Many nest-holes are used annually, presumably by the same pair of birds. The male remains near by during the incubation and assists in rearing of the brood when it is hatched. The family ultimately moves off in a group as the breeding territory dries during the dry season, to join the increasing flocks on the larger pools. Where the breeding territory remains throughout the dry season the family is quite content to stay there until the following breeding season.

In the Northern Territory, although sexual activity begins in the early wet season, the breeding season itself is timed to occur after the rains, that is, in the very late wet season and early dry season. At this time the flooding is over and most pools and swamps are receding so that bare mud or grass is available between the water and the pandanus fringe, and the ideal habitat is most widely distributed. Clutches are begun between February and July, but most are found in May and June. There are very little data available on the breeding season in north-east Queensland. According to North it occurs in the period December to February, that is, considerably earlier in relation to the wet season than is the case in the Northern Territory, but no explanation can be offered.

Although the breeding season is regular there is some evidence that it is affected by the rainfall. In 1964, a year in which the wet season was very late and extended, several birds collected in September were still undergoing active spermatogenesis, suggesting a very extended breeding season.

Nest

The nests are in large hollow limbs or spouts of trees, usually in water or near by. The eggs are laid on the bare wood with a little light-grey down. A typical nest hollow was a hole in a paperbark caused by a falling limb. It was ten inches in diameter and opened into a hollow eighteen inches in diameter and only six inches deep.

Eggs

The eggs are cream in colour with a smooth, lustrous surface. The shell is close grained. Fifty-two eggs from five nests measured in length 55-61 mm. (average 59 mm.) and in breadth 39-45 mm. (average 42 mm.).

Clutch Size

Very few clutches have been described. According to Delacour, the clutch size ranges from 6 to 12 eggs.

Incubation

The incubation period is thirty days.

Status

The Burdekin Duck is not considered a good game duck by true sportsmen. It is very tame and slow-flying and its flesh is coarse and of low quality; but although it provides very poor sport it is often shot by irresponsible and ignorant shooters. Although it is still moderately common in remote areas it is very vulnerable to shooting, being local in habits, sedentary, and easily shot.

It is very uncommon near towns and roads, and a noticeable decline in numbers occurs very quickly in the Northern Territory wherever a new village, agricultural development, mine, or development road is established. Its extreme rarity on the well-populated eastern coast of Queensland, as well as in New Guinea, and its complete disappearance from northern New South Wales are almost certainly due to earlier unrestricted shooting. Suitable habitat for this species is still abundant in those districts, since it has little value for agriculture.

It does not cause any damage to agriculture, since its life habits do not favour the invasion of crops and, in any case, its numbers are too low throughout its range for it to be of any significance. When rice was introduced to the Adelaide River plains, Northern Territory, in 1955, the development itself was on the whole beneficial to the Burdekin Ducks; the irrigation channels provided extra feeding habitat and the water-storage areas extra drought refuges. The ducks did not enter the crops, which provided neither food nor breeding places. They did not enjoy the benefits for long, however, since despite their having caused no damage they were almost eradicated from the vicinity of the ricefields by indiscriminate and pointless shooting by those involved in the development and by tourists and others whose access to the area was made possible by road construction.

The speed with which the numbers of Burdekin Ducks declined on the Adelaide River and elsewhere in the Northern Territory, when road access was provided to areas that had remained inviolate because of swamp and unbridged rivers for centuries, leads me to believe that there is no hope for the species unless effective policing of the protection laws can be arranged in the very forefront of the rapid development that is under way throughout northern Australia.

Key to Plate III

WHISTLE-DUCKS, PERCHING DUCKS, AND DIVING DUCKS

1. Grass Whistle-duck.
2. Water Whistle-duck.
3. Green Pigmy Goose, female.
4. Green Pigmy Goose, male.
5. Wood Duck, female.
6. Wood Duck, male.
7. Blue-billed Duck, male in eclipse.
8. Blue-billed Duck, female.
9. Blue-billed Duck, male.
10. White Pigmy Goose, female.
11. White Pigmy Goose, male.
12. Musk Duck, male.
13. Musk Duck, female.

B.T.W. 1965

Black Duck

Anas superciliosa Gmelin

References

Anas Linnaeus, Syst. Nat., ed. 10, i, p. 122, 1758.
Anas superciliosa Gmelin, Syst. Nat., i, p. 537, 1789. (New Zealand.)

Other Names

Wild Duck, Grey Duck, Blackie.

Description

ADULT MALE. Top of head, neck, and back, dark brown, the feathers edged with lighter brown; underparts brown; throat white; speculum green; underwing white; head pattern is unique, a dark line from the bill through the eye with white or pale yellow above and below; bill lead grey; legs yellow-green; eye brown.

ADULT FEMALE. Plumage is the same as the male but generally lighter in colour. Differentiation of the sexes is difficult without great experience.

IMMATURE. Similar to female.

DUCKLING. Top of head, neck, and back, dark grey or black; underparts yellow, as are spots on the back and rear edge of the wing; face yellow with a prominent black line through the eye.

Size

	Weight gm.	*Length mm.*	*Wingspread mm.*	*Wing mm.*	*Bill mm.*
Adult Male					
Maximum	1400	608	928	284	58
Minimum	870	506	820	230	45
Average	1114	568	896	262	52
Number measured	*131*	*132*	*69*	*139*	*157*

	Weight gm.	*Length mm.*	*Wingspread mm.*	*Wing mm.*	*Bill mm.*
Adult Female					
Maximum	1280	584	898	271	54
Minimum	805	470	750	226	46
Average	1025	534	855	247	49
Number measured	*207*	*105*	*43*	*109*	*107*

Voice

The voice of the Black Duck is typical of the Mallards. The sound most frequently heard is the loud and raucous quack of the female. The individual syllables cover a wide frequency range band, from 0·4 to 3·0 kilocycles per second, there are strong harmonics and much random energy. Each syllable occupies 0·25 second and they are deliberately spaced at 0·20 second intervals. There is very little "descrescendo". The call is quite unlike that of the equally raucous teal in that there is little fall in frequency during its duration and the syllables are shorter and faster.

The usual sound heard from males is the loud courtship "peep" or whistle, uttered during pair formation. The male also has a characteristic hiss used during threat.

Both sexes have a one- or two-syllabled, soft, drawn-out quack similar to the "raehb" and "raebraeb" described by Lorenz for the Mallard. They may be uttered very rapidly in courtship and at other times.

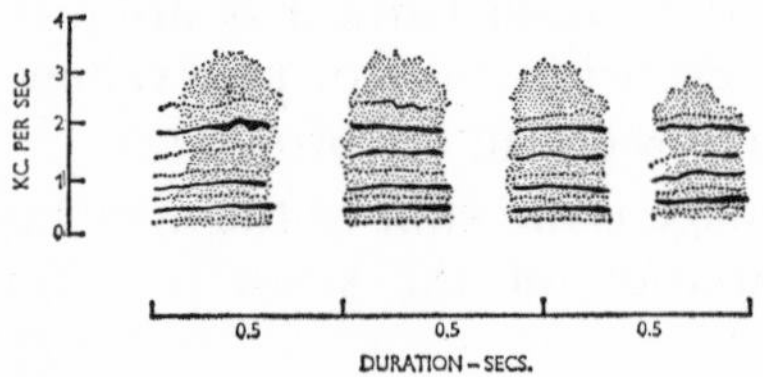

Diagram of sonogram of contact call of female Black Duck.

Routine

Black Ducks can be seen singly, in pairs or flocks, and in any habitat. They are, however, more characteristic of permanent swamps and streams, where they may be on the water or mudbanks; although they commonly perch on timber this is usually a log or a stump from which they can slip into the water. They are never seen clustered all over dead trees, like the Grey Teal.

When disturbed their flight is straight and swift. Teal usually circle and return to swoop over the water, but Black Ducks form a compact flock, ascend to a great height, circle, and move off to another lagoon. They are wary and alert and difficult to approach.

Field Identification

The Black Duck is very easily distinguished from the other common species in the field. In flight it is a dark bird with very swift wing-beats and a long and slender neck. Once learnt, the silhouette is very characteristic. From below it is dark with white underwings, and these immediately distinguish it from the Grey Teal, which does not have white underwings, and from the Hardhead, in which the wings appear wholly translucent, are set much farther back on the body than those of the Black Duck, are smaller in proportion to the body, and have a shorter, swifter stroke.

Flying away, the Black Duck has no obvious and positive mark to distinguish it from the other species, but the Grey Teal has a white stripe near the base of the wing and the Hardhead a prominent white trailing edge to its wings. These species cannot be confused with the Black Duck.

On the water it is a medium-sized duck that differs from the teal in floating lower in the water and having a more slender head and neck, carried more erect. Its high stern distinguishes it from the Hardhead, which slopes towards the water at the rear. When close enough for detail to be seen the facial markings are very obvious and diagnostic. Any duck with a light face and a prominent dark line through the eye is a Black Duck.

Relationships

The Black Duck is a member of the River or Dabbling Ducks, the tribe Anatini. This group includes six genera, of which by far the largest is the genus *Anas*. The genus is distributed throughout the world and includes no less than 38 species, among which are recognized 68 subspecies. The genus is divided into several groups of closely related species—these groups include the Mallards, the Teal, the Shovelers. The Mallard group includes European, American, Indian, and African species as well as the Australian Black Duck. The Mallards are certainly the most numerous and wide-spread group of ducks in the world, and some species the most successful in adapting to the presence of man and agriculture. The Black Duck is probably endemic to Australia, and Amadon[3] felt that it is sufficiently similar to *Anas luzonica* of the Philippines to have been a subspecies of it at some remote period. From Australia it has spread to New Zealand, Polynesia, and Indonesia.

Birds from different parts of its range show a wide variation of colour and size, but interpretation of these is complicated by wide variations in size and colour of local populations. Working from a collection of 273 specimens, Amadon recognized three subspecies.

A. s. superciliosa, the New Zealand Grey Duck, is a very poorly differentiated race; it is indistinguishable in size from the Australian race but is a little paler in colour. Amadon[3] defends the difference by saying "specimens in unworn plumage can probably be separated from *rogersi* with few exceptions". It is now known that there is movement of Black Ducks between New Zealand and Australia, and should it be shown that the volume of this movement is greater than at present thought, it might be necessary to review the race critically. As at present defined, it is found in New Zealand, and on Kermadec, Steward, Great Bernier, Mayor, Kapoti, Chatham, Auckland, Campbell and Macquarie islands.

A. s. rogersi, the Australian Black Duck, is confined to Australia, Sumatra, Java, Kangean, the Lesser Sunda Islands, the Moluccas, and in New Guinea to the southern coast, Arfak Mountains, Southern Highlands, and the Louisiade Archipelago. There is no significant variation in size of the birds in Australia or southern New Guinea, but some populations in Indonesia tend to be smaller.

A. s. pelewensis is smaller than the others and has a wide distribution in the Pacific islands, including the Society and Cook groups, Tonga, Samoa, Fiji, New Caledonia, the Loyalty Islands, the New Hebrides, Santa Cruz and the Solomon Islands, the Bismarck Archipelago, Palau, and the northern lowlands of New Guinea. The birds on many of these islands differ in size from those on others, and it is possible that more races will need to be recognized when larger samples are examined.

Habitat

The Black Duck is found throughout Australia and in all fresh, brackish, and sometimes saline habitats. I have seen them in all kinds of situations, including salt pools on New South Wales beaches, in a pool in dense rain-forest, and in earth tanks and bore drains in the inland. Despite this, however, they are most characteristic of, and most numerous in, relatively deep and permanent water with heavy vegetation. In the inland their most favoured habitats are the cumbungi swamps, and every such swamp contains a quota of Black Ducks; even ground tanks and irrigation channels that become invaded by this weed usually carry a breeding pair or two.

They also breed, but less commonly, in the more permanent lagoons and lignum swamps.

In coastal districts they can be found almost anywhere but are most numerous in the open swamps with sedge, hyacinth, or tea-tree. Every creek and stream on the coast and tablelands, especially if the edges are timbered, carries a quota of resident Black Ducks.

Distribution and Movements

The Black Duck is found as a breeding species throughout the continent, but varies greatly in abundance from place to place,

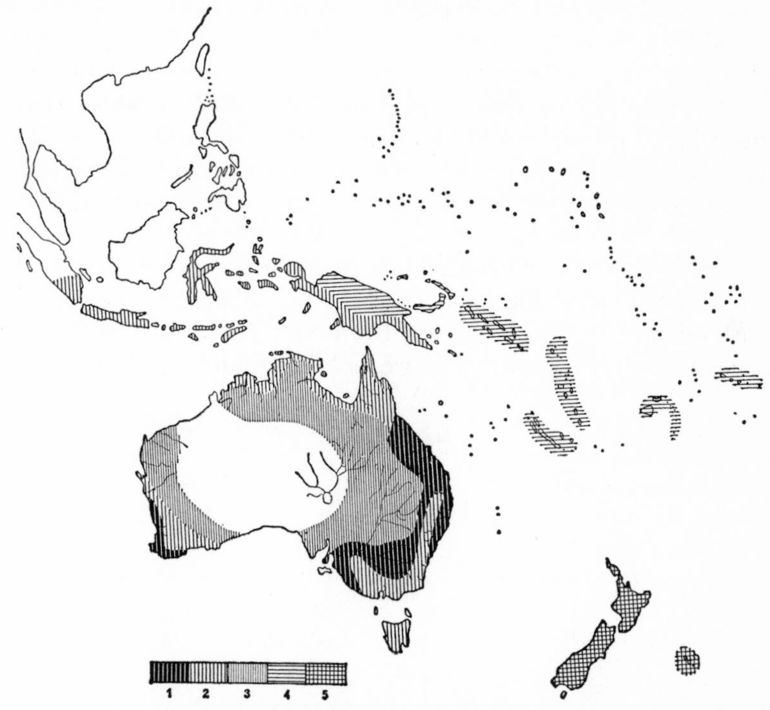

DISTRIBUTION OF THE BLACK DUCK

The square hatching (No. 5) shows the range of the New Zealand Grey Duck *A. s. superciliosa*, except for some subantarctic islands not shown; the horizontal hatching (No. 4) shows the range of *A. s. pelewensis*. The vertical hatchings (Nos. 1-3) show the range of the Australian Black Duck *A. s. rogersi*; the birds breed throughout the shaded area, and the intensity of the shading indicates the relative density of the population; they seldom visit the unshaded areas, but may do so and breed in exceptionally wet years.

according to the distribution of its preferred habitat—deep, permanent, vegetated swamps.

The greatest number are in the Murray-Darling Basin, where it is outnumbered only by the Grey Teal, in the eastern coastal districts from Cairns to Sydney, and in the south-west corner of Western Australia; in the last two areas it is easily the commonest duck. Elsewhere in the tropical coastal areas it is widely distributed but not numerous. It occurs throughout the slopes and tablelands of eastern Australia where every water area has a few pairs. It is uncommon in the arid interior, but, nevertheless, it does exist there whenever there is water. Beyond the continent, in New Guinea, Indonesia, and New Zealand the local races are widely distributed in all available water habitats.

The Black Duck is certainly the most widely spread breeding species and, in the aggregate, probably the most numerous duck in Australia. In the inland the immense nomadic flocks of Grey Teal are very impressive, but they fluctuate greatly in numbers and distribution, whereas the Black Duck is reasonably common, nearly always, nearly everywhere.

Although Black Ducks can and do make impressive journeys—for instance, many from southern New South Wales reach northern Queensland, and they have crossed from New Zealand to Australia—on the whole they are much more sedentary and local than Grey

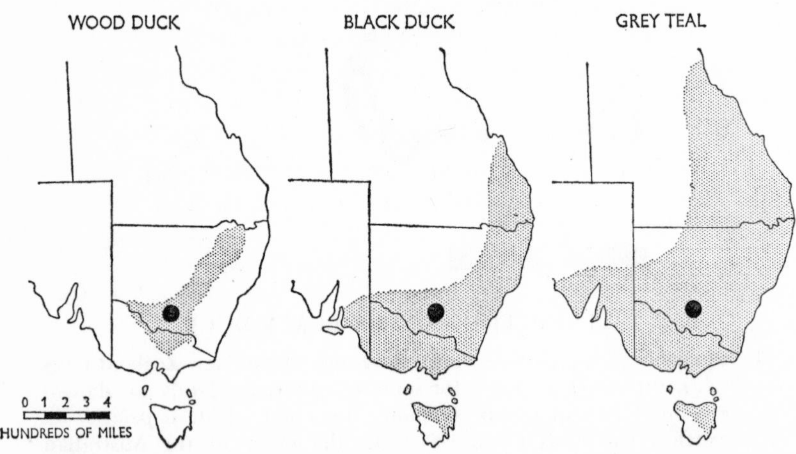

The relative scale of summer movement of three common inland species. Each year birds of each species banded at Griffith, N.S.W., shown as a large spot, disperse throughout the areas shaded. In drier seasons the dispersal is greater, but the same relativity is retained.

Teal.[44] Many marked Black Ducks remain in the same waterhole month after month and even year after year, but teal seldom do. The distance travelled varies greatly. In a typical study, although 58 per cent of both species were recovered within 50 miles of the marking place, 24 per cent of the Grey Teal had moved more than 200 miles, but only 14 per cent of the Black Ducks. None of the Black Ducks moved more than 400 miles, but 8 per cent of the Grey Teal had done so.

In inland south-east Australia there is a fairly regular cycle of movement. During the summer the Black Duck in the inland concentrate on the larger swamps, as the smaller ones decline in level, and during December and January these concentrations reach their peak and many ducks leave the area. Banding has shown that those that leave move in all possible directions—some reach the north Queensland coast, and many reach Tasmania as well as most parts of New South Wales, Victoria, and South Australia. The bulk of the population, however, does not move, and of those that do move most travel in a south-westerly direction along the Murray River and its tributaries to south-east South Australia and western Victoria. At the same time some of the birds already in those districts concentrate and move out in all directions, so streams may move in opposite directions.

In May and June a reverse movement occurs and concentrations form in southern coastal districts, many of these birds turning up shortly in quite large flocks throughout inland New South Wales and the Southern Tablelands. There is some regularity of movements and individuals tend to return to their place of origin to a much greater extent than do Grey Teal.

Despite the basically random nature of the dispersal of Black Ducks that occurs each summer from inland New South Wales there is a regular shift in the population in the south-east. Study of the distribution of banded birds recovered at different seasons shows quite clearly that in summer most of them are south of the place of banding and in winter most of them are north of it. There is a general movement south in summer and north in winter. This movement cannot be called migration, as this term is reserved for a regular biennial movement of the whole population, or very large part of it, between a distinct breeding area and another distinct area. In Black Ducks only part of the population is involved and the individuals move in all possible directions at the same time. The movement is more of a general drift or shift of the centre of gravity of the whole population a short distance north and south, probably due to a learnt experience of better feeding conditions north or south at the different seasons.

In coastal districts regular fluctuations in numbers of Black Ducks have been seen, wherever regular observations have been made. In Western Australia regular counting by J. Ford[33] showed that in a coastal district near Perth there was a regular annual increase in numbers on some swamps, but there was no peak in the winter. He concluded that the concentrations were probably local birds forced into the large swamps by drying of the smaller waterholes. They dispersed again when rain fell. Near Melbourne the Altona Survey Group found a similar pattern—the local birds, reinforced by some from the inland, concentrated each summer and dispersed again in the winter, some returning inland, others to smaller local swamps; in the coastal districts of northern New South Wales the same pattern exists and in both places birds from inland New South Wales regularly occur.

The situation in coastal Northern Territory is similar but in the reverse seasons; here the Black Ducks congregate during the dry season, May to October, but disperse very widely when the monsoonal rain falls and the plains flood. The dry season concentrations in the coastal districts of the Northern Territory are not great and flocks of more than a hundred are rare. There are no extensive inland breeding areas for Black Ducks in the Northern Territory, so presumably the concentrations involve only local coastal birds. In north-east Queensland there is also a concentration of Black Ducks in the winter dry season, the concentration is too great to be explained by local birds and, doubtless, nomads from elsewhere are involved moving to the coast during the dry months and returning inland during the wet months. Each year some Black Ducks that were banded in inland New South Wales are recovered in north Queensland, and birds banded in north Queensland have been recovered throughout much of the east coast. Clearly extensive movements by some birds are involved and the situation is very similar to that which occurs in southern Australia.

When extended dry periods occur movements of Black Ducks are more extensive than usual, but they are very much more conservative than the next species to be discussed, the Grey Teal. Living in more permanent swamps, they are more impregnable to dry weather than the Grey Teal and much slower to leave. The difference was very apparent in 1957 and 1958, drought years, when very little rain fell in eastern Australia. The Grey Teal, extreme nomads, quickly vacated the inland and dispersed over the whole continent and to New Guinea and New Zealand. The Black Ducks, however, preferred to remain inland; some moved out and travelled to coastal districts of eastern and southern Australia, but the majority gathered into immense flocks on the most permanent swamps. They did not move in great numbers until mid 1958, when the inland swamps were seriously declining in level. By this time many of the Grey Teal that had left the area twelve months before were returning inland, searching for refuges, the coastal swamps that had sheltered them having dried out. Had the swamps not been replenished at that time no doubt there would have been as great mortality of Black Ducks as that which had already occurred among the Grey Teal.

Feeding

A typical Dabbling Duck, the Black Duck feeds by dredging the mud in shallow water, by up-ending to secure food from the bottom, by stripping the seeds from plants growing in or overhanging the water, and by filtering seeds from the surface. It often leaves the water and feeds on the bank, but very rarely feeds in stubble fields far from water; this is rather surprising, since elsewhere in the world Mallards and some other River Ducks feed in stubble fields in great numbers, utilizing the waste grain. It utilizes rain puddles away from the swamps, but not nearly to the same extent as do Grey Teal, and it is very much slower to begin feeding on the edge of rising and expanding billabongs. In irrigation districts it visits irrigated fields and at these times feeds on cultivated cereals.

The actual food eaten by Black Ducks varies from place to place, according to the availability of the different plants, but there is a similarity throughout its range. The food is predominantly vegetable and the most important plants are sedges, smartweeds, and grasses; water-lilies are important where they are available. In brief, the most important foods locally are the larger seeded, aquatic, and swamp plants.

In a sample of over 900 stomachs collected in inland New South Wales the food consisted of 54 per cent of seeds and seedheads of swamp plants, 15 per cent of plants usually characteristic of dry land, presumably gathered on the bank and in rain puddles, and 31 per cent aquatic insects.[39] In a sample of over 2,300 Black Ducks from north-east Queensland the food was even more predominantly vegetable and plant materials accounted for 93 per cent of the diet;[69] in a sample of 226 stomachs from Darwin and in 174 from north-east New South Wales the percentage of plant products was 90 per cent and 86 per cent respectively.

In inland New South Wales the birds were collected mainly in the billabongs and lagoons of the Murrumbidgee River and of the Edwards River. In each case the food was quite similar, though the proportions of the different items varied from place to place, according to the birds' feeding opportunities; drying pools were of more importance on the Edward and so there were more insects in the diet and less swamp plants. Over all, seedheads of aquatic and ditch grasses were the most important food, and these accounted for 19 per cent of the total food and included barnyard millet *Echinochloa*, water-couch *Paspalum*, summer-grass *Paspalidium*, and, in irrigated ricefields, cultivated rice *Oryza* was eaten extensively. The next most important group of plants were sedges, mainly *Carex*, which accounted for 16 per cent of the total food, and the smartweeds *Polygonum* and dock *Rumex*, which provided 12 per cent. They also ate appreciable quantities of nardoo *Marsilea*, paddymelon *Cucumis*, saffron thistles *Carthamus*, water-milfoil *Myriophyllum*, and a host of other aquatic and dry land plants in smaller quantities.

The animal food eaten by these Black Ducks was principally insects and molluscs. Insects, mainly the same species of water-beetles Dytiscidae and water-boatmen Corixidae as eaten by the Grey Teal, accounted for 11 per cent of the total food. In Teal they provided 28 per cent. The bulk of the other animal food was larger animals and included freshwater mussels Corbiculidae, up to two inches in length, which provided 13 per cent of the food, and freshwater yabbies *Cherax* and fairy shrimps *Triops*, as well as a large number of smaller and less important water-fleas *Daphnia*, and other animals.

In north-east Queensland, where permanent rich water habitats are more widely distributed, the food was similar but included less animals and dry-land plants than that in the inland. Again sedges were a most important food source and comprised 20 per cent of the total volume of food, but the main plants in this group were the larger species of *Scirpus* and *Eleocharis* that are typical of the tropics. The smartweeds were important also, in the north, and provided 14 per cent of the food. The main difference between the two regions was the great amounts of water-lilies, *Nymphaea* (15 per cent) and water-snowflake, *Nymphoides* (15 per cent), found in the tropical sample; these plants are unknown in the inland. The abundance of water-lilies to some extent decreased the relative importance of aquatic grasses which accounted for only 11 per cent of the total food, though in some months these did account for nearly half the total food eaten.

The smaller samples from north-east New South Wales and Darwin conformed to pattern. In north-east New South Wales, where the swamps are ecologically rather similar to those of northern Queensland, the most important plants were sedges, smartweeds, water-lilies, and grasses, in much the same order of importance. In the Northern Territory, where the vast wet season swamps dry completely in the dry season, there were marked seasonal differences in the food. In the wet season the same major plant groups were eaten, sedges, mainly *Eleocharis,* aquatic grasses, mainly barnyard-grass *Echinochloa,* water-couch *Paspalum,* and wild rice *Oryza,* but in the dry season insects and molluscs were more important and comprised 40 per cent of the total food eaten. There is little doubt that, although the Black Duck prefers to utilize the larger seeds of aquatic plants as food, it is an opportunistic feeder and is capable of utilizing whatever plant or animal food is available at the time.

The food of the ducklings is at first almost entirely of animal origin and predominantly insect. In the inland the most important insects are water-boatmen Corixidae and water-beetles Dytiscidae, but a very great number of small insects are also eaten. By three weeks of age the ducklings eat a large proportion of vegetable food, and by five weeks of age, their food is identical with that of the adults.

Breeding

The breeding season is timed to occur when water areas are most extensive and the swamp plants have developed to provide abundant food. This results in breeding in southern Australia being mainly in the spring and in northern Australia mainly at the end of the wet season, in autumn.

Black Ducks breed in their first year of life if suitable conditions occur. In the Northern Hemisphere Mallard elaborate autumnal displays occur and promote pair-formation within the flocks; these displays intensify during the winter and sterile matings, assisting pair-formation, occur from midwinter onwards. The same sequence, and many of the same display postures, occur in the Black Duck. In southern Australia, in inland New South Wales, and on the Southern Tablelands, pair-forming displays begin in May and continue throughout the winter in the flocks, many birds participating. By spring all Black Ducks are mated and courtship display involving the paired birds intensifies. In northern Australia pair-formation begins in May, in both the Northern Territory and north Queensland, and continues through the dry season in November or December. The pair-forming activities occur each year to what appears to be a fixed seasonal pattern, more or less independent of the weather at the time. The courtship, and finally nesting, however, are very much affected by the weather and its effects on the habitat from place to place and, in some districts, from year to year.

In the extreme south, where the rainfall is almost entirely in the winter and the summers are relatively dry, Black Ducks breed in the winter and spring, July to October, but nests are most common in the period from late July to the end of August. In the Southern Tablelands, where the climate is harsh and cold, the swamps fill during the winter, but there is no vegetative or animal growth in them until the winter ends; breeding occurs in the period October to January, with most nests being begun in October and November. In both areas breeding is extended in wet years and restricted in dry ones.

In northern Australia the timing of the breeding season is the reverse of that in the south.[49] In coastal areas of the Northern Territory the eggs are laid after the monsoon when the swamps have begun to decline. The monsoon usually finishes in March, and by this time the swamps have already begun to decline and are dense with sedges and seeding grasses. The Black Ducks, whose courtship began with the first rains in the preceding October or November, lay the eggs in March, April, and May; occasional nests have been found up to June and July.

In north Queensland the wet season begins in November and quickly replenishes the swamps and nesting cover.[69] The breeding season normally extends from January to April, but in poor wet seasons is restricted both in time and with regard to the number of the local population that breeds. Many undertake courtship display, but if the follow-up rains are not of sufficient intensity fail to breed. Although the north Queensland wet season begins about the same time as that of the Northern Territory the Black Ducks breed appreciably earlier in the former area; perhaps the reason lies in the fact that the Queensland tropical habitats are more abundant in the dry season than those in the Northern Territory and require less replenishment in the wet season before they are suitable breeding places.

In north-eastern New South Wales climatic conditions are not so sharply marked as in the tropics. The main rains are in the summer, but there is sufficient, at other times of the year, to ensure that the swamps always contain water and abundant vegetation—unlike those of the Northern Territory. In this district some eggs are laid throughout the year and every heavy fall of rain is followed by a few nests. However, the bulk of the birds breed in September, October, and November, and nests are much more common at that time.

In semi-arid inland New South Wales there is a regular breeding season in the spring and summer; nests are found between July and December, but the great majority in October and November.[40] The individual birds in the population vary in their response to the factors controlling breeding and not all birds breed each year. The proportion that breeds depends on the suitability of the weather, that is, the amount of rainfall and flooding that has occurred. Although, even in a severe drought, a few Black Duck do breed, most do not and remain in large, sexually inactive flocks. In dry, but not drought, weather most Black Ducks breed, but a few do not receive sufficient stimulation and fail to. In times of major flood they have the ability to breed again at any time of the year to ensure that the abundant water is not wasted and that the favourable conditions for nesting are exploited. When a big flood occurs the birds begin courtship immediately but delay nesting until the peak has passed. This may be any time of the year. All local birds are involved and there is often a considerable influx from elsewhere to breed.

This ability to produce an extra breeding season, or to restrict it, is a useful adaptation to the Black Duck's mode of life. Egg-laying is delayed until the flood peak is over, thus ensuring that there will be ample water; if a flood is not a big one the birds that have begun their sexual cycle do not go on with it and do not lay eggs. If the weather is dry and the breeding habitat not extensive only a few birds breed to maintain the population; the majority conserve their energies for a more favourable time.

Nest

Nests are built in a wide variety of situations. Some are merely scrapes in the ground beneath bushes, others are quite well built and partly woven in clumps of grass, crops, and reeds. They are often placed in the tops of stumps, in tree-holes, or deserted nests of ibis and other water-birds. Where a tree-hole is used it is commonly in a red gum and nearly always in the scar caused by a falling limb, giving a large and shallow hole. Thick tea-trees will often support a nest, as will the top of a staghorn or blackboy, and these sites are often used.

In the inland, tree-holes or elevated sites are the usual nesting places and ground nests are rare. This is presumably because ground cover, in the inland, even on the edges of swamps, is usually sparse and there is little opportunity for ground nesting. In coastal areas and others where ground cover is abundant ground nesting is usual, and nests are sometimes found in grassland or crops far from water.

Clutch

The clutch varies from 7 to 13, but 8 to 10 is commonest. The distribution of size among 75 clutches was as below and the average clutch size was 9·1 eggs.

Number of eggs:	5	6	7	8	9	10	11	12	13
Number of clutches:	2	4	7	11	18	19	9	4	1

Eggs

The eggs are elliptical, usually white but sometimes cream with a pronounced greenish tinge. The shell is smooth and glossy but it is usually dirty from the bird's habit of defecating as it leaves the nest when disturbed. They are laid at daily intervals; 188 eggs from 21 nests measured in length 51-63 mm. (average 58 mm.) and in breadth 37-45 mm. (average 41 mm.).

Incubation

The incubation time is 26 to 28 days.

Development of Young

On hatching, ducklings range in weight from 33 to 35 grammes, the range of bill-length is 12-16 mm., the wing 13-19 mm. and total length 155-160 mm. In captivity the first tail-feathers appear between 14 and 21 days and the first body feathers at 21-29 days. The primaries are visible at 36-45 days and at this age the only down remaining is on the back. The primaries do not achieve their full length until 54-69 days, but most birds are capable of flight 7-10 days before this.

Longevity

Some banded Black Ducks have survived in the wild for at least ten years, but the average life of a wild bird is very much less, and it has been shown by the analysis of band recoveries that the average juvenile Black Duck has a life expectancy of only 15 months.[44] Of a given group of Black Ducks 50 per cent die in the first year, 80 per cent in the first two years, and 95 per cent by the end of three years. Juveniles are more susceptible to early death than adults, and in the first year after banding 69 per cent of the juveniles die, but only 51 per cent of the survivors in subsequent years. Presumably, after surviving one year, the young birds are more skilful at evading the causes of death.

Many Black Ducks are shot and banding has given some idea of the magnitude of this loss. Shooters do not return all the bands they recover, but the number returned indicate that the minimum percentage shot in south-eastern Australia is 13 per cent; 7 per cent are shot in their first year. The rate of harvesting, however, differs greatly from place to place and from year to year, according to the local shooting pressure and the concentration of the birds. In 1957 when the birds were concentrated by drought, 11 per cent were shot in the first year, but in 1959, when they were not, only 4 per cent.

The longevity and mortality rates, as well as the recovery rates, mentioned above are quite normal for ducks that are shot for sport in other countries.

Status

In some seasons the Black Duck is very common in irrigated ricefields in New South Wales and it has been thought that it seriously hinders the growth of the crop. In 1932 officers of the Australian Museum made a brief survey and decided that wild ducks were not a serious pest,[66] and work by the present author in 1952-6 confirmed this.[36] Black Ducks do feed in ricefields, at times, but the damage done is small. They visit the crop when the fields are first flooded, to germinate the seed, and later, before the crop is drained for ripening, and eat some grain. It was found that at germination time the birds visited mainly poorly graded fields and much of the poor germination thought to be due to ducks eating the seed was, in fact, caused by rotting of the seed, owing to the uneven grading of the field. Prior to harvest the ducks ate some rice, but over all this was a small quantity, and the birds still tended to visit uneven crops where there were open water areas to permit landing; well-grown fields were avoided. Their main food in ricefields was barnyard millet, *Echinochloa,* a serious weed of rice and indicative of poorly grown, uneven crops. In a general assessment Black Ducks were considered only a very minor problem in rice-growing districts, even though, occasionally, individual farmers could experience appreciable losses due to them. The New South Wales authorities have met the situation by declining to relax hunting regulations in irrigation districts, except to issue licences to individual farmers to remove birds from their own crops by shooting.

The Black Duck is the premier game duck in Australia and that most sought by sportsmen. Throughout coastal districts it is the chief component of the bag and may comprise 80 per cent of it in some places. In the inland it is sought after by most shooters but is less commonly secured; within the Murrumbidgee Irrigation Area it may comprise 60 per cent of the bag in some years, but in others only 30-40 per cent. In more typical inland regions, among the billabongs and lagoons of the rivers, it comprises 10-20 per cent of the bag. It is considered a good game bird, because of its great wariness, speed of flight, and excellent table qualities. In districts where decoys are used it decoys better than any other Australian duck.

Although its numbers have declined greatly in many coastal districts where drainage has been most widespread, it is still very common in most places and very numerous in some. Given adequate protection and a reasonable attempt to preserve and to restore some of its habitat, there seems no reason why this situation should not continue.

Mallard

Anas platyrhynchos Linnaeus

References

Anas Linnaeus, Syst. Nat., ed. 10, i, p. 122, 1758.
Anas platyrhynchos Linnaeus, Syst. Nat., ed. 10, i, p. 125, 1758. (Sweden.)

Description

ADULT MALE. Head and neck rich iridescent green with a white collar at the base of the neck; breast rich purple; underside of tail black; remainder of underside white with numerous fine dark lines; back brown; rump and tail glossy black; wings brownish grey; speculum purplish blue, bordered at both sides with black and white bars; bill yellow; legs orange; iris brown.

MALE IN ECLIPSE. The male in eclipse resembles the female but has a dull green bill.

ADULT FEMALE. Head and neck buff with brown streaks; the whole body is mottled and streaked with dusky brown and dull chestnut; wings brown; speculum as in male.

Size

ADULT MALE. Wing 260-270 mm.; bill 43-52 mm.; tarsus 38-42 mm. (Delacour). Length 554-678 mm.; wingspread 850-1021 mm. (Kortright).

ADULT FEMALE. Wing 240-270 mm.; bill 43-52 mm.; tarsus 38-42 mm.; length 521-579 mm.; wingspread 770-965 mm. (Kortright).

Field Recognition

The Mallard is very distinctive. In males the green head and white neck ring are obvious, as is the rest of its bright colour pattern. In the hand the purple speculum distinguishes both sexes from all Australian ducks. Females lack the distinctive face pattern of the Black Duck and are much lighter in colour. Overhead Mallards do not show the distinctive white underwings of Black Ducks.

Relationships

The Mallards form a group with world-wide distribution, they include many very similar forms and are by far the most widespread and best-known group of ducks. All are very closely related and most replace one another geographically. There are four groups of closely related forms and three more localized forms.

The main groups are the northern Mallards, *Anas platyrhynchos* of the Northern Hemisphere, the Spot-billed Ducks, *A. poecilorhyncha* of Asia, the Black Ducks, *A. superciliosa* of Australia and the South Pacific, and the Yellow-billed Ducks, *A. undulata* of Africa. More localized forms are the American Black Duck *A. rubripes,* the Philippine Duck *A. luzonica,* and Meller's Duck *A. melleri* of Madagascar.

The Mallard that we are concerned with is the common green-headed bird *A. p. platyrhynchos.* The stock was introduced from England.

Distribution

The breeding range extends across the Northern Hemisphere; Europe, Asia, North America, and north-west Africa. It winters in the southern U.S.A., Mexico, North Africa, and across Europe and Asia to southern China.

It has been introduced into New Zealand where it is now very abundant. It was first introduced in 1867 with one pair from Australia, and in 1893 nineteen and in 1904 four more were imported from England. From 1896 to 1916 from 20 to 170 of the progeny of these birds were liberated each year, and in 1895 the society involved proudly "considered the acclimatization of these ducks an established fact".[7]

The birds multiplied rapidly and, aided by further releases, mainly from North America, spread throughout New Zealand. In many districts it now constitutes most of the shooters' bags.

Australian Occurrence

Mallards, both pure bred and in various degrees of hybridization with Black Ducks and domestic strains of ducks, most of which in turn are derived from the Mallard itself, are common in many city parks and gardens, and in some country towns. It is also occasionally encountered in the wild. I have seen one shot on a billabong near Deniliquin, New South Wales, and once trapped one in association with a recently arrived flock of Black Ducks at Griffith. There is nothing at all to recommend Mallards in the Australian bush and they should be shot on sight.

In some country districts domestic ducks and cross-bred Mallards are allowed access to swamps so that the females may be impregnated by Black Ducks; the progeny are thought to be more efficient call birds than either domestic ducks or Black Ducks. The use of live call ducks is prohibited, anyway, so there is nothing to recommend this dangerous practice, which could lead to the dilution of Australia's premier game duck with very undesirable characteristics inherited from the Mallard strain.

Life History

The habitat of the Mallard, in the Northern Hemisphere, includes all types of water, lakes, ponds, rivers, ditches, swamps, and the sea coast, as well as city parks and gardens. It is one of the most adaptable waterfowl and the most successful. In North America the principal feeding grounds are in the interior in sloughs, lakes, and rivers, but it also freely visits stubble fields and feeds on the fallen grain. The food is very similar to that of the Australian Black Duck and consists of sedges, grasses, smartweeds, and many other aquatic and dry-land plants.

The usual nest site is on the ground, but nests have also been found in trees sometimes far from water, and occasionally in the deserted nests of other birds, and even on the tops of some London buildings. The clutch is usually 10 to 12 eggs, which are very similar in shape and appearance to those of the Black Duck; the incubation period is 28 days.

In the Northern Hemisphere the Mallard is migratory, although less so, perhaps, than many other ducks. In New Zealand the movements of Mallards and Black Ducks have been compared and it was found that the Black Duck was the more mobile. Black Ducks moved throughout the summer and might cover the whole country, and a few even reached Australia; Mallards, however, were rather sedentary and seldom moved far from where they were bred. In the same study it was shown that the Black Duck has a higher mortality rate than the Mallard. Of the Black Duck population 57 per cent die from shooting but only 30 per cent of Mallards. The Black Ducks decoy more readily and so are more easily shot. The Black Ducks needed to rear 4·4 young per pair to replace these losses, but the Mallards only needed to rear 2·9; unfortunately the Black Duck clutch size in New Zealand, 8-9 eggs, is less than that of the Mallard, 10-12 eggs. All these things add up to put the Black Duck at a severe disadvantage in competition with Mallards.

Status

It is unfortunate that the Mallard already exists in a feral state in Australia and, assuming that it is impossible to eradicate them now, they must be very carefully watched until the trends in their populations are determined. It is sometimes argued that exotic waterfowl could be more widely distributed to replace depleted populations of Black Ducks in various districts, but the possible results are not always realized. The acclimatization of fauna to a foreign environment is a very grave matter. Before birds are introduced to Australia deliberately there must be very careful study and consideration of the possible effects on the native fauna and habitats. Fortunately the quarantine regulations, at present, are of sufficient strength to prevent further irresponsible, even if well-meaning, introductions.

To survive and reproduce in a foreign environment an introduced bird must find a suitable ecological niche, that is, a combination of food, shelter, habitat, and all the other things it needs for life. All the niches in an environment are normally occupied by native fauna; if a vacant one had existed then, through evolution, a species would have developed to occupy it. An introduced bird, usually, can only expand in competition with the older resident species. There are three principal results of this competition: (*i*) the introduced species may not be so well adapted to the environment as the native species, which maintains its numbers while the introduced bird remains very low in numbers or disappears; (*ii*) the introduced bird may be more efficient and, by direct competition for food, nesting places, or other living resources, may completely replace the resident species; or (*iii*) where the two are closely related they may hybridize or cross and ultimately produce something very different from either of the original birds; this can easily be far less attractive than either the resident species or the introduced one.

Those who favour the spreading, or protection, of the introduced waterfowl feel that agricultural development has so altered the Australian environment that new ecological niches have been created and could, with profit, be filled by foreign birds without detriment to native species. Those opposed to acclimatization feel, and I think correctly, that as the Black Duck easily adapts to new niches created by agriculture anyway, and the results of an introduction cannot be forecast on theoretical grounds, and have no certain advantage to offer, the dangers involved are too great a risk.

The New Zealand experience is that the introduced Mallard has increased rapidly and the competition has gone against the Black Duck, which is gradually being replaced by the Mallard. New Zealand waterfowl biologists, deploring the dominance of the Mallard in many places, complain:

> We have other districts already endowed with good grey [= Black] duck populations where, because of novelty and the desire to try and improve a good thing, individuals and acclimatization societies desire to breed and liberate Mallards. This is considered most unwise and such attempts should cease as they are contrary to the best interest of those concerned, and will almost certainly lead to the replacement of the grey duck population.[7]

The dangers of its dissemination in Australia are that it is closely related to the Black Duck and has quite similar food and habitat needs. It interbreeds very freely with Black Ducks and proves the dominant strain, so that the characteristics of the native Black Duck are lost in successive generations of the crosses. This is associated with a more sedentary nature than that of the Black Duck and less adaptability to survive in the erratic environment of inland Australia. On theoretical grounds one might expect wide dissemination of Mallards to be disastrous to the Black Duck, which would quickly cease to exist as a species and be replaced by the introduction.

Grey Teal

Anas gibberifrons Müller

References

Anas Linnaeus, Syst. Nat., ed. 10, 1, p. 122, 1758.
Anas gibberifrons S. Müller, Verd. Nat. Ges., p. 159, 1842. (Celebes.)

Other Name

Slender Teal.

Description

ADULT MALE. Feathers of back dark brown with a paler margin, except those of tail and rump; upper wing and coverts dark brown; outer coverts white, as are the tips of inner coverts and secondaries; primaries dark brown; speculum glossy black with bluish sheen, in the closed wing appearing as a black band with a white band above and below; top of head and back of neck blackish brown, speckled with lighter brown; side of head, throat, and chin almost white; under-surface of body light brown with dark brown in centre of each feather; legs and bill black; eye bright red.

ADULT FEMALE. Similar to male but generally paler in colour. Separation of the sexes by their appearance requires very great experience and is then not certain.

IMMATURE. Both sexes are similar to adults but very much paler than females, particularly on the head and neck. They are easily distinguished from adults with practice.

At times Grey Teal of all sexes and ages are reddish brown on the heads, necks, and breasts. The colour is sometimes very bright, almost orange. In these cases they sometimes resemble, superficially, young Chestnut Teal, or possible hybrids between the two teal. The colour is due to staining of the plumage by iron salts from feeding in shallow stagnant water.

DUCKLINGS. Downy ducklings are dark brown-grey on the back and head and lighter underneath. There are two prominent brown stripes on the head, one through the eye and one below it.

Size

	Weight gm.	*Length mm.*	*Wingspread mm.*	*Wing mm.*	*Bill mm.*
Adult Male					
Maximum	670	477	721	220	43
Minimum	395	407	625	175	32
Average	507	445	673	205	37
Number measured	*210*	*208*	*35*	*209*	*210*
Adult Female					
Maximum	602	440	704	243	39
Minimum	350	370	605	164	32
Average	474	418	66	198	36
Number measured	*138*	*149*	*29*	*148*	*148*

Voice

The female has a loud penetrating quack, repeated rapidly—"laughing". It can be distinguished from that of the female Black Duck in several ways. The quacks are shorter, one-tenth of a second compared to a quarter of a second; they are of a higher frequency and greater resonance and the sequence is of greater duration; the quack is repeated fifteen or more times, but in the Black Duck seldom more than six. The male has a muted "peep".

Routine

Grey Teal can be found almost anywhere, in pairs, groups, or flocks, which can be very large and contain several thousands of birds. It

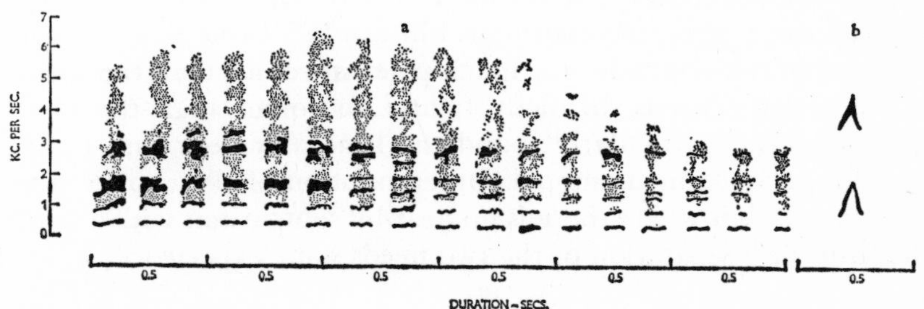

Diagram of sonogram of Grey Teal: (*a*) female, (*b*) male. Compare female call with that of the Chestnut Teal on p. 200.

can be found on the water, on mudbanks, or clustered all over fallen trees. It is usually easy to approach, except when it has been disturbed by shooting, when it is very wary. When disturbed they fly in a compact flock which twists and turns in the air, returning to swoop low across the billabong and rise again very steeply. It usually settles again farther away and may be flushed several times before it leaves the area.

Experiences with teal in inland Australia vary from the isolated birds that rise continually before one from among the fallen timber in near-dry billabongs, and fly silently away through the timber to the next pool, to the exciting view of the immense nomadic flocks on residual floodwater on the plains. Here very many thousands gather in dense groups that cover hundreds of acres of water and, when disturbed, circle overhead in clouds. As one wades through the floodwaters teal rise continuously in masses a hundred yards or so ahead, with a roar of wings, to join the circling flocks.

Field Recognition

The Grey Teal is a small duck that floats high on the water; the head is large and the face and throat very light in colour, but there is no eye stripe. It could be confused with the Black Duck, Pink-eared Duck, or female Chestnut Teal.

In flight the flash of the white on the wing immediately distinguishes it from the Black Duck. Its head is heavier in proportion to its size, the neck is thicker and shorter, and there is a white bar on the wing, and no eye stripe. Overhead it lacks the white underwings of the Black Duck. Confusion with the Pink-eared Duck is only possible on the water at long range, in flight it is very different in many ways. In flight the Pink-eared Duck has a white tip to the tail, white rump, and a white trailing edge to the wing, it carries its head high and the large bill is obvious, and it twitters—all very different to the Grey Teal. On the water the Pink-ear floats higher and carries the head more erect, the enormous bill can be distinguished at great distances, and the bird is very much paler in colour than the teal.

The Grey Teal is distinctly lighter in colour than the female Chestnut Teal, particularly round the head and neck, and the distinction, once learnt, is simple. Differentiation of the two in mixed flocks is easy, but where there is no near-by comparison with a female Chestnut Teal separation of the two needs some experience.

Relationships

A Dabbling Duck of the tribe Anatini, the Grey Teal is closely

Black Ducks, showing (*upper*) alert posture, and (*lower*) feeding methods.
Photos by Ederic Slater

Upper: Part of a summer concentration of Grey Teal.

Lower: Grey Teal resting on the edge of inland floodwater in far western New South Wales. *Photos by Ederic Slater*

related to other Southern Hemisphere teal; the group is collectively known as Austral Teal and comprises the Grey Teal, the Chestnut Teal *A. castanea,* the Madagascar Teal *A. bernieri,* and the New Zealand Brown Teal *A. aucklandica;* all are very similar in size and shape but vary greatly in colour. The Grey Teal and Madagascar Teal are similar in appearance, and the Chestnut and Brown Teal are similar to one another but brightly coloured. The classification of the various forms is still the subject of some discussion.

The Grey Teal is found throughout Australia, Indonesia, New Guinea, and some Pacific Islands, and is self-introduced to New Zealand.[20] The following races have been recognized. *A. g. gibberifrons,* which is slightly smaller and darker than the mainland subspecies, is confined to Indonesia (Java, Celebes, and the Lesser Sunda Islands to Timor). *A. g. albogularis* is confined to the Andaman Islands. It is similar in size to the mainland species but is distinguished by white rings round the eyes and has white elsewhere on the head; the amount of white is very variable. It seems strange that a nomadic bird like the Grey Teal should be found in Java and in the Andaman Islands, as well as occasionally on Christmas Island and in Burma, but has not been recorded from Sumatra. Perhaps it will be found there also eventually. *A. g. gracilis* is the mainland subspecies and is found throughout Australia, New Guinea, Aru and Kei, and in New Zealand; it frequently irrupts to near-by islands, including New Caledonia, Lord Howe, and Macquarie. *A. g. remissa* has been recognized from Rennel Island by Ripley[86] on a small sample. It is said to be smaller than the other races, intermediate in colour between *gracilis* and *gibberifrons,* and to have a smaller bill and lower forehead.

Habitat

The Grey Teal may be found in any fresh, brackish, or salt-water habitat at any time, and can be found breeding in everything from ground tanks to extensive coastal swamps. Its preferred habitats, however, are the billabongs, lagoons, and floodwaters of the inland rivers. At all times most of these have a permanent breeding population of teal, and in times of flood the floodwaters are rapidly colonized by very large nomadic groups. In times of drought and stress inland the birds may move in large numbers to deep lakes in the highlands and to salt-water bays and estuaries on the coast, but at other times these support few teal. The first bird to appear on any newly formed water area of any sort is usually the Grey Teal, and this indefatigable nomad spends its life moving over the continent colonizing all areas of water that form.

Distribution and Movements

The Grey Teal is found as a breeding species throughout Australia, New Guinea, Aru and Kei, and in New Zealand, but because of its extreme nomadism could easily be seen farther abroad. It ranges from ground tanks on the most arid inland plains to the snow-covered tablelands and from city parks in Tasmania to sago swamps in New Guinea. It is, however, more typically a bird of

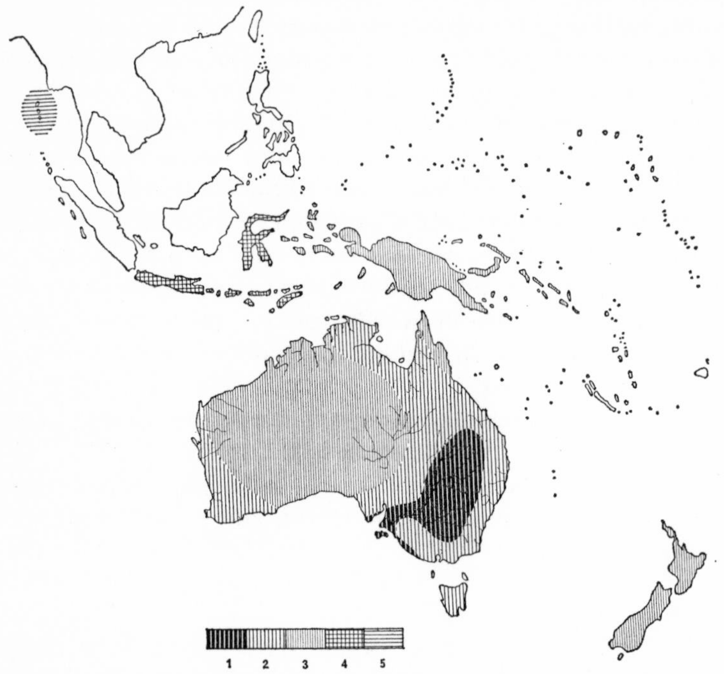

DISTRIBUTION OF THE GREY TEAL

The range of *Anas g. gracilis*, the Australian Grey Teal, is shown by the vertical shading (Nos. 1-3). On the mainland the darkest area (No. 1) shows the main breeding range of the species, where Grey Teal are found in great numbers at all times; the birds are less common but still a numerous species in the area of intermediate shading (No. 2), and in the lightest parts (No. 3) are widely spread but uncommon and only breed in exceptionally favourable seasons. In New Guinea and New Zealand only the total range is indicated. The square hatching (No. 4) indicates the range of *A. g. gibberifrons*, and the horizontal hatching (No. 5) the range of *A. g. albogularis*.

low rainfall country and is best adapted to live in the inland, and there, normally, the greatest concentrations occur.

In eastern Australia it breeds in most districts, but the greatest numbers are in the lagoons and billabongs of the inland rivers. There are few records of breeding on the eastern coast and tablelands. In Victoria there is some breeding, particularly in the south-western districts, and considerable numbers breed in south-eastern South Australia and throughout Tasmania. In Queensland it is not a very common breeding species on the coast, but breeds in great numbers in the south-west, lesser numbers in the northern inland, and in some years in the Gulf country. In Western Australia it is a common breeding species everywhere, except in the Kimberley region where it is usually rare, but at times large numbers of nomads visit that region also. It is widely distributed on the coast of the Northern Territory, and inland small numbers occur wherever there is water.

Grey Teal are very mobile and, while most inland billabongs always support a few, the main populations wander over the continent in an erratic manner.

They are quick to colonize and have established themselves in New Zealand in recent times. The species was first seen there by Europeans in 1866 but had probably occurred there before, since the Maoris had a word for it, *tete*. Between 1866 and the end of the century there were frequent sightings and it became quite common in some places but, over all, it was considered rare and afforded protection from shooting. In 1957 there was a drought in Australia and this resulted in a massive influx of Grey Teal into New Zealand. Since this drought-induced movement, although the numbers have declined, it remains moderately common in New Zealand and probably occupies all the available habitat.

A similar colonization of the subcoastal plains of the Northern Territory occurred between Oenpelli and Darwin in 1957.[38] Repeated air surveys of the region before 1957 had shown that the bird was very rare, but in the middle of that year a massive irruption occurred from the south and immense numbers of Teal arrived; every water area was crowded with them. Many, later, dispersed back in a southerly direction, but great numbers remained and bred, so that Grey Teal became, and still are, very common in the area. Perhaps the groups that are recorded briefly on various islands from time to time, for example, in New Caledonia, are groups that, under more favourable conditions, might have permanently colonized the area.

Concentrations of Grey Teal are usually not static in composition. Individuals are continually arriving and leaving, so that, although the size of the concentrations might not vary greatly, the individuals comprising it can change completely.[43] The size and permanence of a concentration in a given swamp in normal times are probably determined by the amount of food available, but in droughts, when there is little water anywhere, the pools carry more birds than they can support and the whole group must move or perish. Accordingly the scale of movements is determined by the amount of suitable water available, which is, in turn, determined by the conditions of rainfall and flood. When rain is adequate and the swamps and billabongs remain full there is little movement, but in dry times there is more extensive movement, and in drought very wide dispersal indeed. It is reasonable to suppose that individual birds vary in their speed of response to unfavourable conditions, and field observations support the idea. Some birds move very soon after conditions begin to deteriorate. but others are more resilient and remain to the last. Although Grey Teal in permanent swamps seem to be quite sedentary, and some of them really are, as shown by their repeated recapture in the same place, the populations contain a nomadic element that is constantly moving through the area, and sometimes travelling long distances. The most extensive and erratic movements, however, are in the inland populations, which often undertake spectacular irruptions.

Extensive banding by C.S.I.R.O. and by State authorities has shown that these movements can occur at any season and that the usual movements of Grey Teal are explosive random dispersals. The distance travelled is only limited by the availability of suitable habitat on which to stop. The birds disperse and fly in all compass directions, in apparently straight lines, until suitable water is found. If no water is found they continue until they have reached the coast, perhaps on the other side of the continent, and many go on to reach New Guinea or New Zealand, or other islands. Undoubtedly many fly out to sea, fail to find islands, and perish. There is little tendency among those that do find water to return to their place of origin, except by chance in another random dispersal.

It was possible to study one spectacular irruption of Grey Teal in 1957 and 1958.[43] This led to Grey Teal from the Murray-Darling Basin moving throughout the whole of Australia, New Guinea, and New Zealand, at least, and resulted in a great mortality among the birds that failed to find suitable habitat. Many were banded in 1957 at Griffith, New South Wales, after an extensive flood in 1956, and as the floodwater dried these scattered in all directions and flew throughout the whole continent and beyond it. The result of this exodus was that by the middle of 1958 the inland was almost devoid of teal, but every swamp and water area on the coast and highlands carried unprecedented numbers. They were found in large concentrations in city parks and coastal estuaries, and enormous numbers appeared on the coastal plains of the Northern Territory where Grey Teal are normally not common.

It was possible to visit several of these refuge areas and to band large numbers of the birds. It was found that, when the waters began to decline, the birds moved out of each as it became unsuitable. They scattered far and wide over the continent, again in search of water. Any permanent waters that existed soon supported concentrated flocks. One such case was Hume Reservoir, and here birds were recovered that had originally been banded near Griffith and Dareton in inland New South Wales, Sydney, Darwin, Hobart, Naracoorte and Adelaide, Melbourne and Perth—everywhere that Grey Teal had been banded at that time. At the same time birds from the Hume Reservoir and other water areas were moving out, and birds from every banding place were also dispersing in all directions, and were moving through every other banding place all over the continent.

It was apparent that during 1957 and 1958 the teal were flying back and forth across the continent, in all directions, searching for water, in what can only be described as a desperation scatter. Those that found water survived, but the majority of birds were unsuccessful and perished. After 1958 they became very uncommon in eastern Australia and did not begin to recover until there was adequate inland flooding again in 1960.

The crash in numbers in 1958 was not an isolated case, though it is the best documented. A similar crash occurred in 1953 and 1954 when the very large numbers of birds produced by floods in 1951 and 1952 perished. Previous to 1952 periodic abundance, and then great scarcity, characterize the teal populations; each year of scarcity followed a drought when the birds were pushed out of the inland. A similar irruption from the inland is in progress at the time of writing, August 1965.

In years of irruptions the scale of movements, both in the distance travelled and in the numbers of birds involved, is exaggerated, but similar movements, on a smaller scale, occur in most years. Each summer, from inland areas, the teal move in all compass directions and concentrate in coastal districts, or in areas having permanent water, such as along the Murray River and the lakes of the Southern Tablelands. Although the birds move in all directions from inland New South Wales there is a decided preference for southerly and south-westerly directions, perhaps owing to a learnt experience of better-than-average chances of finding suitable habitat in those districts. They stream into south-eastern South Australia, southern Victoria, and Tasmania, from which places erratic dispersal simultaneously occurs. Although there is some regularity in the time of movement, the birds usually leaving in November or December and returning again in March and April, these dates and the numbers of birds are very much affected by the rainfall inland. The drier the summer the greater the movement, and the influx of birds, to the refuge areas, but when there is heavy rain or flood in the inland the volume of the movement is reduced, or it may not occur, since many birds find suitable habitat inland and remain there.

The main movements of Grey Teal are drought-induced dispersion, but some movements strongly suggest that, in addition to being "pushed" by dry or otherwise unsuitable conditions, sometimes they can detect distant rain and move to it. Thus in 1952, Grey Teal were numerous in the Riverina district of New South Wales, and the rice-growers were complaining bitterly. Heavy rain fell in central Queensland, and within two days the birds were rare in the Riverina but abundant in central Queensland. Other examples are the swamps on the lower Richmond River in north-east New South Wales. These are usually dry, but whenever they fill flocks of Grey Teal arrive, almost overnight, some of them bearing bands placed on in inland New South Wales only a few days before. There are so many observations of Grey Teal very quickly reaching newly flooded areas, in large numbers, that there seems little doubt that they do detect the distant rain, but in what manner is not known.

Feeding

Typical Dabbling Ducks, Grey Teal feed by dredging the mud at the water's edge, tipping in the shallows, or by stripping the seeds and flowers from plants in, or overhanging, water. They often filter the surface water, picking up insects and seeds, and seldom move more than a few feet from its edge. They very quickly discover rain pools on the plains and utilize these for feeding and are quick to follow the edge of an expanding water area.

In inland New South Wales 41 per cent of the food in 2037 stomachs consisted of plants that normally grow in swamps, 26 per cent of plants normally growing on dry land, and 33 per cent of animal food.[39] The most important groups of plants were the smartweeds *Polygonum,* which provided 11 per cent of the food, and the sedges, mainly *Carex,* which contributed 18 per cent, and grasses, mainly water-couch *Paspalum,* rye-grass *Lolium,* wallaby-grass *Danthonia, Eragrostis,* and oat-grass *Agrostis.* Most of these grasses normally grow on land and were presumably gathered from rain pools and freshly flooded pastures. The remainder of the plant food consisted of clovers, thistles, nardoo, paddymelon, and many other dry-land and aquatic seeds belonging to a very wide range of plant families. Apparently whatever seed was available at the time was eaten.

Most aquatic insects were eaten including the larvae of midges Chironomidae, mosquitoes Culicidae, caddis-flies, Trichoptera, and dragon-flies Odonata; but the most important animals eaten were the water-beetles Dytiscidae, which included *Berosus,* the commonest animal eaten, and water-boatmen Corixidae. Insects provided 28 per cent of the total food, that is, nearly all of the animal food, the remainder of which consisted of small freshwater mussels, crayfish, and minute crustaceans.

In the inland, and doubtless elsewhere, Grey Teal have no regular seasonal cycle of food, or even an annual cycle. The food eaten at any particular time depends on the level of the water and its condition. When the level is steady the birds remain in the billabongs, cruising the edges, and eating aquatic insects and seeds. When the level rises and floods out through the timber the Grey Teal move with it, feeding on the dry-land insects forced out of burrows and drowned. As the water then moves across the plains, beyond the timber fringe, they still go with it and subsist on the flooded seeds of dry-land grasses and clovers. If the flood is maintained they exhaust this food, but by then water insects have colonized the drying pools and are eaten exclusively. Thus in a flood year they might feed for very long periods entirely on dry-land grasses or aquatic insects, according to the stage of the flood, but in another year they might be restricted to the billabongs and live on sedges and smartweeds for most of it. The very elastic food habit means that Grey Teal can use almost any kind of water for feeding; undoubtedly it is a very big factor in allowing their wide movements, and ensures that they can subsist almost anywhere.

In better-watered tropical areas Grey Teal confine their feeding more strictly to the lagoons. In a sample of 307 stomachs from north-east Queensland the food was almost entirely (97 per cent) vegetable and consisted mainly of products of the lagoons.[69] The major part of the food was sedges, pondweeds, and water-lilies. Grasses were not important and insects very uncommon. In 106 stomachs from coastal Northern Territory, collected in the dry season, the main food items were sedges and water-beetles in about equal proportions.

In many coastal districts Grey Teal resort to saline mud-flats and beaches and clearly feed there. A small sample of fourteen birds from such a habitat near Townsville, Queensland, showed these birds had been eating mainly *Amaranthus*, insects, and molluscs.[69] Birds collected on a saline earth dam west of Alice Springs had been feeding entirely on algae, and several in a salt-water lagoon behind the sand dunes near Evans Head, New South Wales, had fed entirely on small fish and tiny crabs. There is probably no other duck in Australia able to utilize such varied sources of food.

Breeding

The breeding season of the Grey Teal varies throughout its range but has only been adequately studied in the inland, where it is erratic and can occur at any time of the year. In southern coastal districts, and the Southern Tablelands, the breeding season is fairly regular and occurs in the late winter and spring, after the predominantly winter rainfall, but in northern Australia it occurs in the late wet season, that is, in late summer and autumn. In the inland, however, where most of the Grey Teal normally breed, they have no regular season at all and may lay eggs whenever the lagoons, billabongs, and claypans are filled by rain or flood. In the one district this could be midsummer one year, midwinter the next, or it might miss several years.

The initiation of the breeding season is controlled by rainfall and its effects, and there is little doubt that the most important factor is the increase in the water-level of the billabongs.[40] The level of these billabongs is mainly controlled by rain, or melting snow on the mountains, hundreds of miles away from the plains. When there has been heavy rainfall there, so that the inland billabongs abruptly increase in level, the Grey Teal in these billabongs breed, even though locally there may be no rain at all; similarly, I have seen times when heavy local rain, which does not alter the level of the billabongs, failed to stimulate any breeding.

The reaction to a rising water-level in the inland is very rapid. Sexually inactive birds begin to display as soon as the water-level begins to increase, and eggs may be laid only ten days after it began. This very swift reaction ensures that favourable chances to breed are not missed. There is scattered display at all times among most inland flocks of Grey Teal, but only when the river rises, and the water swirls into the billabongs, do they begin courtship in earnest. All over the surface groups swim restlessly to and fro. Some birds fly off to skid down again a few yards away, and other groups break and re-form or fly up and down the lagoon. In the larger groups the water fairly boils as the males vie for the females' attention. If the water-level rise is not maintained display ceases after a few days, and there is no breeding. If the rise in water-level is sustained, but is not great, only the local birds breed, but in a major flood, when water runs for miles across the plains, all the local birds breed, great nomadic flocks appear, and very extensive breeding follows. Every tree and stump contains a nest and many eggs are laid on the ground. At such a time hundreds or thousands of square miles of land are covered by water, the numbers of Grey Teal that breed are immense, and in every depression are large numbers of ducklings. Breeding continues as the water dries, and as it recedes the pools are crowded with hundreds of ducklings from little downy ones up to flappers; frequently many of these perish, as the water dries before they can fly, and many nests are deserted.

The advantages of having a breeding season directly geared to a rising water-level, to a duck that lives in an environment as unpredictable as inland Australia, are obvious. If the birds had a regular breeding season, or one determined by local rainfall, or by most other environmental factors, more often than not, when the ducklings hatched there would be no water for them to swim in.

In addition to providing the breeding habitat, it has been found that flooding, or water-level rise in the billabongs, increases the food available for the ducklings. The insects that form their food also have a breeding season geared to changes in water-level, and a rise in the level of the billabong is rapidly followed by breeding and a great increase in numbers of water-boatmen, Corixidae, the main food of the ducklings; thus the increased number of birds in the billabong are ensured of an increased food supply to support them.

The Grey Teal, apparently, has the ability to abbreviate its pair-forming and courtship displays to fit the environment in which it lives. On the Southern Tablelands the sequence is similar to that described for the Black Duck; pair-forming displays occur in the flocks in autumn and continue through the winter, in preparation for the spring breeding season. In the permanent cumbungi swamps in the inland also, where some Grey Teal breed in most springs, events are similar. In the inland billabongs, however, a sudden water-level rise can be followed immediately by courtship, the pair-forming displays having been either abandoned or compressed into a day or so—a remarkable adaptation to the erratic environment.

Nest

Grey Teal will nest anywhere, on the ground far from the water, in reeds on the edge of it, in hollow limbs of trees, under rocks, or in rabbit burrows. Hollow limbs are the commonest site in the inland lagoons, where the birds usually choose one about six inches in diameter in a tree standing in, or on the edge of, a billabong, and lay the eggs some feet from the entrance. I have seen one nest where the bird entered a hollow branch thirty feet from the water and then descended inside the trunk to lay the eggs at about water-level. When the tree was struck she could be heard scrambling up inside the tree to escape from the limb. She was successful in extricating the young. It is a strange sight to see a duck swim to the base of a tree then fly upwards almost vertically, to land on the end of a hollow limb and crawl into it like a parrot. Once inside they sit very quietly, are hard to flush, and presumably are safe from predators.

The eggs are laid on the bare wood or soil and gradually covered with grey down, plucked from the duck's breast. Small pieces of this down, which stick to the female's body are left outside the hollow and frequently betray the nest site.

Eggs

The eggs are oval or sometimes elliptical in shape and cream-coloured, though they quickly become nest-stained. In length, 126 eggs from 24 nests measured 49-58 mm. (average 50 mm.), and in breadth 35-42 mm. (average 36 mm.).

Clutch Size

Clutches found vary from 6 to 14, although sometimes, when breeding is very concentrated, several birds may lay in the one nest and up to 30 eggs have been found in such a hollow. The numbers of eggs in 54 nests were as follows:

Number of eggs:	4	5	6	7	8	9	10	11	12	13	14
Number of nests:	1	3	9	12	14	7	2	0	4	0	2

Counting the sizes of broods of various ages has shown that although, on the average, 7 or 8 ducklings form a brood, of the youngest age, only 2 or 3 reach the "flapper" stage.

Incubation

The incubation period is 24 to 26 days.

Longevity

The mortality rate and survival of Grey Teal has been studied in banded populations.[44] The average Grey Teal has 1·2 years left to live, though an occasional bird does survive until at least 8 years of age in the wild. Juvenile Grey Teal have only one year to live, but a bird found still alive after its first year can count on the average on having 1·4 years left. These figures are a little less than those for the Black Duck, as might be expected, considering the erratic nature of the Grey Teal's life. There is a greater turnover in their population than in those of Black Ducks.

Of a population of Grey Teal, 60 per cent will die in one year, 80 per cent in two years, and 96 per cent in three years, all greater mortality rates than in Black Ducks. For the Black Duck, the mortality rate declines as the birds grow older and learn to evade the causes of death, but the rate for Grey Teal remains fairly constant throughout life. Juveniles, however, are more vulnerable than adults and 66 per cent of them die in the first year after banding, compared to 53 per cent of adults.

The proportion of the birds that are shot is a little less than for Black Duck, 11 per cent against 13 per cent, but there are great locality and seasonal differences. At Griffith, New South Wales, between 1954 and 1961 the percentage of banded birds shot in the first year varied from 1·4 per cent to 15·2 per cent, with an average of 6·9 per cent. The shooting rate was greatest in the driest years when the birds were most concentrated and least in wet years when they were widely dispersed. Of birds banded in inland New South Wales, 6 per cent were recovered in their first year and a total of 12 per cent subsequently, but at Darwin only 2 per cent were shot in the first year and, near Adelaide, as many as 21 per cent. Clearly the shooting pressure varies greatly from time to time and from place to place.

Status

The Grey Teal is easily the most widespread duck in Australia, and one of the most numerous, being rivalled only by the Black Duck. It forms the greater part of the bag of most shooters in many districts, particularly in the inland ones, and in some places is almost the only game bird. Should its numbers decline greatly, duck-shooting as a sport would probably disappear from the greater part of inland Australia.

Although usually large, the numbers of Grey Teal are very subject to fluctuations caused by drought or flood. It can be present in myriads at times but is greatly reduced in numbers by even one year of drought, and the observer should not be misled by apparent abundance in any one place at one time. These might be the bulk of the continent's population striving to weather a dry period inland. The management of Grey Teal provides some difficult problems for conservation authorities. Its numbers vary from year to year, as can the directions of its movements and the timing of its breeding season. This makes the calculation of permissible bag limits and timing of open seasons difficult. The problems have not yet been completely overcome.

Although it is still numerous its future abundance cannot be considered certain. The main regions producing Grey Teal are the floodwaters and billabongs of the inland rivers of New South Wales and south-western Queensland. In recent years there have been rapid increases in water-conservation and flood-control projects aiming to control and use this water for agricultural and hydro-electrical schemes. Each of these projects aims a blow at the economy of the Grey Teal in a manner from which there can be no recovery. Each such project reduces the frequency of flooding of the inland rivers and so decreases both the frequency and the scale of breeding of Grey Teal. If the birds are to remain numerous it seems certain that their needs will have to be considered during the planning stages of water-conservation schemes, and that some of the structures will require modification to ensure that the important breeding areas are not needlessly destroyed.

Chestnut Teal

Anas castanea (Eyton)

References

Anas Linnaeus, Syst. Nat., ed. 10, i, p. 122, 1758.

Mareca castanea Eyton, Monogr. Anatidae, p. 119, 1838. (N.S.W.)

Other Names

Chestnut-breasted Teal, Mountain Teal.

Description

ADULT MALE. Head and neck glossy green; back dark brown, each feather with a chestnut fringe; rump and upper side of tail black; breast and underside generally chestnut, each feather with a prominent dark-brown blotch; undertail coverts and tail glossy black, on the flank before the tail is a prominent white patch; wing dark brown; speculum dark glossy green with a broad white band forward and a very narrow one behind; bill blue-grey; legs and feet greenish-grey; iris hazel brown.

MALE IN ECLIPSE. In eclipse males are said to be slightly duller; the glossy green head is dull and loses its sheen and the chestnut body colour is mixed with brown. This plumage has been noted in captivity but has not yet been recorded in the wild.

ADULT FEMALE. Similar to female Grey Teal but lacks whitish throat and is very much darker generally; general colour above dark brown, each feather, except those of rump and tail, edged with pale brown; crown dark brown; face fawn with blackish streaks; underside generally pale brown, each feather having a dark centre; speculum as in male.

IMMATURE. Immatures of both sexes resemble the female.

DUCKLING. Similar to those of the Grey Teal, but very much darker; white areas replaced by yellow and grey plumage heavily suffused with chestnut.

Size

I have been unable to measure Chestnut Teal and measurements of large series do not seem to have been published. General texts, however, imply that they are slightly larger than Grey Teal. According to Delacour the measurements of males are: wing 204-231 mm., tail 87-107 mm., bill 40-43 mm., and tarsus 36-40 mm. Those of females are: wing 197-210 mm., bill 37-42 mm. The large series of Grey Teal reported in this book greatly overlap these measurements.

Voice

The sounds most usually heard from Chestnut Teal are the loud multisyllabic quack of the female and the peep or whistle of the male.

Sonographic analysis of small samples of these two calls of the two teal species show very slight differences. The quack of the female and the whistle of the male Chestnut Teal are shown below, those of the Grey Teal on page 185. It can be seen that the whistles of the two males are identical, they cannot be distinguished by the human ear or by sound spectrograph. The quacks of the females are also very similar; there is a tendency for the Chestnut Teal to restrict itself to 7 to 9 syllables, whereas the Grey Teal commonly has up to 15, and the individual quacks of the Chestnut Teal are of a slightly higher pitch.

The differences, however, are so slight that clearly one should examine larger samples of both species before saying that differences are definitely established.

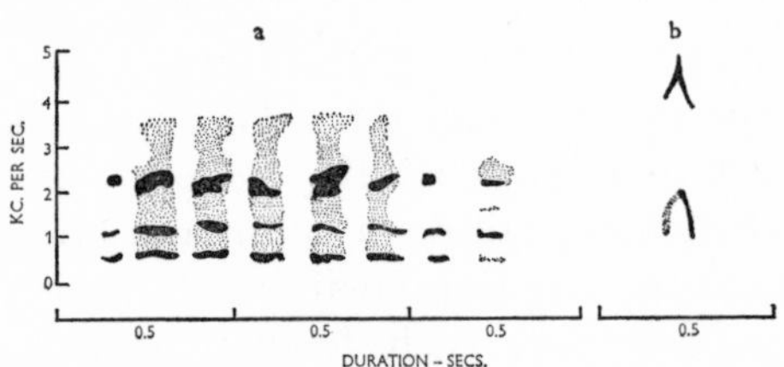

Diagram of sonogram of sounds made by Chestnut Teal: (*a*) female, (*b*) male.

Routine

Chestnut Teal can be found in all situations, swimming, or roosting on logs, rocks, or mudbanks. They seldom leave the water to feed on the bank, even less often than the Grey Teal, but often nest on rocky islands and run with great agility among the rocks. They are usually found in pairs or small groups; although flocks do occur they are always small and there is no equivalent to the immense swirling flocks of Grey Teal. Indeed, except in Tasmania, where large flocks of Chestnut Teal sometimes occur, they are usually found among the larger groups of Grey Teal. The general behaviour of the two species is very similar.

Field Recognition

The Chestnut Teal is a small duck that floats high on the water and may be in groups or small flocks. The general impression is of small, very dark, duck.

The females are similar to those of the Grey Teal, but, being very much darker and lacking the white throat, are quite easily distinguished. The two species are often in the same flock where the difference can be seen and readily evaluated.

The male's dark-green head is very distinctive, and in the distance the whole effect of the bird, even if colour cannot be seen, is very much darker than the Grey Teal. Unlike the Grey Teal, it has a very prominent white patch on the flank near the tail, similar to those of the Hardhead and Shoveler, but the bird is quite different in shape to these species; the Hardhead is low in water and has no visible stern; and the Shoveler has an enormous bill.

Relationships

A typical River Duck of the tribe Anatini, the Chestnut Teal is usually grouped with two other species known collectively as the Austral Teal, all of which live in the Southern Hemisphere and are quite closely related to the Mallards and Green-winged Teal of the Northern Hemisphere. The group comprises, in addition to the Chestnut Teal, the Grey Teal *A. gibberifrons* of Australia, and *A. bernieri,* the Madagascar Teal. All the forms, except one subspecies of the Grey Teal, are confined to the Southern Hemisphere, and that one barely crosses it.

Although they are very distinct species, the Chestnut Teal and the Grey Teal were originally confused at the beginning of this century, and it was thought that only one species inhabited

Australia; the green-headed birds were believed to be immature males and all others females, immatures, or males in eclipse.

Gould strongly suspected that he was dealing with more than one species when describing the "Australian Teal":

> There appears to be two very distinct races of this bird, one of which is much larger than the other; so great, in fact, is the difference in this respect in specimens from various parts of the country that the idea presents itself of their being really distinct species. The smaller race inhabits Tasmania, the larger the western and southern portions of Australia.

That this assumption was correct was not established until breeding experiments were performed in 1882. Ripley[86] attempted to revive the controversy again in 1942 with the opinion that Grey Teal were really a race of the Chestnut Teal, but the surprising opinion received no support anywhere at the time, though unfortunately it has since found its way into some recent literature.

The two teal are very distinct species. The breeding range of the Chestnut Teal completely overlaps that of the Grey Teal and the two nest side by side, the nests often being only a few feet apart. In captivity the two sometimes cross, the hybrids being intermediate in coloration between the two species, but in the wild, although their ranges completely overlap and they breed together in many areas, there is no authenticated record of a natural hybrid. There may occasionally be wild hybrids, but they are obviously very rare. Many birds without green heads but with chestnut breasts shown to the author as possible wild hybrids have all proved to be Grey Teal whose plumage has been stained with iron salts in stagnant water. It seems very likely that the Chestnut Teal is of southern origin and was a very early inhabitant of Australia, probably with a wider range than it has today, and that it has been overlapped by the Grey Teal of more northern origin and better adapted to live in the drying interior of the continent.

Even now there is a difference of opinion on the extent of the Chestnut Teal as a species. There are four very similar green-headed Teal in Australia, New Zealand, and near-by islands. Delacour prefers to consider these to be two species, one *A. castanea,* endemic to Australia, and the other three to be races of a species *A. aucklandica,* endemic to New Zealand. The *Checklist of New Zealand Birds,*[4] however, considers them all subspecies of the Chestnut Teal, *A. castanea.* There is no decisive proof of the relationships

Pair-forming display of Chestnut Teal. *Upper*: The female on the left is mated and repels a rival female. *Lower*: Three males indulge in communal whistling.

Photos by author

Shovelers, male (*upper*) and female (*lower*). *Photos by Ederic Slater*

of the various forms, but their appearance and behaviour are very similar and clearly more work is needed to settle the point.

The forms of the Chestnut Teal, following the New Zealand *Checklist* assumption, would be:

A. c. castanea. The nominate subspecies, the Australian Chestnut Teal, is mainly confined to the southern coastal districts of the continent.

A. c. chlorotis. The New Zealand Brown Teal is slightly larger than the Australian form and not so brightly coloured.

A. c. aucklandica. The Auckland Island Teal is confined to those islands. Following long isolation it has developed into a bird with short wings and very weak powers of flight.

A. c. nesiotus. This form is claimed to exist on Campbell Island, but only a dozen or so have been seen and four collected. It cannot be certain that it is a valid subspecies.

Habitat

The Chestnut Teal is most numerous in brackish coastal lagoons and salt-water estuaries, as well as in the lower reaches of creeks draining into the sea. There is some evidence that in southern Victoria and South Australia it was formerly most abundant in brackish tea-tree swamps, a habitat that has now largely disappeared. It is very abundant in the salt water of the Coorong, South Australia, but much less common in the adjacent freshwater lakes Albert and Alexandrina, these areas being occupied by Grey Teal. In Tasmania, whilst most numerous on the coast, it is found throughout the swamps and lakes of the interior, including the high lakes, and is often found in numbers in Midland lagoons.[89] In the southern highlands of the mainland it restricts itself to the deep rocky lakes, especially where islands occur and is not usually found in swamps and creeks. On the New South Wales and Western Australian coasts it favours mangrove-fringed creeks, swamps, and estuaries, and breeds in brackish, polluted water on Sydney Airport; there are also breeding colonies in some of the mangrove bays of Sydney Harbour.

When it does appear in the inland it may be seen in any water habitat, but most of the breeding that occurs is in billabongs. It often frequents clear lakes in the southern highlands in the non-breeding season but in very small numbers.

Distribution and Movements

Standard texts usually infer that the Chestnut Teal is uncommon or rare; this, however, is not so; within its range and in the correct habitat it is a common duck. The distribution is essentially coastal but in some places extends inland. Its main range is in Tasmania and the coastal districts and off-shore islands of southern Australia, from Sydney in the east to Moora, north of Perth, in the west. In this region it is a common breeding species but its exact status is difficult to determine, because within its range most flocks of Grey Teal include a few male Chestnut Teal and the proportion of the two species in the flock is hard to determine.

Tasmania is the undoubted stronghold of the species. It is widely distributed in rivers, estuaries, swamps, and lakes. Con-

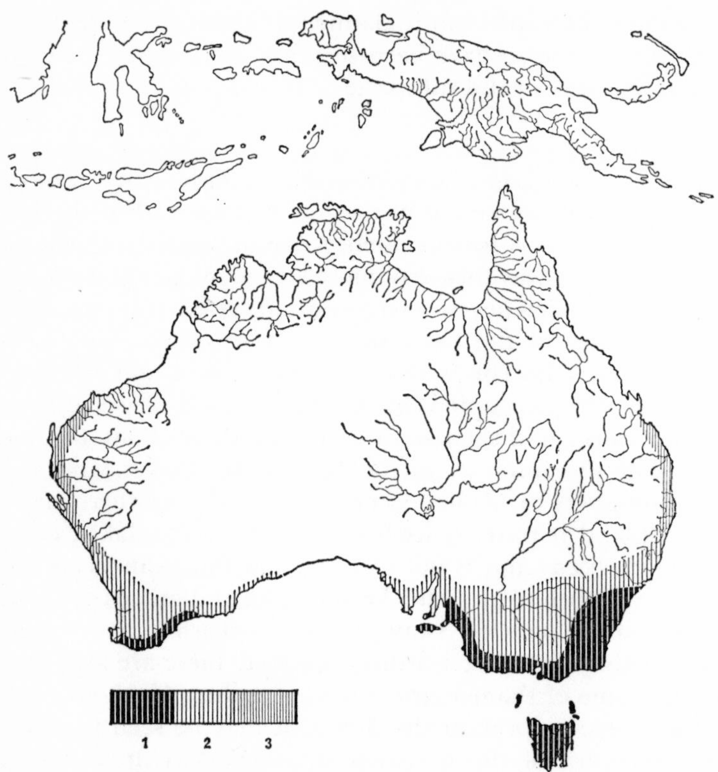

DISTRIBUTION OF THE CHESTNUT TEAL

The darkest shading (No. 1) shows the main breeding range of the Chestnut Teal. The area of intermediate shading (No. 2) is characterized by scattered breeding colonies, and in the lightest area (No. 3) vagrants occur regularly. Elsewhere in Australia vagrants are very unusual.

gregations of hundreds are often seen, especially in lagoons of the Midlands and in the estuaries of the east and south-eastern coasts. It extends through the islands of Bass Strait and off the south coast of the mainland. In coastal districts of the mainland it is less common but widely distributed. In the east its greatest abundance is between Naracoorte, South Australia, and Sale, Victoria; elsewhere on the coast it is represented by isolated, though sometimes quite strong colonies. The largest of these is in the city of Sydney where several pairs breed each year on Kingsford Smith Airport and others in the bays of Sydney Harbour. In Western Australia it is most numerous on the southern coast, especially in the brackish estuaries and lakes east of Cape Leeuwin and between Albany and Esperance. It is widely, though sparingly, distributed through the high plateaux of the southern tablelands and highlands to as far north as Canberra. In this region each mountain lake, with rocky foreshores, supports a small colony of up to about forty birds.

On the distribution map a gap is shown across the coastline of the Great Australian Bight between Eyre, Western Australia and Ceduna, South Australia. The region is arid and there is little surface water; more significantly, few ornithologists have traced the coastline. It seems possible that a close search would show a thin population of Chestnut Teal across the Bight associated with the few sheltered bays and inlets and reasonably fresh springs.

Beyond its main range isolated pairs or small colonies are sometimes found breeding. In Western Australia it has at times bred as far north as North West Cape,[13] and in the east there are several similar records. Hobbs[58] has reported breeding in a flood year, 1956, between Hay and Deniliquin, and each year a few pairs breed on the Murrumbidgee River near Griffith and in the lignum swamps west of Booligal on the Lachlan. These breeding records are much more common in flood years, and in 1951 and 1956 quite significant numbers were bred there. Farther north it has been reported breeding near Gilgandra, and Jackson[61] recorded a clutch claimed to be of this species at Grafton in 1896.

Records of its past distribution are difficult to interpret because of the early confusion between the two species of Australian Teal. For the same reason many of the clutches of eggs reputed to be of this species in museums are of very doubtful origin. There is some evidence, however, that colonies of Chestnut Teal on the New South Wales coast were formerly more common than they are now. Savidge wrote: "The Chestnut Teal (*Anas castanea*) was plentifully dispersed about the large swamps on the Lower Clarence River District; the open water and river courses do not seem to attract it so much as purely swamp country." I have spent much time resident on the far North Coast of New South Wales, and in a lifetime have only seen two or three Chestnut Teal north of Sydney, including the Clarence River swamps. Unless Savidge was still confused with the early nomenclatural difficulty, which seems unlikely, as late as 1914, his remarks suggest a former much more extensive, but quite credible, range in coastal New South Wales.

Little is known of the movement pattern of the Chestnut Teal. The evidence available, however, suggests that it is basically sedentary, but there is some dispersal each summer during which individuals may travel considerable distances.

Wherever they are common there is a regular, annual change in distribution. They are gathered in flocks on the larger lakes and the estuaries during autumn and winter, and in spring and summer disperse. Usually the movement is local and most breed in the immediate vicinity. Most banded birds have been recovered close to the banding place, but there is an element, mainly juvenile, that wanders more widely. Several birds from Tasmania have reached Victoria, having travelled 300 miles. One bird from Maitland, New South Wales, moved inland to Lake Cowal (250 miles) and one from Canberra reached Granya, Victoria (150 miles).

In years of drought there have been occasional records far from the birds' usual range. We collected two adult males near Darwin, Northern Territory, in 1958, 1,500 miles north of their usual limit, and Lavery saw single birds in North Queensland. Probably these, as well as the Chestnut Teal recorded earlier in northern Australia, were vagrants that had become involved in moving flocks of Grey Teal.

Breeding

The breeding behaviour of the Chestnut Teal follows the common pattern of the genus *Anas* when living in mild and regular environments.

The displays have been described in some detail by Lorenz.[71] At Canberra the typical mutual pair-forming displays, with several males vying for the attention of one female, begin in the flocks during March and continue throughout the winter. The mated pairs separate from the flock in spring, commonly in August, when there is less display between the mated birds, and the sexual period with precopulatory display begins in early September. The pairs cruise the edge of the lake, running ashore to examine tumbled rocks and grassy islands for nest sites, or in timbered areas flying up to inspect hollows. The male is less liable to desert the female when the eggs are laid than is the Grey Teal; nearly half the Chestnut Teal broods that I have seen have been accompanied by a male.

There is very little information on the precise extent of the breeding season, but the scanty records suggest that, although it is regular, there are significant regional differences.

At Lake Bathurst, a mountain lake near Canberra at 2,000 feet altitude with a severe winter climate, where there is a small colony of Chestnut Teal, nests have been systematically searched for throughout two years, 1963 and 1964. Of 27 nests examined, no clutches were begun in August, one clutch was begun in the first half of September, and four in the second half. Most were begun in October, four in the first half and thirteen in the second half. The latest clutches were begun in the third week of December. In a study by the Victorian Fisheries and Wildlife Department of a population breeding in nest-boxes near Melbourne, 169 clutches were recorded in 1963-4. Of these, the first were begun in the first week of June and the last in December, most were begun in the period July-November, and the peak of egg-laying occurred in October. It is apparent that in the milder environment of southern coastal Victoria the breeding season began somewhat earlier than in the harsh climate of the Southern Tablelands. There is other evidence from the Coorong, South Australia, at sea level. In November 1964 examination of nests and broods showed that egg-laying had begun not later than 10th August and extended until 1st January, but most clutches were begun in October. The date 10th August was deduced from the age of flappers seen, but as other juveniles on the wing were present, which probably were bred locally, breeding almost certainly began earlier. In any case the observations are sufficient to show that breeding began at about the same time as at Melbourne and earlier than on the tablelands.

Many Chestnut Teal probably rear more than one brood in the season. Many of the females in the Victorian study were individually marked, and of 80 females 41 were seen on one clutch, 27 on two separate clutches, and 12 on three separate clutches. Some females, having left a nest with a brood, returned within a week to begin another one; the fate of the first brood is not known. Others did not return for 20 weeks; most of the birds that laid two clutches, however, returned to begin the second clutch between 2 and 6 weeks after leaving the first brood. With those birds that laid three clutches the interval between the second and third tended to be a little longer than between the first and second.

Food and Feeding

The feeding actions of the Chestnut Teal are those of a typical Dabbling Duck, that is, as for the Grey Teal and Black Duck. Although most standard reference books give generalized statements of the food eaten as "grass, water-weed, insects, etc.", these are probably based on opinion rather than the examination of gizzard contents. There has been no systematic nor, so far as I know, even partial study of the food eaten by Chestnut Teal. Where the two species occur together they feed side by side in the same flock and no doubt secure the same items of food in these situations.

Nest

The nest is a scrape placed on the ground in long grass, rushes, in rock crevices, or in a tree-hole. In the southern highlands rocky or grassy islands are favourite nesting sites; this location undoubtedly saves many nests from predation by foxes, which are numerous on the shore, but many are lost to snakes that abound on some of these islands. In this district no nests have been found in hollow trees, but, according to Sharland,[89] tree-nesting is usual in Tasmania and has also been recorded in Victoria and New South Wales, near Melbourne, Sydney, and Griffith. The species readily adapts itself to nesting in nest-boxes erected for that purpose. The nest down is brownish-grey with lighter tips and centre and is easily distinguished from that of the Grey Teal, being very much darker in colour.

Eggs

The eggs are cream, elliptical, close-grained, smooth and probably more lustrous than those of the Grey Teal; 366 eggs from 42 nests measured, in length, 35-57 mm. (average 52 mm.), and in breadth, 35-41 mm. (average 37 mm.). These sizes do not differ from those of the Grey Teal.

Clutch Size

The clutch usually varies from 7 to 15, although up to 17 have been recorded in the one nest. The numbers of eggs in 59 nests, mainly near Canberra and the Coorong, were as below.

Number of eggs:	5	6	7	8	9	10	11	12	13	14	15
Number of nests:	1	4	10	11	14	8	4	3	3	0	1

In the Victorian nest-box study there was a greater range of clutch size; of the 169 clutches the size varied from 8 to 27. There was apparently some competition for nest sites and more than one female often laid in the nest; 79 per cent of the clutches were in the range of 8 to 13, and 9 and 10 were the commonest numbers of eggs found. Seventy-eight per cent of the clutches in this study were at least partially successful, that is, some eggs hatched. Of the successful clutches 80 per cent of the eggs hatched, but of the whole population 65 per cent resulted in ducklings, of which 3 per cent died in the nest-boxes.

Incubation

The incubation period is 28 days.

Development of Young

After hatching the young spend a day in the nest and are then led from it, but at least sometimes return to rest in it on the first night. In 1952 I saw a brood clamber back into its nest in late afternoon. In more than half the broods I have seen the male remained with them, sometimes until they were fledged. It is very uncommon, indeed, to see a male Grey Teal with his brood. In ducklings reared in captivity the first body feathers appeared between 20 and 29 days of age and the primaries appeared between 43 and 57 days. At 52-65 days of age the primaries were protruding one inch from the sheaths, and at 60-80 days of age the primaries were fully grown, though the young could fly long before this, some at 56 days of age. The juvenile plumage is moulted at four months of age and the birds are fully coloured and capable of breeding at the end of the first year, as are most *Anas*.

Status

Chestnut Teal are not uncommon in coastal districts. It is regarded as a game bird and is legally hunted in some States. It shares with the Grey Teal the qualities of a good game bird, being wary and swift-flying. In Tasmania and some parts of southern Victoria it makes up an appreciable part of the sportsman's bag.

There is no reason why the Chestnut Teal should not be hunted in the places where it is common, but it has declined both in range and numbers since European settlement of the coast line. It seems certain that as the flight of Grey Teal and other waterfowl from the inland to coastal districts declines in volume—and it undoubtedly will with water-conservation works continuing in the

Murray-Darling Basin—Chestnut Teal will come under even heavier shooting pressure than at present. When this occurs it would be foolish to assume that the species will not require special conservation measures. It has a relatively restricted range and is more sedentary and quite different ecologically to the Grey Teal, but is lumped with it and other ducks in most game regulations. There has been no population study of the species and the factors regulating its numbers are completely unknown. It is certain, however, that it is not capable of sustaining the same hunting pressure as the nomadic and resilient Grey Teal or the numerous and widespread Black Duck. It has undoubtedly declined in abundance and there is little doubt that it will decline further, perhaps dangerously, on the mainland at least. The study of its life history, to make sensible management possible, is urgently needed.

Superficially, at least, it appears to be a duck that could be managed efficiently and would rapidly respond to conservation measures. It is reasonably sedentary, and breeding and feeding conditions could easily be improved by the reservation and stabilization of coastal lagoons and the protection from stock of the cover around them. It readily adapts itself to breeding in predator-proof nest-boxes. It is to be hoped the facts of its population regulation will soon be studied in detail.

Shoveler

Anas rhynchotis Latham

References

Anas Linnaeus, Syst. Nat., ed. 10, i, p. 122, 1758.
Anas rhynchotis Latham, Index Orn. Sup., p. 70, 1801. (N.S.W.)

Other Names

Spoonbill, Blue Wing, Blue-winged Shoveler, Stinker, Whistling Teal.

Description

ADULT MALE. Crown of head and chin brownish black; remainder of head and neck blue-grey with a brilliant green gloss; there is a white crescent on the face before the eye; back and rump black with green gloss more distinct on rump; tail dark brown; front of neck and breast dark brown, each feather with broad light-brown tip and a white crescent; remainder of underside deep chestnut, each feather having a broad black edge and black bands; on each side of the tail there is a prominent white patch, each feather being crossed by several fine black lines; wing quills brown and upper wing coverts powder blue; scapulars black crossed with several broad white bars; speculum dark green with a broad white band in front; bill olive brown; legs and feet bright yellow; eye bright yellow.

MALE IN ECLIPSE. The male in eclipse lacks the white face crescent, green gloss, and white rump patch, and although easily distinguishable from the female, since it remains considerably brighter in colour, has a general resemblance to it.

ADULT FEMALE. The female is much duller than the male and has no white face crescent or green wash to the head and neck, and the speculum is much duller. The chin and sides of the head are buff, the crown and nape dark brown; the remainder of the upper surface dark brown, each feather edged with light brown; the under surface is pale chestnut, each feather having a dark-brown centre; bill black; feet and legs greenish grey; iris brown.

IMMATURE. The immature birds of both sexes are similar to the female but paler in colour. Both have brown eyes and greenish-grey legs when very young, but by four months of age the yellow coloration of these parts is apparent in the male.

DUCKLINGS. Dark brown above and yellow tinged with brown below; there is a broad yellow stripe above the eye and a prominent dark-brown band from the bill, through the eye, to the back of the head; trailing edge of wing yellow, and there is a yellow spot on each side of the back; when hatched the bill is no larger than that of other ducklings, but by 14 days of age it has grown very large in proportion to the ducklings and is distinctly spoon-shaped.

Size

	Weight gm.	*Length* mm.	*Wingspread* mm.	*Wing* mm.	*Bill* mm.
Adult Male					
Maximum	852	530	825	261	67
Minimum	570	450	720	210	56
Average	667	495	777	239	61
Number measured	*76*	*72*	*42*	*74*	*72*
Adult Female					
Maximum	745	490	790	297	62
Minimum	545	460	730	210	57
Average	665	477	759	238	60
Number measured	*70*	*101*	*42*	*102*	*69*

Voice

Shovelers are very silent and are seldom heard. The male has a soft "took took" and a guttural grunt uttered in display, and the female a very soft, husky quack. They also have a soft chatter when flying.

Routine

Shovelers are occasionally found in flocks of up to three hundred birds, but these occasions are rare and related to dry weather or drought. The typical distribution of Shovelers is in small groups or pairs, widely dispersed. They are commonly associated with other ducks, particularly Pink-eared Ducks, Grey Teal, and Black Ducks, and the first sign of their presence is usually the sound of the very distinctive whirr of their wings or the sudden flash of yellow legs.

They are very quiet and unobtrusive, resting during the day in dense cover. They are rarely seen on the edge of the swamp and never in trees. They are very wary and, when associated with teal, are always alert and swimming restlessly to and fro long before the teal have shown any alarm. The flight is swift and direct, but probably no swifter than that of the teal; they do not join in the swooping movements of teal, usually leaving the flock at that time.

Field Identification

The best field marks for the Shoveler are the heavy bill, which is very obvious in all situations, and the bright-yellow legs of the male.

It is a medium-sized duck that floats low in the water, much lower than the teal, Pink-eared Duck, and Black Duck, but similarly to the Hardhead. At long distances the white patches on the male's rump show up clearly and both sexes are readily identified by the shape of the head and enormous bill. The top of the bill and the forehead form a straight line, so that the bird has no visible forehead. This is unlike the Pink-eared Duck, which also has a huge bill, but a very distinct forehead.

The Shoveler springs into the air almost vertically, with a loud whirr of wings, and this wing-beat, unlike that of other Australian ducks, continues throughout the flight and is a good field mark. It flies very swiftly and directly and seldom returns to cross the lagoon again. In flight the bright-yellow legs are obvious in the male and are quite diagnostic for the species, but the blue shoulder patches, so obvious in the bird in the hand, are only noticeable in the field at close range.

Relationships

The Shovelers are included in the large genus *Anas* and, within this genus, are included in a group of rather similar birds known as the Blue-winged Ducks; these are distinguished from the others by similar plumage and behaviour. The large bill is characteristic of the Shovelers but not of Blue-winged Ducks generally; none has a shovel bill at hatching.

The group includes the Garganey, *A. querquedula* of the Northern Hemisphere, which has occasionally reached Australia as a vagrant, the Blue-winged Teal, *A. discors* of North America, the Cinnamon Teal, *A. cyanoptera* of North and South America, and the four shovelers: *A. platalea,* the Red Shoveler of South America, *A. smithi,* the Cape Shoveler of South Africa, *A. clypeata,* the Northern Shoveler of Europe and North America, and *A. rhynchotis,* the Australian Shoveler.

The Australian Shoveler is restricted to Australia and New Zealand and within it two subspecies have been recognized: *A. r. rhynchotis* is restricted to Australia, including Tasmania; *A. r. variegata* is a little more brightly coloured than the Australian form and is restricted to New Zealand and occurs on some off-shore island groups as a vagrant.

Habitat

The Shoveler can, at times, be found in any habitat, but it has a strong preference for the more permanent, heavily vegetated swamps—the cumbungi swamps of the inland and the tea-tree swamps of coastal districts. In these situations there are nearly always a few Shovelers present as permanent breeding residents. They are also found, in the non-breeding season, in lagoons and billabongs associated with other ducks, but I have never seen them breeding in these habitats, except during times of flood when they may be found breeding in all types of floodwater.

Distribution and Movements

Shovelers have been recorded at one time or another in most parts of Australia. They are occasionally seen in the tropical regions, but most of the records refer to occasional vagrants and the main distribution is in the south. Everywhere the Shoveler must be considered rare compared to all other southern ducks, except the Freckled Duck.

As with many other Australian ducks, the determination of its exact breeding range is difficult because of frequent nomadic movements that obscure its more usual distribution. Its rarity is a further complication. There is little doubt, however, that the main numbers now occur in the deeper swamps of the Murray-Darling Basin, in south-east Australia, and in Tasmania, and that these are its main breeding areas. Elsewhere in the eastern States it is unusual. There are very small numbers in the permanent lakes of the Southern Tablelands, and vagrants can often be found on the New South Wales and Queensland coasts as far north as Cape York; in times of drought these vagrants may occur in quite considerable flocks for brief periods. Inland in times of flood the Shoveler can be found very widely but sparingly distributed, and it has bred as far north as

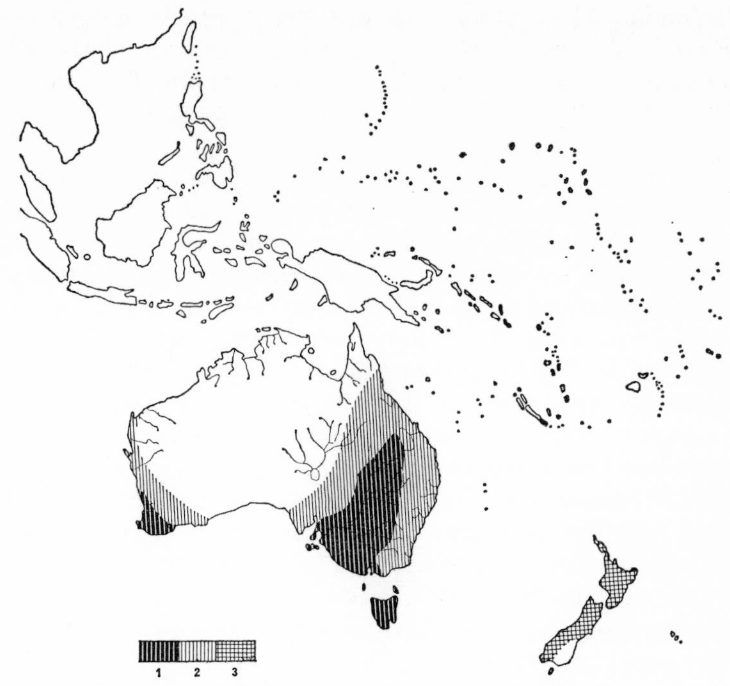

DISTRIBUTION OF THE SHOVELER

The vertical shading shows the range of *A. r. rhynchotis*. The darker shading shows the breeding range, and in the area with lighter shading vagrants regularly occur but seldom breed. The square shading shows the range of *A. r. variegata*.

the Gulf of Carpentaria. This event, however, was unusual. It is very uncommon indeed in the inland deserts and has never been recorded in the Northern Territory or the Kimberley Region of Western Australia. In Western Australia it is rare and is mainly found in the coastal districts of the south-west corner. It straggles inland when water is available, and has been recorded as far north as Point Cloates.

Published information on its earlier abundance is no more precise or satisfactory. What there is, however, suggests that it was formerly much more abundant in the coastal districts of south-eastern Australia than it is today, a not surprising fact in view of its habitat preference for the permanent, heavily vegetated lagoons that were formerly abundant and widespread in these districts. It was "fairly numerous" on the Clarence River and "very common" on the Richmond River in north-eastern New South Wales at the turn of the century,[82] and in the same period it was a significant bird to market hunters near Melbourne. Shovelers are almost unknown on the New South Wales coast today and, although they still occur, they are unusual near Melbourne.

Inland they were apparently never very abundant. North[82] gives some idea of their previous numbers in South Australia, writing of Lake Alexandrina, "the Shovelers were found in every part of the lake and passage. . . . These birds are fairly plentiful at times and in 1899 visited the reedbeds in great numbers." In New South Wales and South Australia 1888 and 1889 were years of very severe drought, and a similar passage would describe conditions in Lake Alexandrina today and in the 1957-8 drought. Shovelers were "very common" on Lake Boga in the early 1900s but are no longer. Hall[53] recorded that "To only a limited extent [do] they nest in this district", writing of the Murray River near Kerang. North recorded that they were "fairly numerous" on the Lachlan River and a "rare species" in southern Queensland. The status today inland seems rather similar to these accounts.

A quaint idea has arisen and is perpetuated in some textbooks that the rarity of the Shoveler, or its decline, is due to massive hunting by aborigines. The myth may have arisen with North, who described aboriginal hunting methods on the same page as the status of Shovelers, but he certainly did not infer that the two were linked. Shovelers were never very abundant compared to other ducks, but there is evidence that their numbers have further declined since settlement. They are very rare now in some districts where formerly they were regularly seen. It is unlikely that the decrease has been much greater relatively than that of the other ducks; it is most marked in those districts where other ducks have declined most.

Even if the decline in Shovelers had been greater than that of other ducks it would be unfair to blame the aborigines, since it has continued long after they were detribalized and ceased to depend on hunting for food. European occupation can be blamed for any decrease in numbers and distribution of the bird. In coastal districts, where its greatest populations were, the rich swamps, its preferred habitat, have nearly all been drained and converted to pasture. Inland its nesting habitat, the grass- and lignum-covered edges of swamps and lagoons, has been trodden and eaten by sheep and feral pigs and invaded by countless introduced foxes. There is little nesting cover and little chance of a clutch surviving the pigs and foxes. The wonder is that the predominantly ground-nesting Shoveler has survived at all.

Very little is known of its movements, but what observations there are suggest that it is fairly sedentary and that its movements are very much less extensive and more regular than those of the Grey Teal and, usually, only local in extent. In the inland swamps Shovelers are present in every month of the year, but seem to move about from swamp to swamp a great deal. Similarly in south-east Australia small numbers are always present. It is probable that the usual movements of Shovelers are local concentrations and small-scale dispersals in accord with the changing extent of the habitat in winter and summer.

On the Southern Tablelands a few are always present on the richest lakes, those that are sufficiently sheltered to have some submerged vegetation, and breeding is regular. The nests are likely to be found in the same place year after year, an observation that suggests a considerable degree of permanence of individual pairs. Several meadows, lucerne fields, and districts generally in southern Australia also are regularly favoured as nesting places for Shovelers, and in the present state of knowledge it seems probable that individual birds have a very strong homing tendency. The Northern Shoveler is a true migrant, but has been shown to return each year to the same meadow to nest; only careful colour-banding of individual birds will show if the Australian Shoveler has the same ability.

In the inland Shovelers are always present in the permanent swamps, and regularly breed there, but in other seasons groups wander to the lagoons and billabongs of the rivers. Despite this apparent regularity of movement floods are invariably followed by a small but noticeable increase in the numbers of Shovelers in most districts. Where the flood is regular the influx is regular, but where it is erratic then so is the influx. Every incoming flock of teal seems to include one or two Shovelers, but whereas, following major flooding, the influx of Grey Teal is numbered in tens of thousands, that of Shovelers is in ones and twos. As the floods recede they gather into small flocks and the local numbers decline as some move out.

The scale of the nomadic movements is influenced by the severity of the dry period, and in a drought, such as that of 1957 and 1958, can be quite extensive. In 1958 unusual concentrations and large flocks formed in inland New South Wales and elsewhere. I encountered several groups numbering up to five hundred birds.

These large groups travelled more extensively than usual—one at least reached the Jardine swamps on the tip of Cape York Peninsula and others were seen in North Queensland—but, strangely, no Shovelers were found in the enormous concentrations of drought-refugee ducks in the Northern Territory, despite careful search.

Feeding

Shovelers are more local in their daily movements than most other ducks. Once established in a swamp they, together with the Pink-ears, seldom move beyond it. Their daily routine is confined to the swamp, sleeping during the day on mudbanks or floating in deeper water, and feeding by day in the shallows. They seldom take foraging flights from the swamp that shelters them at the time.

The bills of all surface-feeding ducks are provided with hairlike lamellae on the edges, through which the water or mud is strained, so that the food is retained. This adaptation to food-collecting is highly developed in the Shoveler and the specialization of the bill is only exceeded by that of the Pink-eared Duck, in which the lamellae are finer and longer and through which the flow of water can be controlled more carefully by means of large membranous flaps. The bill of the Shoveler is large, measuring $2\frac{1}{2}$ inches in length; it is $\frac{5}{8}$ inch wide at the base and $1\frac{1}{4}$ inches at the widest part near the tip.

With this efficient filtering bill it is not surprising to find that Shovelers are usually found in habitats where the water is fairly permanent and might be expected to contain much floating food, so that dabbling in mud or stripping of seeds from plants is unnecessary.

With the exception of the Pink-eared Duck, the Shoveler is more typically a surface-feeding duck than any other. It swims rather more rapidly than the Pink-ear, but in the same manner, with the bill and half of the head, or the whole head, immersed. The bill chatters rapidly and the water is filtered through the hairlike lamellae on its fringe, retaining edible items. Communal feeding is common; the group forms an echelon or rough arrowhead formation and cruises along, each bird keeping station with its bill at its neighbour's flank, feeding on animals disturbed by its paddling feet and motion. Sometimes the leader swings round so that the party moves in a circle and he also gains something from the formation. They also hurry over the water, snapping from side to side, presumably catching quick-moving insects, and occasionally stand in shallow water and dredge the mud or up-end as do teal and feed from the bottom.

There has been no thorough study of the food eaten by the Shoveler, but in 47 stomachs that were collected near Griffith, New South Wales, representing most months of the year, 76 per cent of the food was of animal origin and 24 per cent consisted of plant materials.[39] The plant materials were almost entirely seeds with few flowers, stems, or other plant parts, suggesting that they had been filtered from the surface and not stripped from growing plants. There were seeds of a very wide variety of plants, including sedges, grasses, smartweeds, docks, paddymelons, nardoo, and clovers, but no particular plant was of special importance, either in respect to the volume of food or the frequency with which it was eaten. Presumably, as might be expected, the Shoveler does not select particular plants but merely utilizes whatever is encountered while filtering the water.

There was some animal material in every stomach examined; of the animals identified, insects were of outstanding importance and contributed nearly half of the total volume of food. They were found in every stomach. Of the insects, beetles were most numerous, and the commonest insect, and also the most important single food item, was the water-beetle *Berosus* sp., which provided 17 per cent of the total food. In addition to beetles considerable quantities of water-boatmen, Corixidae, were eaten and one of these, *Corixa eurynome,* accounted for 9 per cent of the food. Both these insects are also of considerable importance to the other dabbling ducks of the inland. One third of the Shovelers had eaten shells and these accounted for one fifth of the total food; both bivalves and univalves were eaten, but the commonest were the small *Lenameria* and *Isidorella.* Some freshwater mussels, *Corbiculena,* were also eaten. Most of the shells were tiny, most of them were less than an eighth of an inch in diameter, but some were surprisingly large, one freshwater mussel was nearly three-quarters of an inch in diameter. The only Crustacea found were a few minute ostracods.

Breeding

There has been no detailed study of the breeding of the Shoveler. The display resembles quite closely that of the European species and in some ways is not unlike that of the Pink-eared Duck. The courtship is performed on the water, usually far from the shore. The female swims along followed by one or more chattering males, who frequently swing their bills upwards and grunt. Sometimes a male will dart in front, raising the feathers of his neck and head and turning the back of the head towards her. There is constantly the soft chattering. The female raises and lowers her bill parallel to the water with increasing rapidity and takes wing, to be followed swiftly by a male or two, and they twist and swoop through the air. Copulation is on the water, afterwards the male swims in circles, grunting and chattering and swinging his head up and down.

The male and female select the nest site together, and soon after the eggs are laid he moves off and she hatches and rears the brood alone. I have seen nothing to substantiate the claim that the male "takes a share of incubation duties, and indeed is more often at the nest than the female".[89] According to Kortright,[67] in the Northern Shoveler polyandry is common, the female associating with two males, but this has not been recorded or suggested yet for the Australian species.

Shoveler nests are not often found and so it is not possible to record the exact breeding season throughout its range. Textbooks usually credit it with having a regular breeding season, from August till December. This is, no doubt, true in coastal districts with regular climates, but in the inland it can be just as erratic in its breeding season as other inland ducks. In any flood of sufficient severity to induce the breeding of teal and Pink-eared Ducks, there are sure to be a few Shoveler nests, no matter what season it is.

Nest

The Shoveler more commonly nests on the ground than do most other Australian ducks. The nest is a depression in the ground, lined with dead grass and usually containing a little down. It may be placed in the shelter of a tussock, in a growing crop or grass or, occasionally, in a bare pasture with very short grass and little or no cover. It is usually quite close to the water's edge, but sometimes nests are found a couple of hundred yards from the water. Some Shovelers nest in stumps, usually on the open top of a low dead stump standing in water, but I have never seen one in a hole covered at the top.

Eggs

The eggs are elliptical or oval, and creamy white with a faint tinge of green; the shell is smooth but not so lustrous as some other ducks. From 18 nests 120 eggs measured in length 51-57 mm. (average 54 mm.) and in breadth 36-40 mm. (average 37 mm.).

Clutch

The clutch size is usually 9 to 11, but there are no quantitative data.

Incubation

The incubation period is 24 days (Delacour).

Status

The Shoveler is not common enough to be "deliberately" hunted, but in many places is shot with other ducks whenever it appears. It is a very wary and swift-flying duck, testing the marksman's skill, but is not considered a good table bird. At the present time it is legal game in some States, but the wisdom of this must be seriously questioned, owing to its rarity and declining numbers, at least until its life history has been thoroughly studied and something of its population regulation is known. In the field it is easily recognized and "mistakes" by shooters should be few. It does not visit crops or newly sown pastures and so its presence has no economic implication.

The Shoveler has probably always been an uncommon duck, but as drainage of swamps continues it will undoubtedly become more so, unless special steps for the preservation of coastal habitats are soon taken. In the inland its main remaining habitats are the few cumbungi swamps, which are grazed heavily to the water's edge, so that it is denied adequate breeding cover.

Northern Shoveler

Anas clypeata Linnaeus

References

Anas Linnaeus, Syst. Nat., ed. 10, i, p. 122, 1758.

Anas clypeata Linnaeus, Syst. Nat., p. 124, 1758. (Sweden.)

Description

ADULT MALE. Adult male Shovelers are among the most colourful of ducks. Head and neck bright iridescent green; breast pure white; underside rich chestnut, paler to rear; undertail black; there is a conspicuous patch on the flank; back brown with lighter edges to the feathers; shoulders blue; greater coverts grey; primaries black; speculum bright metallic green with white border front and rear; iris yellow; feet yellow; bill greenish-black.

MALE IN ECLIPSE. In eclipse plumage the adult male resembles the female.

FEMALE. Very similar to the female Australian Shoveler.

Field Identification

In the wild, at rest or in flight, the male is a typical Shoveler, but is distinguished from the Australian Shoveler by the brilliant green head and white breast. Differentiation of the females of the two species in the wild would be very difficult. Perhaps the observer should hope to see a male or two.

Size

ADULT MALE. Wing 230-252 mm.; bill 62-70 mm.; tarsus 32-37 mm. (Delacour); length 457-546 mm.; wingspread 737-843 mm. (Kortright).

ADULT FEMALE. Wing 215-235 mm.; bill 59-69 mm. (Delacour); length 432-513 mm.; wingspread 693-805 mm. (Kortright).

Distribution

According to Delacour, the range of the Northern Shoveler includes the whole Holarctic region except the extreme north; it winters south, sometimes across the equator. One of the most widespread species of the Northern Hemisphere, it breeds all around the world up to, or just beyond, the Arctic Circle, except in north-eastern America. It winters south to Mexico (Tehuantepec), Louisiana, Florida, Africa south to Lake Victoria, Persia, India, Ceylon, Burma, Siam, Indo-China, southern China, Formosa and Japan. Stragglers have been recorded as far as South Africa, Australia, and the West Indies.

Australian Occurrence

The only record in Australia is that of Gould and I can do no more than quote:

> . . . I must ask my ornithological readers both in Australia and Europe to take my word for the occasional appearance of the bird in Australia. When I visited New South Wales during the rainy season of 1839, all the depressed parts of the land were filled with water, and the lagoons here, there, and everywhere were tenanted by hundreds of Ducks of various species, and every now and then one, two, or more beautifully plumaged Shovelers were seen among them; but I did not succeed in shooting one of them and must have left the matter in doubt as to the particular species if the late Mr. Coxen of Jarrundi had not had the skin of a splendid old male in his possession, which he had himself shot and which after careful examination I found to be identical with *Spatula clypeata* of Britain and the European continent.

Unfortunately "vermin" destroyed Mr Coxen's specimen before it reached a Museum, so we are left only with Gould's word. It is impossible to imagine a man of Gould's knowledge to be mistaken, but no more specimens have been seen, and so the Northern Shoveler has been admitted to the Australian list of birds on the basis of a sight record. Perhaps a reader of this note will secure a properly authenticated specimen and settle the point.

Relationships

The Northern Shoveler is closely related to the Australian Shoveler,

Key to Plate IV

RIVER DUCKS AND FRECKLED DUCK

1. Black Duck.
2. Freckled Duck, male.
3. Freckled Duck, female.
4. Freckled Duck, male in breeding plumage.
5. Grey Teal.
6. Chestnut Teal, female.
7. Chestnut Teal, male.
8. Pink-eared Duck.
9. Hardhead, male.
10. Hardhead, female.
11. Shoveler, male in eclipse.
12. Shoveler, female.
13. Shoveler, male.

B.T.W. 1965

and its position in the family has been described in the life history of that species.

Life History

The Northern Shoveler has a very wide range and uses a great variety of habitats, usually fresh water but sometimes brackish. In North America it is widely distributed but most abundant in the central and western parts, where it is essentially a freshwater bird of the sloughs, swamps, and sluggish creeks. The prairie regions of the middle west provide its most desirable range; the swamps in this region are dense with *Phragmites,* and prairie grasslands are extensive and dotted with small swamps. A *Phragmites* marsh in a prairie is very reminiscent of a cumbungi swamp in the Riverina, and the preferred habitats of the Northern and the Australian Shoveler are very similar. In Canada Shovelers cruise the sloughs and jump from the meadows just as they do in Australia, and in their whole economy, appearance, behaviour, and general ecology one is constantly impressed by the similarity to the Australian Shoveler.

The feeding methods are identical with those of the Australian species and the food eaten of very similar composition. It consists of 70 per cent vegetable material and 30 per cent animal. The plant food is mainly the seeds of sedges, pondweeds, grasses, and smartweeds. The animal food consists of molluscs, insects, and a few crustaceans. There is not much doubt that the Shoveler in North America occupies exactly the same niche that our species does in Australia.

The nest is typical of Shovelers; a depression in the ground lined with dry grass and some down. The nest is usually in long grass and may be a long way from water, but is more usually close by the boggy edge. There seems to be no record of Northern Shovelers using elevated nest sites as the Australian species sometimes does. The clutch size varies from 7 to 14, but 8 to 12 is the commonest. Incubation period is 21 days and the young fly at 6 weeks of age. The eggs are very similar in size and appearance to the Australian Shoveler. They are pale olive-buff on greenish grey in colour, with a pronounced greasy feel, and average measurements are 50 mm. by 18 mm.

Garganey

Anas querquedula Linnaeus

References

Anas Linnaeus, Syst. Nat., ed. 10, p. 122, 1758.

Anas querquedula Linnaeus, Syst. Nat., p. 126, 1758. (Sweden.)

Description

ADULT MALE. Head and neck brownish chestnut streaked with white; crown of the head and throat black, there is a white stripe over the eye; back and tail blackish brown; breast brown with fine white lines and the rest of the underparts white with fine black wavy lines; scapulars black with a broad central white line; wing coverts bluish grey; speculum light green between broad white bands.

MALE IN ECLIPSE. The males resemble the females except for the wings, which remain in the breeding plumage.

ADULT FEMALE. Dark brown above and almost pure white underneath; upper breast brown; wing coverts grey-brown; speculum olive-brown with white edges; throat white, and there is a dark line from the bill through the eye.

Size

Stuart Baker gives the following measurements:

Adult Male: Length 404-414 mm.; wingspread 635-693 mm.; wing 187-205 mm.; bill (from gape) 46-48 mm.; weight 303-484 gm.

Adult Female: Length 376-394 mm.; wingspread 584-648 mm.; wing 187-205 mm.; bill (from gape) 46-48 mm; weight 303-484 gm.

Distribution

The Garganey is a Northern Hemisphere duck. The breeding range extends from Great Britain across Europe and Asia to Kamchatka, but not to North America. The northern latitudinal limit to the breeding range is about 64 degrees north and the southern limit corresponds to a line through Spain, Crimea, Turkestan, and Manchuria. In the Northern Hemisphere winter it migrates south to southern Europe, Africa as far as the Congo and Nyasaland, southern Asia, Malaysia, the Philippines, and Indonesia. It apparently reaches New Guinea fairly regularly during migration. Prior to 1964 it had only been recorded from the Kapara and Oriomo Rivers, but Hoogerwerf[60] found it to be fairly common near Merauke. He writes:

> . . . this teal proved to be of rather common appearance in the rice-fields of Kurik and along the shore between the Maro and Bian Rivers during the winter months of the temperate zones, though there were considerable annual fluctuations during my stay in New Guinea. . . . I counted 60-70 specimens on 20th, 24th, and 26th January 1961; on 30th January of that year and on 7th March 1962 about 150 were seen. Along the shore their numbers were smaller as a rule but on 11th March 1962 about 100 were counted along the beach. . . . On 16th January 1963 I secured a solitary specimen at Manokwari in a small freshwater pool near the aerodrome Rendani. In accordance with Gyldenstolpe Bergman found the species rather numerous on Lake Atinju (Vogelkop) in February 1948, when 5 were secured.

Australian Occurrence

There are three records in Australia. Two birds were shot by W. Shaw at Lake Connewarre in southern Victoria in 1896. There is also an old mounted specimen in Melbourne Museum collected by C. Hooper at Lake Colac. A further bird, a male in eclipse, was collected on 20th February 1965; it was shot on Lake Buloke, near Donald, Victoria.

There is no reason to doubt that the records refer to wild birds, not aviary escapees. It is now known that there is extensive movement of Grey Teal and other waterfowl between Australia and New Guinea, and it is not unreasonable to expect an occasional Garganey to become involved in these movements and to reach Australia as a straggler. The point of entry would, most probably, be Cape York Peninsula, an area seldom visited by ornithologists, and occurrence there could be more common than is usually thought.

Relationships

The Garganey belongs to the group within the tribe Anatini collectively known as the Blue-winged Ducks. The group comprises the Garganey, the Blue-winged Teal *A. discors* of America, the Cinnamon Teal *A. cyanoptera* of America, and the Shovelers. Blue-winged Ducks are specially adapted to filter feeding and have strong similarities in behaviour, plumage, and colour pattern.

Life History

Remarkably little has been recorded on the biology of the Garganey. They are not numerous in western Europe, where they occur usually in pairs or small groups in shallow swamps with dense cover. They seem to be more abundant in the Soviet Union, where they are common throughout the steppes, forests, and some deserts, but are not found in the tundra and mountains. During the northern winter they congregate in large flocks in the Mediterranean countries, Africa, and Europe; smaller numbers move through Indonesia to New Guinea and occasionally Australia.

The food has not been studied but seems to be similar to that of other Blue-winged Ducks, consisting of both plant and animal items and including a rather large proportion of animal material for a surface-feeding duck. The feeding methods are similar to those of the other members of the group.

The nest is usually in long grass or reeds near water. It is a scrape in the ground and is lined with down, which is grey with white tips and centre. Brooding and care of the young is by the female.

The clutch size varies from 7 to 16, but is usually 8 to 11; no quantitative data have been published. The eggs are creamy buff in colour with a greasy texture. According to Hartet they measure in length 35-48 mm. (average 45 mm.) and in breadth 30-36 mm. (average 32 mm.). The incubation period is 21 to 22 days.

Pink-eared Duck

Malacorhynchus membranaceus (Latham)

References

Malacorhynchus Swainson, J. Roy. Inst., 2, p. 18, 1831.
Anas membranacea Latham, Index Orn. Sup., p. 69, 1801. (N.S.W.)

Other Names

Pink-ear, Pinkie, Pink-eye, Whistler, Widgeon, Zebra Duck, Zebra Teal, Whistling Teal.

Description

ADULT MALE. Top of head, neck, back, and wings, brown; side of head white with fine light-brown bars, a dark-brown patch surrounds the eye and extends to back of neck, there is a small pink patch behind the eye and a narrow white ring around it; neck and undersurface white, covered with fine brown lines; rump white; undertail buff; there is a white trailing edge to wings and a subterminal white band on tail; eye brown; legs lead-grey; bill spoon-shaped with membranous flaps on edges near tip, leaden grey.

ADULT FEMALE. As for male.

IMMATURE. Immature birds of both sexes resemble the adults but are generally paler in colour and the pink patch is smaller and less distinct.

DUCKLING. General colour above light brown; underside of body and throat light grey or white; sides light brown with light-grey patch behind wing; wing light brown above and grey below; top of head and neck dark brown; face grey with a large dark patch through and surrounding the eye. The bill is spatulate. In the flesh they give the general impression of a teal but are only superficially similar.

Size

	Weight gm.	*Length mm.*	*Wingspread mm.*	*Wing mm.*	*Bill mm.*
Adult Male					
Maximum	480	448	713	213	74
Minimum	290	384	574	172	44
Average	404	418	650	197	67
Number measured	*77*	*80*	*67*	*46*	*82*
Adult Female					
Maximum	423	418	657	200	67
Minimum	272	364	573	152	53
Average	344	392	618	188	61
Number measured	*81*	*84*	*67*	*67*	*83*

Voice

The contact call of the male, uttered in flight, at rest and with uplifted bill in threat display, is a chirrup; see (*a*) below. That of the female is similar, but at a lower pitch and of more uniform frequency throughout its duration; see (*c*) below. They are very easily distinguished. In fighting there is a continuous trill; see (*b*) below.

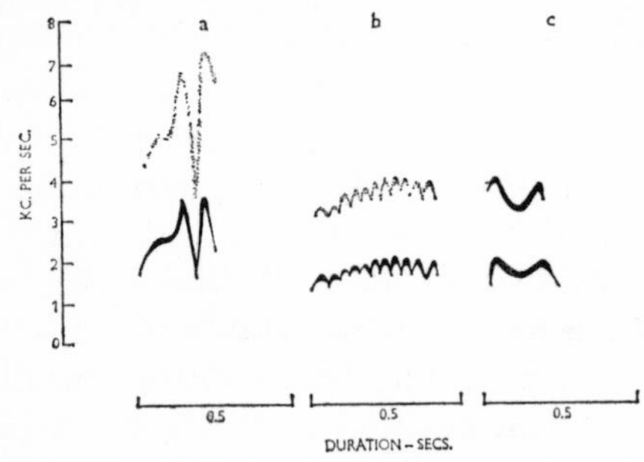

Diagram of sonogram of sounds made by Pink-eared Ducks. Their function is described in the text; (*a*) shows the contact call of the male and (*c*) that of the female; (*b*) shows the trill used in the fighting threat.

Routine

The Pink-eared Duck is usually seen in flocks, sometimes very large flocks, and is frequently associated with Grey Teal on shallow water. It is less commonly seen in timbered or vegetated swamps or lakes, but does occur there. It is more aquatic than the Grey Teal and seldom leaves the water except to roost on its edge. It perches readily on fallen trees but usually only a few inches above the water.

It is usually very tame and often allows the observer to approach closely, especially when breeding. When flushed it flies in dense clouds round the waterhole, refuses to leave, and usually settles again near by. The flight is slower than that of the teal, but otherwise similar. In flight it is very noisy, chirping continuously; usually the the first indication of Pink-eared Ducks in a flock of teal is this characteristic sound.

It is usually found roosting on the edge of the water or feeding away from the shore; it is less dependent on the edge of pools for feeding than other Dabbling Ducks. It never dives, except when wounded or in display. It walks well but seldom does so except in shallow water.

Field Recognition

The Pink-eared Duck has a very characteristic shape that, once learnt, is the best means of identification, but specific field marks are also available.

On the water it is a small, light-coloured duck that floats high and, even at a great distance, the heavy bill is very obvious. It has a distinct forehead, unlike the Shoveler, which also has a large bill. In the Shoveler the top of the bill and the top of the head form a straight line, there being no forehead. The Shoveler also floats lower in the water than the Pink-eared Duck, is very dark in appearance, and has quite distinct field marks of its own, so the two are rarely confused.

In flight the Pink-eared Duck is very distinct from other ducks; it flies swiftly but, except when harried, with a much shorter and slower wing-beat than the teal. The head is held high, with the neck not so extended as in other ducks, giving the bird a quite characteristic appearance. The white bands on the topside of the wing and tip of the tail and white crescentic mark on the rump are very noticeable and diagnostic. In flight it usually utters a chirrup that identifies it immediately. Overhead the body is light, the tail is dark and has a white edge, the enormous bill is again obvious.

The Pink-eared Duck is a very distinctive little duck in every way and is easily identified.

Relationships

The Pink-eared Duck was considered by Delacour and Mayr[27] to be an aberrant member of the tribe Anatini, but they expressed reserve on this judgment because so little was known at the time of the bird's behaviour or life history. Since then more information has been collected. The bird, with its bizarre plumage and lack of speculum and of sexual dimorphism, is clearly very different to other ducks.

The downy duckling has now been described[34] and although its eye stripe is different in shape and its ground colour is brown rather than yellow, which sets it apart from the typical *Anas* duckling, it does have a general similarity with the ducklings of some of the Blue-winged Ducks of that genus, for example, the Ringed Teal, *Anas leucophrys*. The brown colour, the shape of the eye stripe, and the distribution of white spots elsewhere on the body, are also quite similar to those of the ducklings of the Cairinini, and it could be concluded that the colour pattern forms a link between the two tribes. It differs from all other ducks because of the large spatulate bill. The Shovelers hatch with a normal bill and develop the spatulate shape later. The presence of the spatulate bill at hatching, however, is not an argument for separating *Malacorhynchus* from other groups, since the plankton-feeding habits of the downy ducklings demand such a bill. Presumably its shape is merely an adaptation to the food habits of the ducklings.

The trachea, usually considered to have phylogenetic significance, has been previously undescribed. It is unlike those of Anatini in several respects. It is not uniform in section, but tapers considerably and uniformly to the syrinx. The bulla is very poorly developed, almost not existent. It is just discernible and is slightly rounded and slightly extended towards the left side. It is closer in appearance to that of the pigmy geese, Cairinini, than to that of the Anatini.

The calls are all whistles and remarkably similar to those of the Green Pigmy Goose, but quite unlike those of the Anatini.

The displays have not been studied in detail, but there are sufficient observations to show some general similarities, as well as many differences, to the Shovelers and other Anatini. The feeding and ritualized foraging of Shovelers are well known and have some similarities to those of the Pink-eared Duck. Both species feed in groups, and although it has been said that the Pink-eared Ducks rarely forage in "trios or larger groups" the statement is incorrect; group feeding is just as common as pairs.

In Shovelers the display of ritualized feeding is usually performed face to face and is stationary. In Pink-eared Ducks the position is different, the heads are either face to face or side by side and turned inwards, the bills are completely immersed. Each bird then revolves, counter-clockwise, so that bills follow one another round the circumference of a circle about four to six inches in diameter; they maintain position relative to each other. As a variation each bird immerses its bill beside another's flank, the two being head to tail, they then swim slowly in tight circles. The whole flock often becomes involved in the display and the pool is then covered with small groups of rotating birds. Males that try to join a rotating group are usually repelled by all those already present.

Other aspects of the pair-forming display are quite unlike the Shovelers. The commonest is the uplift call, which is very similar to the threat display. The bill is rapidly tossed upwards with extended neck, it is then rapidly lowered with a drawn-out whistle. The action is carried out in flocks and often sets off a chorus of similar actions by other birds of both sexes, but often also leads to the male being attacked.

A mated male defends the vicinity of the female and when threatening other birds may swim silently towards the intruder with neck outstretched, opening and closing the bill, but more usually rushes across the water with neck erect and the bill swinging repeatedly to 45 degrees elevation, uttering a loud trill; fighting often results. Following a successful encounter the male raises the body from the water and flaps vigorously or makes several shallow dives. This is very unlike other Dabbling Ducks, including Shovelers, but quite similar to the pigmy geese, Cairinini.

The bobbing of the head to signify flight intention is very rarely seen in Pink-eared Ducks, whereas in most Anatini it is very common, but its form and that of lateral headshaking and of preening behind the wing are very similar in Pink-eared Ducks and the Anatini. The "drinking" aspect of sexual display, which is also absent in Shovelers, has not been seen, nor have many other aspects of the typical *Anas* display. Male Pink-eared Ducks, unlike most Anatini, often remain with the female and defend the nest area during incubation and assist in the raising of the brood. Copulation, and the display associated with it, have not yet been observed. There is not a great deal in the birds' behaviour to suggest the Anatini, but likewise there is only a little to suggest the Cairinini.

From a study of skeletons Woolfenden[101] found several peculiarities and, whilst retaining the bird in the Anatini, considered it a very distinct genus. It is of interest that he was unable to separate the two tribes Anatini and Cairinini on the basis of osteology, though in the field these are clearly distinct groups of closely related birds. The Pink-eared Duck has characteristics of both groups and could, on present knowledge, be included in either of these two, or in an intermediate one, according to the breadth of one's definition of a tribe. Because its life habits as well as its form more closely resemble the Anatini than the Cairinini, however, I prefer to retain it there at present rather than erect a special intermediate monogeneric tribe.

Habitat

Generally a duck of the inland plains, the Pink-eared Duck can be found at times in all habitats there, but shows a very strong preference for the shallow open expanses of residual floodwater or rain-filled claypans. If shallow water is not available Pink-eared Ducks will congregate for brief periods on deep lagoons, billabongs, and swamps before moving elsewhere, but rarely breed in numbers in those situations. Extensive breeding is most common in areas of temporary shallow water, but small groups do live and breed in some permanent swamps.

Distribution and Movements

Like the other nomadic species—and the Pink-eared Duck is the extreme nomad—it might be found anywhere in the continent at some time. However, it is essentially a duck of the dry inland, and mostly lives in areas having less than fifteen inches of rainfall each year. Where the low-rainfall areas reach the coastline, as in parts of Western Australia and South Australia, it is regularly found in coastal areas, but elsewhere on the coast and highlands it is a rather rare visitor. Each summer small numbers reach the coasts of Victoria, south-east South Australia, and the south coast of Western Australia, and the movements are very much greater in times of drought. It is, however, rare, even in times of drought, for it to visit the eastern and northern coasts of the continent. It very rarely reaches Tasmania and does not breed there.

Its nomadic range potentially covers the whole continent and its breeding range most of inland Australia, wherever rainfall or flooding can produce extensive pools of shallow temporary water among nesting sites such as lignum, tall bluebush, or dead timber. Most breeding occurs and populations are greatest where these conditions occur most frequently. Suitable breeding conditions occur most often, on a large scale, in the Murray-Darling region, and usually most Pink-eared Ducks are bred there, but small numbers also occur and breed fairly regularly in south-east South Australia and in the southern parts of Western Australia.

Clearly its main habitat, shallow receding floodwater, cannot be a permanent feature of the arid inland, so wide movements are

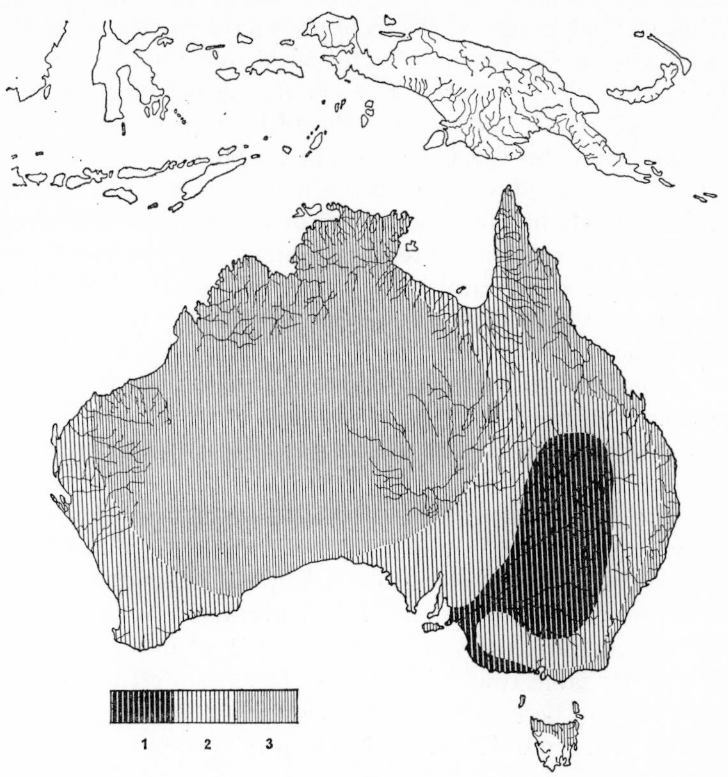

DISTRIBUTION OF THE PINK-EARED DUCK

The darkest shading (No. 1) shows the principal range of the Pink-eared Duck, where large numbers are found in most years. The intermediate shading (No. 2) is characterized by smaller populations, and breeding may occur throughout in favourable years. In the zone with the lightest shading (No. 3) Pink-eared Ducks are uncommon; they visit the coastal areas only in times of drought and the interior in times of unusual rainfall.

necessary for it to survive. Its nomadic movements are, like those of the Grey Teal, erratic, but even more spectacular. When Grey Teal move there is a small resident population that remains behind, but this is not so with the Pink-eared Ducks; when they vacate a district they usually do so completely and very few, if any, remain.

Following a flood, because of its food habits, the Pink-eared Duck can remain in the residual water longer than the Grey Teal, and usually stays in steadily increasing concentrations until the water is almost gone, then moves *en masse* quite suddenly. In 1957 and 1958, following the very extensive floods of the inland, there was a drought and an exodus of ducks generally, followed by a population crash of some species, and in this period spectacular concentrations of Pink-ears occurred. As the water dried the teal left the inland and flew to the coast, and the Black Ducks and Hardheads sheltered in the permanent cumbungi swamps, but, in the absence of rain to fill claypans or floods to form new areas of feeding habitat, the Pink-eared Ducks remained in the residual waters. They gathered in ever-increasing flocks of ten and twenty thousand birds on the dregs of the declining waters; chirping hordes thronged every pool. At the same time large flocks began circulating in near coastal areas and also in some very arid ones in search of refuge habitat. Large concentrations developed in high mountain lakes, in city parks, and even in some salt-water estuaries. I saw some in the tropical lily lagoons on the Northern Territory coast where the aborigines claimed not to have seen the species before, flushed some from a shallow rock pool a few feet in diameter in the rocky hills near Alice Springs, and saw some in mangrove swamps in north-east New South Wales, all most unusual habitats. This movement was an exaggerated one due to drought, as was that of the Grey Teal in the same period, and it had the same result. Pink-eared Ducks suffered a great mortality and did not become really abundant again anywhere for several years. Usually the movements and mortality are not nearly so extensive.

Having left a district, they do not return there unless suitable flooding occurs to recreate their habitat. Many of the inland floods are due to rainfall or snow melting on the mountains hundreds of miles away from the site of the flooding, where there might have been no rain, but Pink-eared Ducks detect the flood and colonize it. When the river flood is small, and only fills the lagoons and billabongs, it is ignored by the ducks and none arrive. When it is swift, so that clear water runs down the effluents, a few Pink-eared Ducks arrive, but there is no great influx. Only when the flood is broad and slow and great sheets of dirty water spread slowly over the plains do they come in great numbers, and one suddenly discovers that the Pink-eared Duck has become the commonest local bird, almost overnight.

When it returns to a district it sometimes does so in really immense numbers. John Hobbs,[57] describing the aftermath of the 1956 flood in the Riverina, wrote:

> Soon every depression, swamp, and creek was swarming with Pink-ears. . . . during that day we threaded our way along other creeks where, owing to lignum and blue bush, visibility ahead was at no time more than 40 yards and not once would there have been less than two broods in sight. From earlier and subsequent investigations I know that a similar density of birds prevailed throughout the country between Wanganella and Moulamein, a direct distance of 56 miles. Thus with a knowledge of the creeks and depressions in the area it is possible to estimate with some degree of accuracy, that an absolute minimum of 90,000 pairs were breeding between those two centres.

Hobbs was describing a small part of similar conditions that prevailed along the Murray, Murrumbidgee, Lachlan, and Darling rivers for several thousands of square miles. Wherever there was shallow floodwater and suitable nest sites many thousands were nesting, but a few months later they had all left and remained uncommon in those districts for years.

Feeding

The Pink-eared Duck secures food by filtering water or sometimes mud through its large bill. The bill is fringed with a dense layer of very fine lamellae and is so arranged that, when partly open, water can be drawn through the tip, but when the bill is closed this aperture is closed and the water is expelled laterally through the lamellae. These act as a fine screen or filter and retain the microscopic plants and animals that form the bulk of the diet.

The birds usually feed in very shallow water where they cruise slowly along with bills immersed in the water, right up to the eyes, filtering the food organisms from it. They often swim in echelon so that each bird has the advantage of animals disturbed from the bottom mud by the one in front. In slightly deeper water they swim with their heads and necks immersed so that the bill is trawled along as close to the bottom, where food organisms are most numerous, as possible. Sometimes they stand in the mud on the edge of the water and, filling the bill with mud, expel it through the lamellae. They have been seen up-ending like ordinary River Ducks, but this is uncommon.

The food secured consists of microscopic animals and plants, plankton.[39] In 138 stomachs animal food accounted for 94 per cent of the total, and of this insects provided 79 per cent by volume. All these stomachs contained some animal food, but 86 per cent contained also some plant food. The animals most commonly found, after insects, were miscroscopic water-fleas, copepods and ostracods. The most common plant foods were freshwater algae and small floating seeds of clovers and smartweeds.

The types of food eaten clearly explain the bird's preference for shallow, stagnant water. It is only here that microscopic animal life is really abundant and concentrated. The Pink-ear can stay in floodwater until it is practically dried up, long after other ducks have been forced to move, and still find abundant food. Fresh water is a disadvantage and, should the river rise and freshen the stagnant pools, the ducks leave the district as their food becomes too diluted to collect economically.

Similarly, in large deep swamps and lakes the actual density of the small food items is low, so the numbers of Pink-eared Ducks that such places support are low, probably just because the birds find food-collecting uneconomical, except in the shallow edges, which are restricted in extent compared to the size of the body of the water, and in the centre of some deep swamps where local concentrations of copepods occur in association with floating, rotting, masses of cumbungi. Stomachs examined from lakes and swamps contain essentially the same food as those collected in the floodwater pools.

It is unusual to find a duck that lives in a very erratic environment to be something of a food specialist, and one might think it would be very dangerous for it to be so. Of the two most successful nomadic species of the inland, one, the Grey Teal, is adapted to live on almost every edible product of the billabong and adjoining plains according to its availability, but the other, the Pink-eared Duck, is specialized to feed on items of very variable occurrence that are only numerous at a particular time of the life of a pool. Of the two, the Grey Teal seems to be the more successful, as might be expected, and although its numbers do fluctuate widely following drought and flood these fluctuations over all are not nearly so frequent or so great as those of the Pink-eared Ducks.

Breeding

As the Pink-eared Duck spends its life searching for residual floodwater, which is erratic in time and location of occurrence, it cannot fit a regular breeding cycle into its nomadic existence. It has no regular breeding season and can breed at a different time and place each year; if conditions are generally unfavourable it does not breed at all.

Its sexual cycle is initiated by, and geared to, rising water-levels.[40] In this situation it is similar to the Grey Teal, but there are important differences. The Grey Teal has a hair-trigger reaction and lays eggs very soon after the increase in level begins, so that the broods are sometimes hatched before the water reaches its peak. The Pink-eared Duck needs extensive shallow water for the ducklings, so cannot afford to lay until it is assured that this will be available. If the rise in water-level is slow and slight, so as merely to fill the billabongs, it has no visible effect on the sexual cycle. If, however, it is rapid, and the water floods through the effluents and spreads onto the plains, display begins in earnest and the birds rapidly come into breeding condition. Even then they do not lay immediately, but wait until the peak of the flood has passed and the pools are declining.

Fresh floodwater contains little or no food; it requires to be colonized by insects, and these, in turn, need time to reproduce and build up in numbers. Similarly the microscopic plant and animal life only gradually increases in quantity and does not become really concentrated until the water-level is declining quickly. If the birds laid eggs as soon as the water rose the ducklings would be abroad before there was sufficient food for large numbers of young. By postponing egg-laying until the peak of water-level is past they ensure that the ducklings are hatched at a time when food is abundant. Breeding studies in inland New South Wales have shown that, usually, synchrony is achieved between hatching of the young and a great increase in concentration of the food organisms in the water.

This need to synchronize the broods with a food that is most abundant in drying pools sometimes calls for precise timing and is fraught with some danger. Egg-laying must cease when sufficient time remains for the ducklings to fly before the pools dry. This, usually, is successful, but the mechanism to cause cessation of laying at the correct time is not known. Sometimes timing is not successful and the ducklings have to travel overland to deeper pools, which become crowded. Even then the water sometimes goes before the last young have flown and many die in the mud.

Standard textbooks imply that the Pink-eared Duck has a regular breeding season in the spring and early summer, but this is not so. Although there is a superficial regularity in some places, this is coincidental with the fact that these places have a fairly regular cycle of flooding, or of filling of swamps, and so some Pink-eared Ducks tend to breed at a similar time each year. Thus, in southern Australia, where winter rainfall is the rule, they breed more often in the period August to October than at other times, that is, soon after the rain, and in more northern districts, where the rainfall is predominantly in summer, they breed more often in the period March to May than at other times.

The only real regularity in breeding is in relation to the stage of water-level changes and in comparison with the breeding season of other species. In general the Pink-eared Duck breeds in a declining water-level and later than the Hardhead, which in turn is later than the Black Duck and the Grey Teal, usually the first duck to breed when the water-level increases. The breeding season of all of these species is controlled by changes in water-level, but each needs a different type of water for breeding and so times its breeding season to occur when that water is available. The sequence can be disrupted at any time if unexpected changes in the flood's progress occur, and the full sequence does not necessarily follow should, for instance, the flood only be minor. In this case probably only the teal will breed.

These adaptations towards an erratic breeding season, geared to changes in water-level caused by flood or rain, are a very efficient way to ensure that in the unreliable climate of the inland the birds only breed when suitable food for the ducklings is available and that they do not miss the sudden and unexpected occurrence of these conditions.

Nest

The nests are built in elevated situations from a few inches to at least thirty feet high, always over water. They are built on the tops of fence-posts, logs, stumps, on flat limbs, in tree-holes, in tree-forks, lignum bushes, saltbush, bluebush, or in old nests of Coots, *Fulica atra,* Native Hens, *Tribonyx ventralis,* and other water-birds. Sometimes they are built over the eggs of the other birds, suggesting that they have usurped the site. They readily breed in four-gallon drums and on flat boards hung in trees. When breeding is extensive many birds will lay in the one tree-hole and several nests are found built one on top of another. I have seen sixty eggs in one hollow. When breeding of Pink-eared Ducks is really "on" in some of the box swamps of the plains, the number of nests seems only limited by the number of sites available.

The nest is a rounded mound of down about ten inches in diameter in which the eggs are buried. The down is dark grey with a lighter centre. Some down is placed in the hollow when the first egg is laid and continually added to during laying and early incubation. When brooding the duck carefully covers the eggs with down each time she leaves the nest, unless she has been suddenly disturbed, when they are left uncovered.

Eggs

The eggs are oval but more pointed at the smaller end than those of other ducks. They are smooth, white or creamy white in colour; the shell is compact and greasy.

In 21 nests 144 eggs measured in length 46-53 mm. (average 49 mm.) and in breadth 34-38 mm. (average 36 mm.).

Clutch Size

The clutch varies from 3 to 11 eggs, but 6 to 8 is commonest and the mean of 47 clutches was 6·7 eggs. The distribution of clutch size in these 47 nests was:

Number of Eggs:	3	4	5	6	7	8	9	10	11
Number of Clutches:	1	3	9	12	10	7	3	1	1

From 122 nests near Griffith, New South Wales, in 1956, a flood year, an average of 6·4 ducklings hatched, but only 4·7 survived to fly.

Incubation

Incubation takes 26 days.

Status

Pink-eared Ducks rarely go near any agricultural crop and do not damage them, so they have no effect on the economy.

The attitude of the various States towards the Pink-eared Duck as a game bird varies. In New South Wales, where most are bred, they are rigidly protected, but they are legal game in the neighbouring States. Such a situation appears farcical when it is appreciated that these highly nomadic birds range over the whole continent and the same individuals visit each State. Surely the approach should be uniform.

There is little doubt that the Pink-eared Duck could support a shooting season as well as most ducks, and very much better than some, for example, the Freckled Duck. They are, however, very poor game birds, being very tame, slow on the wing, too easy to shoot, small, and poor table birds. I have seen irresponsible shooters fill their bags with them during the day, but throw them away as "better" birds are secured. Open seasons on Pink-eared Ducks seem to help make this thoroughly unsporting practice simpler to achieve without detection.

They are still very numerous in the inland, though subject to violent fluctuations in numbers. The continuation of their abundance, however, is less certain than that of the Grey Teal, owing to their almost complete dependence on shallow floodwater for breeding and food. As described in the life history of the Grey Teal, the whole trend in water conservation is to reduce or prevent the flooding of the inland rivers, and thus to prevent extensive breeding of the Pink-eared Duck. Unless provision is made to permit some flooding inland Pink-eared Duck numbers must decline very greatly as water conservation continues to control the rivers.

Hardhead

Aythya australis (Eyton)

References

Aythya Boie, Tag. Reise Norwegen, pp. 308, 351, 1822.
Nyroca australis Eyton, Monogr. Anatidae, p. 160, 1838. (N.S.W.)

Common Names

Brownhead, Copperhead, Coppertop, Widgeon, Punkari, White-eyed Duck, White-winged Duck, White-eye, White-wing, Barwing.

Description

ADULT MALE. General colour above, head, neck, back, rump and tail, rich dark brown; underside, throat and neck, same as back; breast rich dark brown deeply suffused with rufous; lower breast white, the feathers mostly with brown bases and white tips, but some wholly brown, so that the appearance of the lower breast is usually more or less mottled; abdomen dark brown; undertail coverts white; wing brown with a rufous or chestnut tinge on upper coverts; outer primaries brown, the remainder white with brown tips; secondaries brown with a conspicuous broad white band across them; bill black with slate-blue bar at tip; nail black; legs and feet grey; webs slate-grey; iris white. No eclipse plumage has been recorded.

ADULT FEMALE. Similar to male, but generally lighter in colour. The bar on the bill is much narrower and paler than in the male; iris brown.

IMMATURE. Both sexes are similar to the female, but paler, and white parts of underside are more mottled; iris hazel brown.

DUCKLING. The downy duckling is light brown above and suffused with pale yellow; breast, belly and underside of the tail, pale yellow; underside of the wing pale yellow, and there is a small yellow patch immediately behind the wing; sides and underside of the head and neck, pale yellow; top of the head and back of neck, light brown suffused with yellow; legs and feet blue-grey; bill, upper blue-grey, lower pinkish white with blue edge; iris pale brown.

Size

	Weight gm.	*Length mm.*	*Wingspread mm.*	*Wing mm.*	*Bill mm.*
Adult Male					
Maximum	1100	587	815	243	50
Minimum	525	417	672	183	35
Average	902	491	769	215	45
Number measured	*105*	*106*	*59*	*99*	*105*
Adult Female					
Maximum	1060	544	794	186	49
Minimum	530	421	635	234	34
Average	838	473	737	217	42
Number measured	*88*	*90*	*46*	*88*	*91*

Voice

Normally Hardheads are silent, but the male has a soft, wheezy whistle and the female a soft, harsh croak.

Routine

Hardheads are nearly always seen on water, alert, or flying swiftly overhead with other ducks; they are seldom seen on the shore and never in trees. Small flocks are common and sometimes very large rafts of several thousand birds occur on extensive lakes. It is a bird of deep water and is usually in the deep, still reaches of large swamps or lakes, but is equally at home in the swift, turbulent creeks of the inland rivers in flood, where it swims swiftly among the lignum, even against the current, diving frequently to come up some distance away, swimming rapidly. It is very difficult to approach, because of both its wariness and its habit of floating on open water. It rises almost vertically, gaining height and speed very rapidly indeed, and flies swiftly with a characteristic wing-beat.

Field Identification

In flight the Hardhead is very swift and direct; the wings are noticeably narrower than those of the Black Duck and set farther back on the body. They beat rapidly with an audible sound and the longitudinal white bar across them is obvious and is diagnostic. From below the small, narrow, pointed wings set far back on the body, have a translucent appearance and the whole silhouette is very distinctive.

On the water it appears as a medium-sized, dark-coloured bird, floating very low. It is slightly smaller than the Black Duck, and at a distance is more easily distinguished from it by the head, which appears proportionally larger and is held lower, and by the absence of the conspicuous eye stripe of the Black Duck, than by the difference in size. The body usually slopes down to the water at the rear, whereas in the other ducks, except the Musk Duck and the Blue-billed Duck, there is a distinct stern. Sometimes it floats higher and then the white sides of the undertail coverts are noticeable.

On the water, at a distance, it can sometimes be confused with the Blue-billed Duck, which also floats low in the water and has a prominent head. The light-coloured bill of the Hardhead can, in some lights, appear pale blue, making confusion with Blue-billed Ducks possible.

Relationships

The Hardhead belongs to the tribe Aythyini, the Pochards, which comprises fifteen species and is represented throughout the world, but mainly in the Northern Hemisphere. Pochards are close relatives of the River Ducks Anatini, but spend more of their time under water. Twelve of the fifteen species, including the Hardhead, belong to the genus *Aythya.* Included in the genus is the Canvasback *A. valisineria,* the premier game duck of North America, and the European Pochard *A. ferina.* The Hardhead is Australia's only Pochard.

Three subspecies have been described, but none of them can be accepted as differing significantly from the mainland form. The subspecies that have been proposed are:

A. a. papuana. Collected in the New Guinea Highlands, the birds were the same size as mainland specimens but were "darker, more chocolate-chestnut on the head, neck, and much darker on the lower abdomen, thighs and flanks".[86a] The colour of Hardheads is very variable, both with age and among individuals of the same age. It is probably not possible to separate the race on subjective descriptions of the colour of a small sample; certainly specimens I have examined in New Guinea did not differ from the normal ranges of Australian specimens.

A. a. ledeboeri. The birds were collected in East Java and separated as a subspecies on the basis of very small and insignificant colour differences.[8] The race has also been rejected by Delacour and by Ripley.

A. a. extima.[75] A small number of birds breeding on Banks Island had the following range of size:

6 males: wing length 193-211 mm., culmen 42-45 mm.
5 females: wing length 189-196 mm., culmen 41-45 mm.

These sizes, however, are completely overlapped by those of the much larger sample of mainland birds whose measurements are summarized above.

Habitat

The Hardhead can be found, at times, in most habitats, but shows a very strong preference for extensive areas of deep water, especially if these carry abundant cover in the form of emergent vegetation. In the inland its favourite haunts are in the permanent cumbungi swamps and lignum creeks and on the Southern Tablelands it frequents deep mountain lakes, but rarely, if ever, breeds in them. It is quite common at times on the freshwater lakes at the mouth of the Murray River and in the swamps of the east coast.

Distribution and Movements

In addition to Australia, Hardheads occur in East Java, the Celebes, New Guinea, New Caledonia, and the New Hebrides, and formerly occurred in New Zealand.

In my opinion the name allotted to the birds "Australasian White-eyes" and the description of their distribution in general works gives a false impression of the status of the Hardhead beyond the mainland. "From Tasmania, Australia, and New Zealand north to eastern Java, Celebes, New Caledonia and the New Hebrides live White-eyes very similar to (*Aythya*) *innotata*. . . . They vary a good deal individually and their size increases slightly and gradually from north to south."[26]

The passage suggests a widespread distribution of resident populations, but this is probably not so. A better interpretation of the pattern of distribution is that it is a continental species that frequently undergoes irruptive movements. At these times flocks spread widely over the Pacific and Indonesian islands and some establish themselves as breeding groups for a time, then, usually, die out. It is possible that ultimately one or more of these colonies will become permanently established, but there is no decisive evidence of its having happened yet.

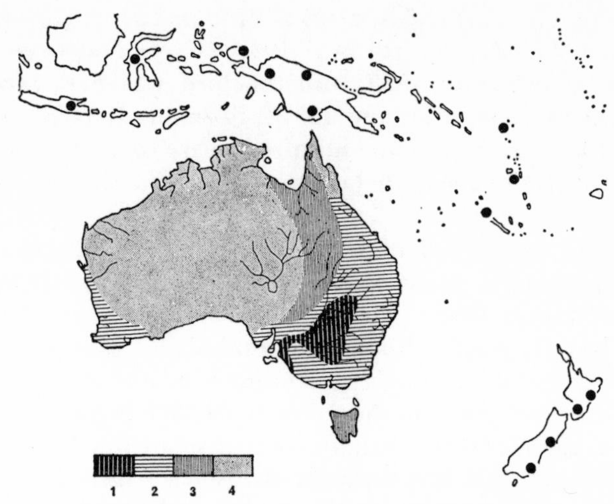

DISTRIBUTION OF THE HARDHEAD

Breeding occurs throughout the areas shaded 1-3, the populations being greatest in the area with the darkest shading and least in that with the lightest. Elsewhere in Australia (No. 4) vagrants occur and may occasionally breed. The spots show populations outside Australia, whose status is not certain.

The best documented occurrence of the Hardhead outside Australia was that in New Zealand. It was first seen there in 1867, but, as the Maoris had a native name for it, it was probably of more ancient origin.[100] According to Buller it was quite common in parts of the North Island and it was later reported at Lake Ellesmere and in the Otago district on the South Island. By 1895 it had disappeared, except for one sighting in 1934. This population was undoubtedly one resulting from a recent invasion from Australia, which almost succeeded in establishing itself permanently.

There is no reason to believe that the other island populations are different to the former New Zealand one. Some populations have been reported breeding, for example, in the New Hebrides, where "Natives say an odd one occasionally nests", but the extent or permanence of no colony is known. In a few cases, for example, in the New Guinea Highlands, Hardheads have been seen more than once, but usually this is not the case, or the records are very widely spaced in time. It is significant that most of the island records followed droughts in Australia when irruptions might have been expected. Thus the Hardhead was first seen in New

Guinea in 1894, following disastrous droughts in Australia, and it was then not collected there until 1938. There had been a severe drought in Australia in 1937, and the bird was next reported in New Guinea in 1960, after the 1957-9 drought. It is also probably significant that during several hundred years of Dutch occupation the Hardhead was not seen in Java until the same time—presumably it is a very recent invasion.

Today the stronghold of the Hardhead in Australia is in the deeper swamps and lagoons of the Murray-Darling basin and in the lakes of south-east South Australia; it is most numerous on the lower reaches of the Lachlan, Murrumbidgee, Murray and Macquarie rivers, where it breeds in considerable numbers. It is quite common in some years on the New South Wales and Queensland coasts and a few birds breed there. Whilst small numbers are found on the inland slopes and tablelands of eastern Australia, these areas are mainly drought refuges for the species and breeding records are few. It is generally distributed throughout Victoria, particularly the western part, but few breed there. It is numerous in the lakes of Tasmania in most summers, but, according to Sharland, there is no record of its having bred there.

In Western Australian the greatest numbers are found in the south-west where it breeds regularly, but at times it visits the north in great numbers. Carter considered it next after the Grey Teal in abundance at North-west Cape. In the inland of Western Australia and the arid interior of the continent generally it could be found anywhere occasionally, but is uncommon and the birds seen are probably vagrants. It is very uncommon in the wet tropical districts of the north and does not breed there normally.

Although it is still a common duck in many places the Hardhead has declined in numbers greatly, more than most other ducks of south-eastern Australia. Details of its primitive numbers are very few, but what there are indicate the extent of the decline when compared to the present situation. In 1914 Savidge reported from north-east New South Wales: "The White-eyed duck (*Nyroca Australis*) is perhaps the commonest duck inhabiting the district, and may be seen on the large swamps on the lower Clarence; also on the clear stretches of water on the upper reaches of the river above Copmanhurst." At this time the birds were also very numerous on the other rivers of the New South Wales North Coast, and one shooter was able to secure three hundred on one morning near Coraki, on the Richmond River. Until the early 1930s Hardheads (known locally as Copperheads) formed a considerable part of the shooters' bag on these rivers, but today they are seldom seen in the district, and never in numbers.

The coastal rivers of the North Coast of New South Wales formerly had large swamps in their lower reaches, and behind the levees in their middle regions, and these swamps were replenished by flood almost annually. Nowadays most have been drained for agriculture and flood mitigation, and all low-lying areas of land are abundantly provided with deep drains so that floodwater is rapidly returned to the river. The habitat of the Hardhead has been almost completely destroyed in that area.

According to Campbell, at the end of the last century it was "exceedingly numerous" on the Gippsland Lakes in Victoria—it is now one of the less common ducks there. At that time also North's correspondents recorded that, whilst the Hardhead greatly outnumbered other ducks on the coastal rivers of New South Wales, on the inland rivers it was one of the less common ducks. It is ironic to reflect that today the Lachlan and the other inland rivers of New South Wales are considered to be the main stronghold of the Hardhead. It is a fair assumption that the numbers on the Lachlan have declined since 1900, but even so they now outnumber the coastal populations many times. It suggests how great the decline on New South Wales coastal rivers has been by comparison.

The steady and continued drainage of deep-water swamps on the coast effectively removed the breeding populations in those districts and, at the same time, removed the drought refuges of the inland birds. In the inland, the drainage of deep-water swamps and the ever-increasing utilization of water for irrigation purposes, with a resultant decrease in frequency of flooding and permanence of the deep lagoons and swamps, strike further blows at the Hardhead's chance of survival in number. The bird is in greater danger than any other game species in southern Australia.

Its movements are not fully understood, since very few have been banded and there have been few recoveries. However, from these few recoveries and aerial observations of concentrations in the inland, together with the reports of observers throughout Australia, it is possible to piece together what are probably the main movements.

The main populations are found in the lignum and cumbungi swamps of the Lachlan, Murrumbidgee, and Macquarie rivers. As these swamps decline in area during the summer, great concentrations of Hardheads develop and some birds move out, mainly south to the Murray River, and there is a general movement of the population in this direction. Many remain in the swamps and lagoons of the Kerang and Wakool districts, but great numbers move along the Murray to its mouth and lakes, where in most years there are very large concentrations. They do not seem to move to the south-eastern parts of South Australia in great numbers. Coastal observers in New South Wales, Victoria, and Queensland have not been able to establish a regular pattern of rise and fall in the local concentration, showing that large regular movements do not occur east to the New South Wales coast or south much beyond the Murray River.

Despite this fairly regular south and westerly movement some scattering occurs, and in New South Wales ducks banded near Griffith have moved north to Bourke and elsewhere. The movements are potentially nomadic, but, owing to the bird's need for deep water and the fairly regular cycle of the abundance of this habitat, generally declining each summer inland, but more often than not remaining extensive on the lower Murray River, they follow a somewhat regular movement pattern.

In times of drought inland the south-westerly movement is much increased in volume and the birds evacuate the inland. Such an exodus was seen in 1957 and 1958 when the Hardheads weathered the drought for a time by gathering into very great concentrations on the deeper waters. They remained long after the ducks that depend on shallower water—Grey Teal, Pink-eared Ducks, and even the Black Ducks—had irrupted from the inland.

Near Griffith there were at least 50,000 Hardheads on Barrenbox Swamp, and 80,000 gathered on Lake Brewster during 1958. Towards the end of that year, however, they were forced to move and flocks of 1,000-2,000 appeared all over the coast and tablelands. Very great concentrations developed on the Coorong in South Australia, on the lakes of western Victoria, and on the Southern Tablelands of New South Wales. What was apparently one of these flocks reached Townsville, north Queensland. Following this exodus, and the associated mortality, as might have been expected, the number of Hardheads in south-eastern Australia declined greatly and some years were needed for the population's recovery.

Feeding

Unlike the Dabbling Ducks, Hardheads are able to feed by diving in deep water. In diving they spring forward and disappear beneath the surface, with hardly a ripple, to appear sometimes thirty or

Upper: Male (front) and female Pink-eared Duck. *Photo by Ederic Slater*

Lower: Pink-eared Ducks filter-feeding. *Photo by author*

Upper: Male and female Hardheads; note prominent white eye of male.

Photo by Ederic Slater

Lower: Group of nomadic Hardheads with a Magpie Goose, far from their usual range, on a tropical lagoon, N.T.

Photo by author

forty yards away, swimming rapidly. They may remain under water for a full minute. Their diving ability makes food available to them that most other ducks cannot reach. Despite this, they are also able to secure food in the manner of Dabbling Ducks, by dabbling in shallow water, up-ending, and by stripping seed from growing plants, and they secure most of their food in this manner. Their feeding is confined to water and they seldom, if ever, come onto dry land. Feeding is mostly confined to the deep, still reaches of swamps and lagoons, but they sometimes make foraging flights beyond them and have been known to invade ricefields and feed on the ripening grain.

Despite its diving habit, the Hardhead is largely vegetarian and a surprising amount of the food eaten is available on the surface or the edges of the swamps. The food in 193 stomachs collected in inland New South Wales consisted of 74 per cent plant material and 26 per cent animal material.[39] Of the plant material, 26 per cent was made up of seeds and flowers of sedges and 22 per cent of grasses, mainly aquatic grasses. The most important sedges were *Carex*, and these plants, by providing 18 per cent of the total food, were the most important single food item. The grasses eaten were very varied: they were mainly aquatic forms, and included water-couch *Paspalum distichum*, oat-grass *Agrostis avenacea*, rice *Oryza sativa*, and barnyard millet *Echinochloa crusgalli*. Smartweeds *Polygonum*, dock *Rumex*, and the seeds of paddymelon *Cucumis myriocarpus* formed significant parts of the diet. All these plants are freely available to the birds without deep diving. Water-milfoil *Myriophyllum*, which comprised 9·4 per cent of the food, was the only deep-water plant found in significant quantities.

In a sample of 231 stomachs collected in north Queensland the food was also predominantly vegetable, plant items amounting to 96 per cent of the total. Here also the plants eaten, although many were characteristic of deep water, were freely available on the surface. Water-lilies accounted for 22 per cent of the volume, smartweeds 26 per cent, and sedges 21 per cent, and there were smaller quantities of submerged aquatics. Apart from the difference in the availability of some plants, the vegetable food eaten was similar in type to that eaten in inland New South Wales. Water-lilies do not occur in the inland and in north Queensland apparently replace grasses in the diet of the Hardheads; the northern birds ate practically no grass-seed. It is surprising to see that smartweeds were not very important in the inland, where they form the principal food of the Dabbling Ducks, but were very important in the north.

The animal food in the inland comprised 15 per cent aquatic insects, mainly beetles and water-bugs, 10 per cent molluscs, and smaller quantities of yabbies *Cherax* and smaller water animals. The average size of the molluscs eaten was quite large—one freshwater mussel was 1½ inches long by one inch wide, but these were easily crushed by the powerful, muscular gizzard. The insects most commonly eaten were, as for the Black Duck and Grey Teal, mainly the beetles *Berosus* and *Dytiscus,* the two commonest water insects in the Riverina. Similarly the common water-boatman, *Corixa eurynome,* was eaten by all three species in significant numbers. The molluscs were mainly *Lenameria* and *Isidorella,* neither of which was of much importance to either Black Duck or Grey Teal, presumably usually living in deeper water than that in which these species can feed. This collection did not include any shrimps; Hall watched a flock catching shrimps in mid air as they skipped and sprang to avoid a flock of feeding coots.[53] Hardheads are also very commonly seen associated with feeding Pelicans and Swans and feeding on animals disturbed by these birds. Morse[81] examined a specimen whose gullet contained a carp 2 inches long.

By and large the food eaten is very similar to that of the Black Duck and the Grey Teal, but where competition exists there are important differences. In one swamp, where presumably the same food was available to all, I found that the Black Duck preferred to eat all vegetable material (98 per cent). The Grey Teal also ate mainly plants (94 per cent), but the Hardhead included 20 per cent of deep-water animals in its food, utilizing forms unavailable to the dabbling species.

Breeding

Nothing substantial has been recorded concerning the courtship and pair-forming processes of the Hardhead, apart from general statements that they are similar to that of the other Pochards of the world. The display of Pochards is not unlike that of the River Ducks. Like that of most Australian ducks, the breeding season varies from place to place, both in timing and reliability. In general it can be said to occur later than that of the Black Duck in any year and to be less regular.

The timing of the breeding season is related to the distribution of rainfall or its effects on the habitats. In south-west Australia, where the rain is predominantly in the winter, breeding occurs in the spring. The records of Mr Reg Taylor of Benger show that the first clutches are found in October and the latest in mid-November.

These dates can be compared to those of the Black Duck, which in that region breeds in the period June to October. On the North Coast of New South Wales the main rain is in summer and clutches are begun when the swamps are at their highest level, in January and February. The few nests reported from the summer monsoon zone of northern Australia were found in April and May, that is, at the opposite season to southern Australia, but with the same temporal relationship to the rainfall.

In inland New South Wales Hardheads are always present in the deep permanent cumbungi and lignum swamps and breeding occurs there. In one such swamp we are engaged in a regular monthly sampling programme of Hardheads. From this work it is apparent that the sexual cycle of the Hardhead begins in August and males produce spermatozoa between September and December; the clutches are begun in the same period. Some annual variation in the breeding season occurs, but it has not yet been possible to relate this to environmental factors.

Beyond the permanent swamps Hardheads are found in lagoons and swamps of the river frontages and plains, and in these habitats the breeding season, like that of other inland ducks, is related to changes in the water-level. When a flood moves slowly down the river, filling the billabongs, swamps, and flood country, first the Grey Teal breed, followed quickly by the Black Ducks, then the Hardheads, and finally the Pink-eared Ducks. Generally the Grey Teal ducklings are beginning to hatch and the Black Duck clutches are complete before the Hardhead lays. If the winter is dry and the swamps do not fill the Hardheads do not breed. This is unlike the Black Ducks, some of which do manage to breed no matter how dry the season. It does need to be really dry, however, to prevent all the Hardheads, and complete failures are uncommon. If the winter is exceptionally wet and flooding is extensive, breeding is also extensive and prolonged.

With these restrictions, in the inland, there is a strong tendency for Hardhead breeding to begin in October each year, but the bird also possesses the ability to breed at any time of the year that extensive flood occurs, as does the Black Duck, to ensure that favourable opportunities are not missed.

Nest

Hardheads most commonly build their nests in dense reeds, tea-trees, lignum or cumbungi, and usually over water several feet deep. In the lignum swamps of the Lachlan and Macquarie rivers, which are dissected by numerous deep channels of clear water, the nests are usually built in bushes on the edge of these channels at water-level. In a flood year on the Lachlan and other inland rivers the birds breed at the height of the flood when the water in the channels is deep and swift-flowing. As the incubation proceeds and the floods subside the nests are left a couple of feet above water. The nest may also be built in thick sedge, where a substantial base is trodden down, or in the butts of flooded trees, or occasionally in thick grass beside the water, usually on an island.

The nest itself is usually carefully built of woven reeds, sedges, or lignum sticks, and is much neater and more compact that those of the two other ducks that nest in similar vegetation, the Blue-billed Duck and the Musk Duck. It frequently has a canopy built over the top. There is much down with the eggs and this is grey-brown in colour.

Eggs

The eggs are creamy white with a close-grained glossy shell; 105 eggs from 15 nests measured in length 49-65 mm. (average 57 mm.) and in breadth 37-45 mm. (average 42 mm.).

Clutch Size

There are no quantitative data, but the clutch varies from 6 to 18, with 9 to 12 being the commonest number found. The large size of the clutch in some nests makes one wonder if Hardheads sometimes parasitize other pairs' nests, as does the related *Aythya americana* of North America.

Incubation

The incubation period is 25 days (one clutch).

Status

In rice-growing districts, in some years, the Hardhead visits rice crops towards the end of the growing season and consumes the ripening grain; it also eats large quantities of crayfish and other animals, many of which are harmful to the crop's levee banks. Its attacks on rice crops are usually very local, being confined to the vicinity of the cumbungi swamps used as reservoirs for drainage water from the fields, and are erratic in occurrence. They only occur in dry years when more than usual numbers of ducks have been forced into the irrigation areas. In the aggregate the damage done by Hardheads to rice crops is negligible, though at times much publicized.

It is one of the most important and most sought-after game ducks in Australia. As a game bird it has few equals and only its more restricted range and smaller numbers make it less important than the Black Duck. It flies very swiftly and is wary and quick to fly away; it is difficult to hit and, owing to a very dense plumage and apparently great stamina, is hard to kill. When wounded it swims and dives expertly and is hard to retrieve—perhaps more crippled Hardheads are lost than any other species. The table qualities are very high.

Pochards, throughout the world, have relatively restricted breeding areas, owing to their need for deep, rich, permanent swamps, and they have suffered greatly from agricultural development. The Australian species is no exception and has declined from being the most numerous coastal species and present in large numbers over a wide area of south-eastern Australia to one that is now rare on the coast and only locally common elsewhere. There is no doubt that the decline has been caused by drainage and flood-mitigation works, and there is also no doubt that as these works continue the remaining populations of Hardheads will further decline. Serious doubts are held for its survival as a common species.

That many water-storage areas could potentially provide habitat for Hardheads if suitable edges, deep, but not too deep, to support dense vegetation were provided, cannot be doubted. The accidental creation of first-class Hardhead habitat by the formation of drainage swamps in the inland suggests a way in which this fine bird could be simply and economically conserved if thought is given to its preservation by the State authorities in time. Time is short.

Source of Data

The more detailed study of the life history of the Hardhead has only recently been begun, by C.S.I.R.O. Division of Wildlife Research. This account is based on unpublished results of this study and earlier, less comprehensive study.

Wood Duck

Chenonetta jubata (Latham)

References

Chenonetta Brandt, Icon. An. Russ. Nov., Av. 1, p. 5, 1836.
Anas jubata Latham, Index Orn. Sup., p. 69, 1801. (N.S.W.)

Other Names

Maned Goose, Blue Duck. The latter name is of very recent origin in Western Australia.

Description

ADULT MALE. Head and neck brown with a mane of elongated black feathers; lower back, tail coverts and tail, black; scapulars grey with broad black edges to the feathers; upper wing coverts grey; speculum brilliant green edged with white; breast mottled grey, black, and white; abdomen and undertail black; sides of breast and flanks grey with very fine, closely spaced wavy black lines; bill olive-brown; legs and feet olive-brown; iris brown.

ADULT FEMALE. General colour above grey-brown; scapulars edged with black; back, rump, and tail, black; wing speculum green edged with white; head and neck pale brown, there is a whitish line above and one below the eye; breast and flanks brown, each feather crossed with a white band; lower breast, abdomen, and undertail, white.

IMMATURE. The immatures of both sexes resemble the female but are lighter in colour. A few finely barred flank feathers can be found under the wings of immature males at 3 months of age and are the first outward signs of the bird's sex.

DUCKLINGS. Top of head, neck, and topside generally grey-brown with two white spots on back and white trailing edge to wing;

underside white; face white with a prominent dark line through the eye and another below it.

Size

	Weight gm.	*Length mm.*	*Wingspread mm.*	*Wing mm.*	*Bill mm.*
Adult Male					
Maximum	955	505	850	290	31
Minimum	700	463	760	254	24
Average	815	482	796	272	28
Number measured	*45*	*46*	*31*	*46*	*46*
Adult Female					
Maximum	984	489	843	284	31
Minimum	662	443	771	252	22
Average	800	467	784	266	27
Number measured	*26*	*29*	*15*	*28*	*29*

Voice

The characteristic sound of the Wood Duck is the long-drawn-out and mournful "new" of the female's identity call. With its well-developed harmonics it covers a frequency range of from 0·3 to 2·0 kilocycles per second and the pitch is low; it is drawn out to 1½-2 seconds in time. The call of the male is shorter, one second, and of a higher pitch, up to 2·5 kilocycles per second with the accent on the higher harmonics. The only other sounds I have heard Wood Ducks make are a continuous low-pitched "cluck" or conversation note of short syllables—see (*a*) in the diagram—and a similar cluck at a higher pitch and of greater volume used by females when mating.

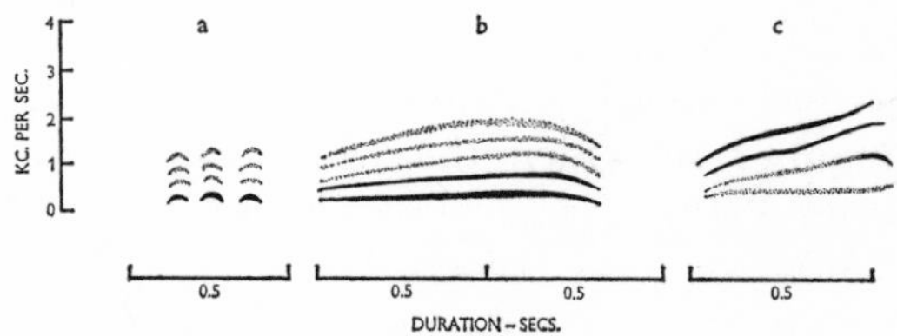

Diagram of sonograms of sounds made by Wood Ducks, showing (*a*) the "cluck" of the female, (*b*) the identity call of the female and (*c*) of the male.

Routine

The Wood Duck is found in flocks that can number two thousand or more birds. They are usually on land and seldom in water; the most typical places are on the edges of swamps or ground tanks and on lightly timbered river margins. Individuals occasionally perch in green trees. No matter where it is encountered it is certain that this extremely shy and wary bird will have seen the observer first; accordingly it is nearly always seen flying silently away or frozen into an alarm posture. The birds freeze with head and neck extended and silently watch. Other ducks raise their heads when alarmed, but usually also become restless and mill around, sometimes quacking. Not so the Wood Duck, it remains motionless and silent and often escapes detection or slips silently away.

On land they run swiftly from place to place, but on water their swimming is slow and awkward. They are slow-flying compared to the Dabbling Ducks and usually fly low to the ground, threading their way through the timber, calling their mournful cry.

Field Recognition

On land the Wood Duck has a very characteristic shape and posture, with long legs and extended neck, and can be confused with no other. On water it is light-coloured and floats higher than other ducks and, though there are no obvious specific field marks, at a distance the shape is very characteristic. In both situations its light colour and dark head are very useful aids to identification.

Overhead, the black undertail and lower abdomen, which form a triangle pointing forward, immediately distinguish the male; the female has no black, but the coarsely speckled breast and abdomen resemble no other duck. Flying away, the wing-beat is slow and there are large obvious white patches on the wings near the body. The Mountain Duck also has large obvious white wing patches, but these are on the shoulders.

I have often been struck with the general similarity of the flight pattern and manner in which the white wing patches of Wood Ducks and Green Pigmy Geese move during flight. There can be no confusion, however; the Wood Duck is light in colour and large in comparison to the Green Pigmy Goose, which is very dark in colour and small in size.

Relationships

The Wood Duck superficially resembles a small goose in appearance; it has a gooselike bill and lives by grazing in a similar manner to the geese and, for these reasons, is sometimes called the Maned Goose. This is an unsuitable name, since the bird has no relationship to the geese and is a member of the subfamily Anatinae—a duck.

Within the subfamily it was formerly considered to be related to the Shelducks *Tadornini*, apparently because of a superficial resemblance to them in shape. However, its life habits and behaviour, and the pattern of the downy young, are very similar to those of the tribe Cairinini, the Perching Ducks, and it is considered by Delacour to belong in this group, where it is associated with, among others, the Carolina Duck *Aix sponsa* of North America, the Mandarin Duck *A. galericulata* of Asia, the Muscovy Duck *Cairina mochata* of South America, and the pigmy geese *Nettapus* spp. There is no reason to doubt that it is related to these birds, but its nearest relative among them is not yet known, though there are many obvious similarities in its behaviour with that of both the Carolina Duck and the pigmy geese.

Habitat

The Wood Duck's preferred habitat is lightly timbered country near water, where there is short grass or herbage beneath the trees. The water can be anything at all—an earth tank, lagoon, or swamp. It is particularly common in the timbered fringes of the inland rivers of New South Wales. It is seldom found in dense or extensive swamps and then, usually only on the edges. It is practically never found in thick forests or where the water is brackish or saline.

Distribution and Movements

The Wood Duck can be found anywhere on the continent and has been recorded in some of the most arid areas, living on a tank or spring. Because of its habitat requirements it is most numerous in the better-watered parts of the inland and on the tablelands of the south-east to as far north as Toowoomba in Queensland, in south-east South Australia, and in western Victoria, particularly in areas devoted to mixed grazing and inland farming. It is widely distributed throughout eastern Victoria, coastal New South Wales, and coastal Queensland, but is nowhere numerous in these districts. It is rare north of Rockhampton and very rare in the Northern Territory.

In Western Australia it does not extend north of the Kimberley Ranges and is uncommon in the extreme south, but during the last few years has been extending its range southwards, throughout the wheat-belt and elsewhere, except in the heavy forests. This

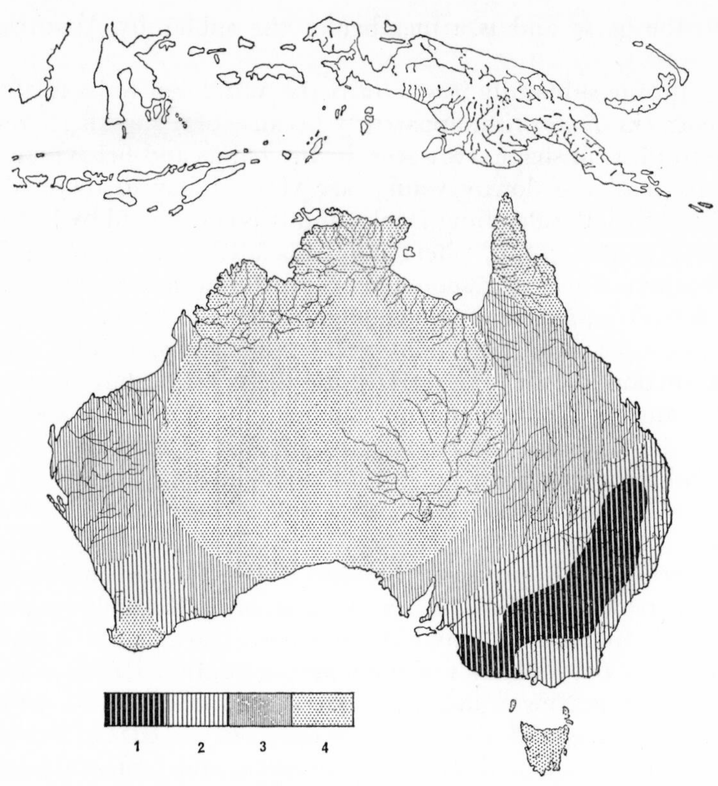

DISTRIBUTION OF THE WOOD DUCK

The greatest populations of Wood Ducks are found on the slopes and tablelands of eastern Australia (No. 1), but considerable populations occur in the region marked No. 2, and more scattered breeding populations in the region marked No. 3. They occur only as vagrants in the area marked No. 4.

increase in numbers and extension of range in Western Australia has been closely watched and documented by local naturalists, and it seems very likely that a similar extension of range also occurred in eastern Australia at an earlier period. The effects of large area agricultural settlement are such that Wood Duck habitat is often improved. The scrub is cleared, coarse, long native grasses, normally avoided by the birds, are grazed short, improved pastures are established, providing abundant green food, and extensive cultivation of wheat leads to a ready source of food in the stubble. The large number of stock dams provide convenient camping places.

In the really dry inland, throughout the Centre, the Wood Duck is very widespread but rare, its occurrence being strictly limited to the few springs and moist places that exist. It occurs fairly regularly in Tasmania, as a visitor from the mainland, but has not been found breeding there. On a few occasions it has reached New Zealand, but has not formed any permanent colonies.

The Wood Duck is more regular in habits and more sedentary than many ducks. After breeding it gathers into flocks which may number up to 2,000 birds but more commonly are less than 100, and each flock locates itself on a camp. The camp sites are traditional and in most years flocks of Wood Ducks locate themselves there. The site may be almost anything—a ground tank, irrigation canal, river bank, or a bare piece of ground on the edge of a billabong. The ground becomes trodden bare and littered with feathers and dung and is easily recognized. The flock spends the day in the camp and flies out to feed in the late afternoon, remaining on the feeding ground all night, to return at dawn. The feeding ground may be a green pasture, or crop, or stubble field, and is visited nightly until the food is exhausted or the birds are harried too much, when they select another one. Feeding might be several miles from the camp, but more usually one of the requirements of a camp site is a near-by food supply. In going to and fro the large flocks seldom move as one body, but small groups follow one another at intervals along the same route, a habit well known to, and frequently taken advantage of, by shooters.

The formation of flocks and the time that camps are occupied, vary with the locality and climate. On the Southern Tablelands flocks usually occupy the camps in May and disperse again in July or August, but in very dry years they may flock as early as February or March and not disperse until October. Similar variations are apparent in other districts according to the rainfall regime.

Although Wood Ducks are found on each camp site in most years, whether they are the same flock or not depends largely on the locality and its climate. Near Canberra, where there is regular rainfall, numbers of birds from different camps have been marked, by means of coloured bands on their legs, and it was found that many of the same birds returned each year. A few returned to one tank for five winters. Presumably where there is no need to move far during the summer the chances of returning are very high. In the Riverina, in inland New South Wales, however, once the flock leaves its camp at the beginning of summer the birds do not usually return to the same place; in fact, very few are ever found again in the same district. It seems that the camps are merely places that, for a combination of reasons, are attractive to Wood Ducks, so that when the birds are moving their chances of attracting a flock are high. Where they do not move far the chances of the same flock returning are high, but where they move more widely the chances are correspondingly less.

In the spring the flocks disperse and smaller groups move more widely throughout the district and breeding begins. The pairs locate themselves on creeks and tanks until breeding is over, when the family groups drift towards the larger bodies of water and flocks build up again to move round the country following the food supply, until they become settled on the camp. Wood Duck flocks are more stable than those of most other Australian ducks and are formed of closely knit family groups. If a group of birds are marked together they often remain in the same locality together year after year, or are shot together, perhaps hundreds of miles away and months later. The flock behaviour of the species, however, has not been studied.

It is nomadic, its movements being controlled by rainfall and the availability of the green herbage that comprises its food. It does not move nearly so far or so often as the Grey Teal or the Black Duck. Of banded birds that were subsequently shot 75 per cent were within 100 miles of the banding place, compared to 55 per cent for the Black Duck and 35 per cent for Grey Teal. Only 8 per cent moved more than 200 miles, compared to 22 per cent for Black Duck and 33 per cent for Grey Teal.[38]

It has been possible to trace the movements of birds from three concentration areas. These three places, Griffith, New South Wales, Naracoorte, South Australia, and Lake George, New South Wales, provide a range of climates. Griffith is semi-arid, Naracoorte is regularly watered by winter rainfall and the summers are dry, and Lake George is a high mountain environment. The amount of movement was directly related to the aridity of the region.

In the summer in which they were marked there was little movement among the birds from Lake George; none left the highlands and none travelled more than 200 miles, most remaining in the immediate neighbourhood. From Naracoorte many birds remained in the district, but considerable numbers moved throughout the western districts of Victoria and a few along the Murray River to as far east as Albury, New South Wales, 300 miles away. From Griffith, as the summer progressed, there was very wide movement and all the birds left the area; a few moved west, one as far as

Broken Hill, but most moved 200-300 miles to the south-western slopes and distributed themselves throughout the well-watered wheat-growing areas, particularly around Condobolin and Lake Cowal. In the next winter there was further movement. The birds from Lake George still remained in the district; those from Naracoorte moved a little farther through western Victoria. Those from Griffith moved more widely and some travelled as far as Warwick, Queensland, 600 miles; none of these birds ever returned to the inland plains, according to band recoveries.

Feeding

The Wood Duck grazes green herbage. An area is selected, which could be several miles from the camp, and is visited nightly, until the food is exhausted. They then select another area and the flock moves to it in a body. If a green crop is within the feeding range of the flock it comes in for its share of attention, but unless it is the only greenstuff in the area is not especially attractive. In wheat-growing districts it freely grazes in stubble fields and the extension of wheat-growing has been thought to be one of the reasons for the extension of the Wood Duck's range in Western Australia.

A good feeding area may be favoured by several flocks. In one case, an irrigated ricefield near Griffith, flocks from seven different localities arrived each night; one of these flocks was travelling seven miles in a direct line to the crop. In another case near Canberra flocks from four localities, within a radius of four miles, arrived each evening. The flocks mingle on the feeding area, but whether there is complete separation when they return to the camps is not known.

The stomachs of nearly 600 Wood Ducks from the Riverina contained less than one per cent animal food—a few backswimmers and one small mussel.[39] The remainder of the food was all plant material and nearly all vegetative material—there were very few seeds. Grasses were most important and comprised 4 per cent of the food, including water-couch *Paspalum*, rice *Oryza*, summer-grass *Paspalidum*, couch *Cynodon*, rye-grass *Lolium*, and wallaby-grass *Danthonia*, and a great number of others. There were 17 per cent of sedges and 13 per cent of smartweeds, and the remainder of the food consisted of numerous herbs, including milk thistles, saffron thistles, medicks and clovers, and paddymelons. Of the total food, 60 per cent was from plants that normally grow on dry land, reflecting the fact that the birds often feed far from the water.

Throughout the year the food eaten parallels the abundance of the various plant groups. The grasses and legumes are most important during summer and autumn, their main growing period. The herbs are most important in the cooler months, the only time of the year that they are abundant on the dry plains, and the marsh plants, sedges, smartweeds, and dock are mainly eaten in winter when the swamps are full. Apparently Wood Ducks primarily seek green herbage and the species comprising it are of little importance.

Downy ducklings have different food habits to their parents and feed entirely on insects. When very small, as the mother grazes, the ducklings eagerly hunt the tiny insects, the small flies, midges, and beetles disturbed by her from the green grass, and at this stage their food is completely derived from animals. Throughout their pre-flying life the importance of this type of food declines and by the time they are three or four weeks old they eat mainly herbage and by six weeks eat nothing else.

Breeding

The courtship displays of the Cairinini are as a rule rather simple and, although the display of the Wood Duck has not been studied in full, it seems to be no exception. The female incites the male, swinging her head from side to side and calling sharply, until she is pursued by one or more males, who hurry after her, bobbing their heads and swelling their breasts. The activity may be on land when the group runs in and out of the timber, or may be on the water when the group sweeps along in the current, periodically coming ashore to hurry in and out among the weeds, then back to the river to be swept away. The mated pair search for the nest site together, flying silently through the timber to perch in any tree with a suitable hollow, which both inspect.

In common with that of many other Australian ducks, the breeding season is variable and is largely controlled by rainfall. For many River Ducks the most important factor controlling breeding seasons is alteration in water-level, but for the Wood Duck, to which the depth of water in the swamp means little, as it normally neither lives, feeds, nor breeds in swamps, the amount of green grass available is of greater importance. Accordingly rainfall and not water-level is the principal factor in initiating breeding, since this ensures that there will be a bounteous food supply for the young.

In districts where the rainfall is regular, as in the southern highlands, the breeding season is quite regular. The main rains fall during the winter and accordingly the Wood Ducks breed in the spring, September and October, when it is warm enough for grass to grow. If the winter and spring are dry, as they occasionally are, little or no breeding occurs. In north-eastern New South Wales, where the winters are relatively dry, but not so that there is no green grass, and the main rains fall in the summer, the Wood Duck breeds throughout the whole year and one is liable to encounter ducklings at any time, though the bulk of the breeding occurs in January, February, and March, following the rain. In areas subject to summer monsoons the main breeding occurs after the main rains in February and March.

In the semi-arid inland the breeding season is erratic and is controlled by rainfall. It can occur at any time of the year in response to heavy rain. On the average, conditions for breeding are most suitable in spring and most breeding occurs then, in August and September. In the winter rain has a more lasting effect, because of the lower evaporation rate, than in the summer. Accordingly less rain is required to initiate breeding in the late winter and spring than in the summer. In dry years no nests are started and the Wood Ducks leave the district.

When the nesting site has been selected and the eggs laid the male takes station near by and prepares to defend the locality. If the nest is far out on the plains he usually stations himself on the nearest tank and defends this against other drakes, ready for the day when the ducklings are hatched and require living space. When the young hatch they jump from the nest and float to the ground; their departure is hastened by the female flying repeatedly from the ground to the tree, calling loudly. On the ground they are assembled and set off to the nearest water, which could easily be a mile or more away. The adult birds walk in front and a long string of ducklings hurry along behind. If disturbed the parents attempt to attract attention by flapping along the ground while the young scatter and freeze to escape detection. Until the young are able to fly the family remains near water, even though it might be only a small pool on the plains. They then move off together and join other family groups as they congregate into flocks in more extensive camps.

Nest

The nests are invariably in tree hollows and, in my experience, usually in green trees. The tree can be anywhere, overhanging a lagoon, in a flooded timber fringe, or far out on the dry plains a mile or more from water. The eggs are laid in the hollow spout on the bare wood and subsequently covered with down. The down is light grey in colour, almost white in the centre and at the tip.

Eggs

The eggs are oval or elliptical and vary in colour from cream to creamy white, with a close-grained, smooth, lustrous shell. The measurements of 88 eggs from 12 nests were: length 53-62 mm. (average 57 mm.), and breadth 40-45 mm. (average 42 mm.).

Incubation

Incubation time is 28 days.

Clutch Size

There are no quantitative data, but according to North[82] the clutch is 9 to 11. This covers the size of the few clutches I have counted.

Mortality

The numbers of Wood Ducks in the milder tablelands and coastal districts do not fluctuate greatly, but inland the species is subject to greater fluctuations than most others. In years of adequate rainfall breeding is regular, and in years of exceptionally heavy rainfall, such as occurred in 1951 and 1956, almost continuous; the survival of young is high and very large numbers of Wood Ducks develop wherever there is suitable habitat. In dry weather these concentrations disappear and Wood Duck become uncommon. In dry weather the Grey Teal disperse to the extremities of the continent in search of refuge and the Black Ducks are able to find temporary refuge in the permanent swamps, but as soon as the green grass and herbage dries off the Wood Ducks must move or perish.

There is some movement of Wood Ducks annually and in dry weather this becomes more extensive, but it never approaches, in scale or the distance travelled, that of the Grey Teal or Black Duck. Few reach the coast and the majority perish inland. The rapid turnover of Wood Duck populations is well illustrated by their mortality rate computed from banding recoveries. In the first year after marking 80 per cent of the birds died and in subsequent years 60 per cent of those surviving died. The first-year mortality rates for Grey Teal and Black Duck are 56 per cent and 58 per cent respectively. Clearly population turnover is much more rapid in Wood Ducks than in the other two species.

The Wood Duck carries a heavier shooting pressure than the two other common game ducks, the Black Duck and Grey Teal. This can be seen from a comparison of the numbers of banded birds shot. Of banded Wood Ducks, 12 per cent were shot in the first

Upper: Wood Ducks feeding on grass and sedges on the edge of Lake George, N.S.W. Mountain Ducks, Black Swans, and Pelicans behind.

Lower: Alert posture of male Wood Duck. *Photos by Ederic Slater*

Upper: Small summer camp of Wood Ducks on a stock dam, Canberra, A.C.T.
Photo by author

Lower: The construction of numerous large stock dams of this type throughout the semi-arid inland has assisted in extending the range of the Wood Duck. (The animal drinking is a Red Kangaroo.) *Photo by Ederic Slater*

year, compared to 7 per cent for Black Duck and for Grey Teal, and after 6 years the percentages that had been shot were 15, 13, and 11 respectively. It is more meaningful, however, to compare the recovery rates in the one district and when this is done for south-east South Australia the percentages are 30 for Wood Ducks, 11 for Black Ducks, and 17 for Grey Teal. These figures are based on the numbers of bands recovered and returned to the Banding Office, but it is well known that not all shooters return the bands, so the figures are underestimates, perhaps gross underestimates.

Status

Wood Ducks have a long history as a nuisance of green crops. In 1921 they invaded the infant Murrumbidgee Irrigation Areas and destroyed the first crop of peas and other vegetables to be grown. The first crop of rice grown in the same district was heavily attacked, and with the expansion of rice-growing in the Murrumbidgee and Wakool areas, some of the best Wood Duck habitat in the continent, they have clashed heavily with the rice-growers and have figured in a more or less continuous controversy between growers and conservation authorities since then.

The relationship between Wood Ducks and rice cultivation was investigated by Kinghorn[66] of the Australian Museum in 1931, and later, in 1951-55, independently by the author.[36] Both studies showed that the Wood Ducks did graze some rice crops, particularly neglected ones, and if not scared off were capable of destroying part of the crop by trampling and grazing, but that one or two, even heavy, grazings did not harm the ultimate crop at all and might even help stimulate tillering. The main damage is done where birds are allowed to feed undisturbed for several nights in the one place, and then a large area of the young crop can be completely destroyed. Farmers sometimes suffer a loss, but in the aggregate the damage done is small. The authorities in New South Wales, where all the irrigated rice is grown, have met the problem by issuing licences to individual farmers to shoot ducks in their crops and by permitting a special open season in the affected districts when the crop is germinating.

On the tablelands of New South Wales, and elsewhere, they sometimes attack newly sown pastures and damage them. Again, although individual pastures may be damaged, over all they are not a serious pest of improved pastures. It is also sometimes claimed that their droppings foul the grass, particularly in the vicinity of ground tanks.

The Wood Duck is considered a good game bird, though inferior to the Black Duck and Grey Teal in table quality, the flesh being coarse and rank. It is extremely wary and difficult to stalk and does not decoy. The usual method of hunting Wood Ducks is by pass shooting or by beating creeks and billabongs, the shooters being hidden ahead of the beaters, or two groups of shooters may walk towards one another from each end of the billabong. They fly relatively slowly compared to many ducks, a fact that confuses many shooters, and are much harder to kill, usually requiring one gauge heavier shot than Black Ducks.

They are numerous over a very wide area and there is evidence that they have been, to some extent, favoured by agricultural development. Although heavily shot, the species is very secure and with proper control of hunting could remain numerous for a long time yet.

Green Pigmy Goose

Nettapus pulchellus Gould

References

Nettapus Brandt, Icon. An. Russ. Nov., Av. 1, p. 5, 1836.
Nettapus pulchellus Gould, Birds of Australia, 7, p. 4, 1842. (Port Essington, N.T.)

Other Names

Pigmy Goose, Green Goose, Goose-teal, Green Goose-teal.

Description

ADULT MALE. Crown of head dark green crossed with bars of brown; back and scapulars dark glossy green; tail coverts and tail dark glossy green freckled and barred with grey; chin grey; neck solid glossy green all around; face has very prominent white patch below eye; mantle and flanks grey, each feather having several broad crescents of dark green or brown; undertail dark brown; bill, dark greenish-grey culmen, lower mandible pink; legs and feet greenish grey; iris dark brown.

ADULT FEMALE. Differs from male in having crown not so green and not distinctly barred; neck, not solid green all around, hind neck green but remainder white, each feather having several broad white or green bars giving striped appearance; face below the eye extending to hind neck and chin pure white with some dark-grey flecks.

IMMATURE. Both sexes at first resemble females, but face, chin, and neck are heavily spotted with dark brown, that colour predominating. By two months of age males begin to develop solid green neck.

DUCKLINGS. Hind neck, back, and upper side of tail, dark brownish grey; underside light grey; underside of tail dark grey; crown of head dark brown; face light grey, there is a dark eye stripe and less white above eye than in White Pigmy Goose; wing dark brown above and grey below, with a white trailing edge; bill, culmen greenish yellow, mandible pink, legs and feet greenish yellow with yellow webs; eye dark brown.

Size

	Weight *gm.*	*Length* *mm.*	*Wingspread* *mm.*	*Wing* *mm.*	*Bill* *mm.*
Adult Male					
Maximum	430	360	600	180	28
Minimum	300	305	480	160	23
Average	310	332	581	172	25
Number measured	*47*	*49*	*24*	*49*	*50*
Adult female					
Maximum	340	344	590	180	29
Minimum	245	300	530	150	21
Average	304	326	565	169	25
Number measured	*26*	*28*	*16*	*28*	*28*

Voice

The sounds made by Green Pigmy Geese are musical whistles and trills. The sound most frequently heard is the shrill contact call of the male, "*pee-whit*", see (*a*) in the diagram, uttered continually in flight or at rest. It is not certain if the female also possesses this call, but she certainly has a whistle, with declining frequency and amplitude, "*pee-yew*", see (*b*), uttered in like situations. The alarm call is a high-pitched whistle, "*whit*", uttered singly or as two rapid syllables, see (*c*). The sound used during fighting and threat is a rapid high-pitched musical trill (*d*). As noted in the life history of the Pink-eared Duck, there is, surprisingly, a general similarity in the structure of the calls of these two species.

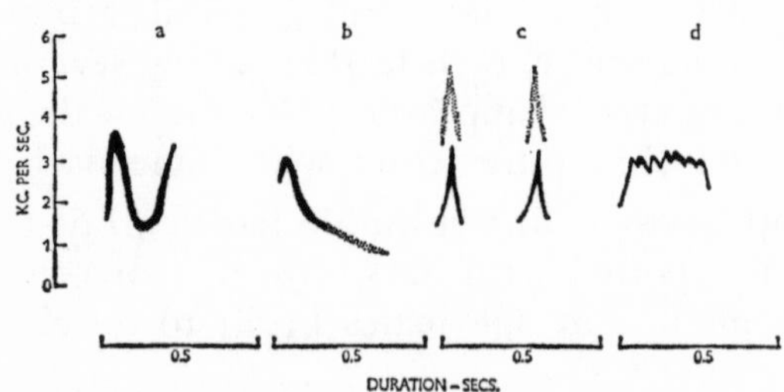

Diagram of sonograms of sounds made by Green Pigmy Geese. Their function is described in the text.

Plumage

A distinct eclipse plumage has not been definitely established, but in the non-breeding season birds are frequently collected that suggest its probable presence.

One such bird collected on the Adelaide River, Northern Territory, on 2nd May 1965, is held in the C.S.I.R.O. Division of Wildlife Research collection. It is an adult male with testes undergoing post-breeding regression; the tail and wings are in moult. The plumage is as a breeding male, but the entire face and chin are white freckled with dark-grey as in the female; the neck is not solid green, the hind neck is dark green, but the sides and foreneck are mottled grey and white with a few green feathers, mainly on the sides. It differs from the female only in that the black and white barring on the neck is replaced by an uneven mixture or mottling.

Routine

Green Pigmy Geese are nearly always found in small groups among the blue water-lilies of tropical lagoons; there is no more attractive experience in Australia for the observer of waterfowl than to watch the vivid green birds threading among the lilies. They are usually in pairs or small groups, but in the dry season flocks of two hundred or more have been seen, though even then the pairs retain their individuality and the flock is a congregation of family groups or pairs. To see more than fifty in a concentration is unusual.

They are wholly aquatic and, except when flying, are nearly always in the water, swimming, resting, or feeding. Lilies grow in the deepest water, and in the early morning and late afternoon the Pigmy Geese swim to the shore to cruise in shallow water, feeding on emergent plants, but during the heat of the day return to the lilies to float motionless in the clear pools among them. They occasionally rest on the water's edge in the shallows, and where there are fallen trees clamber awkwardly out to rest on branches just above water-level. Usually they swim up and crawl out, but very occasionally fly, to the timber and perch with much effort to secure balance and much wing-flapping. I have never seen one fly to a tree to perch except on the entrance of a nest hollow before entering. I have never seen a Pigmy Goose in the wild beyond the edge of the water and find it hard to understand Keartland's note (in Mathews) that he had seen them "feeding on the grass like ordinary domestic geese". Captive birds placed on the land are very awkward and walk with difficulty. In captivity they sometimes leave the water to secure seed on the bank, but are very ungainly and prefer not to come ashore.

Although usually tame they are very alert and freeze, with head erect, to watch the intruder or swim together uneasily. They spring from the water at a low angle and fly swiftly, low down, in direct lines, whistling incessantly. Even when on small lagoons Pigmy Geese are hesitant to leave them, and merely move to another clear pool among the lilies until disturbed again.

Field Recognition

Green Pigmy Geese are small, very dark ducks that float high on the water, swim slowly, and seldom dive. If the observer is close enough to detect colour the brilliant green is diagnostic.

Males are easily distinguished from White Pigmy Geese by the solid dark neck and white face patch. Females are more difficult. At close range the darker neck, the darker flanks, and the comparative lack of white over the eyes of the Green Pigmy Goose are satisfactory field marks, but at greater distance identification is difficult since the general pattern of dark and light areas of the plumage is very similar.

When the bird is flying away the white wing patches sharply contrast with the dark plumage and are a certain field mark; they are very much larger and more obvious than the white on the wing of a Grey Teal and are at the base of the wing rather than at the tip, as in the White Pigmy Goose. The movement of the white wing patches in flight is very reminiscent of those of the Wood Duck. The Green Pigmy Goose overhead is very distinctive. When seen from below no other duck has a dark throat and neck contrasting with a pure white body.

Relationships

The pigmy geese belong to the tribe Cairinini, Perching Ducks of the subfamily Anatinae, and as such are related to the Wood Duck and several Northern Hemisphere genera.

The pigmy geese, genus *Nettapus*, are the smallest of all Anatidae and are confined to the tropics. There are three species, *N. auritus* of Africa, *N. pulchellus*, the Green Pigmy Goose of Australia and New Guinea, and *N. coromandelianus*, which has an extensive range in India, Asia, Indonesia, and Australia. There are no geographic races of the Green Pigmy Goose.

The name "goose" has apparently been incorrectly given to these birds because of a "gooselike" bill; this, however, is merely an adaptation to grazing on aquatic vegetation and the bird has no relationship to geese, in the true sense, beyond that they are both waterfowl.

Habitat

The preferred habitats of the Green Pigmy Goose are the deeper, more permanent freshwater lagoons and lakes of the tropics, especially those that support numerous water-lilies and sub-emergent aquatic vegetation; these plants provide most of the birds' food. In northern Australia water-lilies are confined to coastal and subcoastal freshwater lagoons, which are permanent or nearly permanent and in which there is some circulation of water. Accordingly the habitat is very restricted in extent in the dry season, but is more widespread during the wet.

In the dry season the birds gather on the deeper, more permanent swamps and lagoons of the plains and forests and also in water-storage areas where suitable habitat has been formed. They may also gather in some numbers on those parts of the larger lakes where there are a few water-lilies, such as Lake Finniss on the Adelaide River and Barmaroo-Gjaja on the South Alligator, Northern Territory; these lakes also have much sub-emergent vegetation. They avoid the streams, shallow pools, and brackish water generally at all times.

In the wet season the greatest numbers remain in the lagoons that have persisted through the dry, but spread much more widely over them, since deep-water conditions are greatly extended at this season. Numbers also leave the lagoons and lakes and may be found distributed through the deeper parts of the spike-rush and wild-rice swamps on the low black-soil plains, wherever the water is deep enough to prevent the growth of spike-rush and to allow the deep-water flora to develop.

In southern New Guinea the habitat is very similar but more permanent, owing to more equally distributed rainfall, than in northern Australia, and the birds' habitat preferences are the same. They are abundant in every deep permanent swamp and lake between Port Moresby and the international border. Many New Guinea swamps are heavily overgrown with reeds and in these the birds avoid the dense growth and are found in the more open, deep parts of the area.

Distribution and Movement

The Green Pigmy Goose is found in tropical Australia as well as in southern New Guinea, Buru, and Seran. There are also records from

Geelvink Bay in northern New Guinea and in the Celebes and Moluccas. These last records are probably of stragglers.

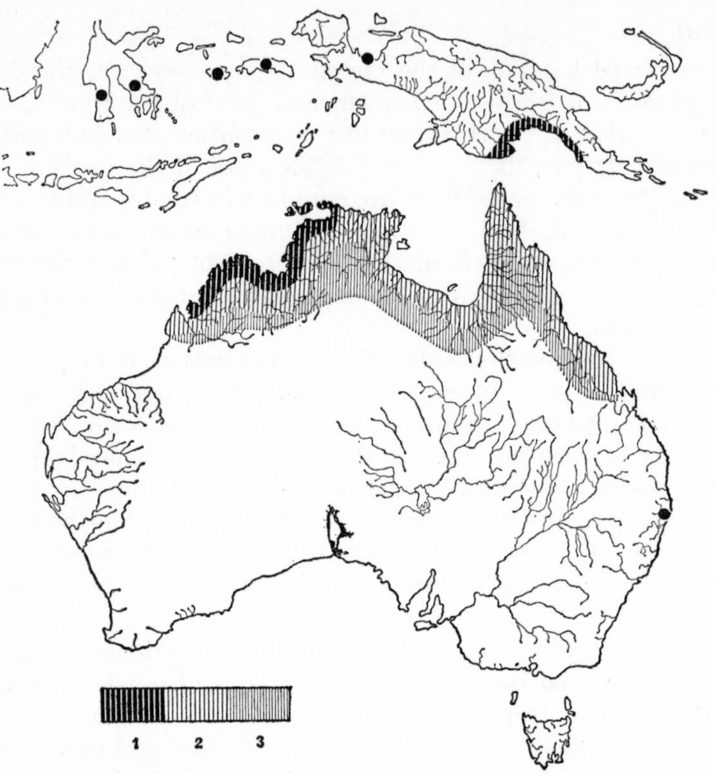

DISTRIBUTION OF THE GREEN PIGMY GOOSE

The densest populations are in the area with the darkest shading, but the bird is also a common breeding species throughout the area with intermediate shading (No. 2). In the lightest-shaded area (No. 3) the birds occur as vagrants. The black spots indicate recent isolated records of vagrants.

In New Guinea it was very abundant, in 1964, in every lagoon and lake surveyed in the Port Moresby district, the Gulf of Papua and the Western Districts as far inland as Lake Balimo and Lake Murray. In Lake Balimo, a very large area of swamp, were the greatest numbers of Green Pigmy Geese that I have ever seen, they were rising continuously in front of the canoe throughout the day. There could not have been less than two thousand in the area. In southern New Guinea suitable lagoons and lakes are very much larger and more numerous than in northern Australia and local populations of Green Pigmy Geese are accordingly very much higher. The western limit of the population in west New Guinea has not been recorded, but the failure of Hoogerwerf[59] to refer to the species, after a study of waterfowl of several years' duration at Merauke, suggests that it is not numerous, if it exists there at all. There is suitable habitat near Merauke and farther west, so its absence would be difficult to explain; certainly it was seen on lagoons not ten miles east of the border.

The record from Geelvink Bay on the north coast of New Guinea, at present, must be considered exceptional, since the species was not seen during an intense air survey of most water areas of northern New Guinea in 1964, nor has it been collected or seen during repeated collecting expeditions to the Wewak-Maprik region by the C.S.I.R.O. Division of Wildlife Research in the period 1960-5, nor is it known to the European and New Guinean hunting communities in that area.

In Australia its distribution is rigidly controlled by the availability of deep lily lagoons and it is normally restricted to the coastal and subcoastal strip from the Fitzroy River, Western Australia, to Rockhampton, Queensland. Throughout this region it is found in most suitable lagoons. In the Northern Territory it is present on every river, but although it has been seen as far inland as Newcastle Waters it is seldom more than forty miles from the coast. It occurs on the lower reaches of the rivers of Arnhem Land, but is not common, presumably because lagoons are not extensively developed there. On Cape York Peninsula it is widely distributed on the lower reaches of the rivers draining the west side and widely distributed but not common on the east coast where lily lagoons are few. It is more numerous between Darwin and Oenpelli, Northern Territory, than anywhere else, apart from Lake Balimo in New Guinea.

The Green Pigmy Goose is very local in habits and has the same pattern of small-scale seasonal movements as several other tropical species. In the wet season it is generally distributed throughout the forests on the low divides and over the flood-plains of the rivers where, although most common in the flooded lagoons, it is also found in the deepest parts of some of the spike-rush and wild-rice swamps. In this season it penetrates farther inland than it does in the dry season, the more inland lagoons being full and deep.

In the dry season on the Adelaide River, as the plains and lagoons dry, it concentrates on the more permanent water areas. Many birds leave the plains and gather on the lagoons in the forests, and others concentrate on the few large lakes and lagoons on the plains. Those that have spent the wet season nearer the coast leave it and move inland as the stringers decline and become brackish and saline.

On the other Northern Territory rivers the movements are similar but modified to suit the hydrological conditions of each river. The Wildman has very few black-soil swamps in the wet season but some deep paperbark-fringed lagoons. It supports small numbers of pigmy geese in the wet, but these leave almost completely in the dry season. The South Alligator and the Mary rivers have numerous billabongs and lagoons in their middle reaches, but these, in general, are not deep, are bare of vegetation, and do not shelter large numbers of pigmy geese for this reason. The most important dry-season refuge areas are the lagoons of the East Alligator and the Adelaide rivers, and of these the greatest areas are probably Fogg Dam, an artificial water-storage area near Darwin that shelters many hundreds each dry season, and Manton Dam, which provides the Darwin water supply; both areas are sufficiently deep and permanent to grow water-lilies at all times.

There is little doubt that individuals move from one river to the other to seek dry-season refuge, but, as very few have been banded, the point cannot yet be proved. At the end of the wet season the concentrations disperse and the birds spread generally throughout the subcoastal strip for breeding.

The movements in north Queensland are of the same type as those in the Northern Territory, but many fewer birds are involved. Thus Lavery[69] showed that in the Boyle River Basin, where pigmy geese are never numerous, the birds could not be found in the wet season. No doubt they are widely distributed and breeding then, but during the dry season concentrations of up to forty built up in the area. The groups were located on the few deep permanent lagoons. This is quite in accord with events elsewhere, including the situation on the west coast of the Cape York Peninsula, where Gulliver (in Mathews[74]) described a dispersal during the wet season and subsequently a concentration on the remaining lagoons during the dry, until these lagoons became low in level and brackish. In 1964 I visited many lagoons along the east coast of Cape York Peninsula during the dry season and found that most had a few pigmy geese, but whereas on lagoons in the Northern Territory similar in size and ecology one might have expected twenty or thirty birds, on Cape York there were never more than four or five.

Although the birds have strict habitat requirements, and seldom move beyond their breeding range, they occasionally do so. In Western Australia there was an unconfirmed report as far south as

North-west Cape and in 1965 one bird was shot at Moora (Serventy personal communication). In Queensland J. Liddy reported an isolated occurrence at Mount Isa, over two hundred miles from the coast. In 1956, an abnormally wet year, a Green Pigmy Goose was shot at Tucki, near Lismore, New South Wales, and its wing seen by the author. These vagrants, however, are very exceptional and the Green Pigmy Goose is more sedentary and more restricted to the tropics than any other Australian duck.

Feeding

The Green Pigmy Goose is one of the most aquatic of ducks; it seldom leaves the water, and its feeding is confined to it. In the wet season, when the lagoons are full and the water-lilies and aquatic grasses are in flower, it spends its time swimming among the plants, grazing on the flower-heads and seeds and occasionally dipping under water for sub-emergents. It often flies forwards a short distance, low down, and then continues feeding. In the dry season when water-lilies are not flowering it moves near the shore and feeds on sub-emergent vegetation, and in shallow water uses a remarkably coot-like dive to secure under-water vegetation up to twelve inches below the surface. This is grasped with the bill and pulled to the surface, where it is broken off by a vigorous shaking of the head. Each pair of birds occupies a small feeding territory and spends the whole day there, within a few square yards, diving continuously. The male vigorously attacks any other pigmy goose that approaches, but it is not known if he is defending the feeding area or the female who is usually in it. Pigmy geese have occasionally been seen swimming in deep water close to overhanging banks and stripping seed from dry-land grasses. The only other common feeding behaviour is a filtering action of the surface water to secure floating seeds and, very commonly, the white flowers of paperbarks, which are abundant in the wet season. Ducklings have been watched feeding in the same manner and diving continually in deep water, coming up each time with a fragment of plant material.

The food eaten is almost entirely of plant origin. Seventy-six gizzards collected in the Adelaide River valley contained 99 per cent vegetable food. The few insects were aphids, spiders, one caterpillar, and a few tiny beetles, all probably collected accidentally with the vegetation. Every gizzard contained vegetable food, but only six of the 76 had any animal material.

Twenty-seven of the gizzards were taken in the wet season; of these, seeds and buds of water-lilies were found in 80 per cent and made up 40 per cent of the volume of food. Grasses, mainly the small seeds of *Echinochloa colonum* and *E. sagnina*, accounted for 30 per cent of the food eaten, and *Chara* (8 per cent) and *Potamogeton* (14 per cent) for most of the remainder. There were small quantities of a very wide variety of other plants, all aquatics.

In the dry season the food was very similar, though the importance of the plants differed. At this season the lagoons are relatively low and the water-lilies, though still growing, flower very sparsely and often not at all, while the sub-emergent growth is nearer the surface, owing to the decline in water-level. At this season these under-water plants were of greater importance to the birds than in the wet and 28 per cent of the volume of the food eaten consisted of *Potamogeton* leaves and stems, 10 per cent was *Chara*, 14 per cent was leaves and buds of water-lilies, and the remainder consisted of numerous aquatic weeds, mainly leaves and stems, usually unidentifiable, but including *Nymphoides*, *Urticularia*, *Sesbania*, and *Monochoria*.

The food eaten in north Queensland is rather similar to that eaten in Northern Territory,[69] though of course the distribution and availability of plants vary from place to place, so local differences occur. In 22 gizzards from Townsville seeds or buds of water-lilies were present in 28 per cent and accounted for 30 per cent of the total volume of food. Hydrocharitaceae provided 23 per cent of the total volume and was present in 41 per cent of the gizzards. Grasses, pondweeds, and Characeae each accounted for about 10 per cent of the volume, and miscellaneous aquatic plants brought the volume of vegetable material up to 96 per cent of the total. Plant material was present in every gizzard and animal food in only 16 per cent. The most common plants eaten were water-lilies, barnyard-grass, and floating pondweed. The few insects were possibly casually acquired along with the vegetable material and consisted of weevils, aphids, and various larvae.

Breeding

The birds are always found in pairs or small groups, presumably family parties. This fact, together with the frequent observation that the male vigorously defends the area around the female from other pigmy geese at all times of the year, strongly suggests that the pair bond lasts for more than one breeding season, possibly for life.

Fighting between males is very frequent. The threat consists of a rapid up-and-down swing of the bill similar to that of the Wood Duck; following this the bird attacks, trilling loudly, with bill open, and severely buffets the other male. It may attack sometimes by flying up and alighting beside the intruder with flailing wings; the opponents spring in and out of the water and frequently dive to escape one another. I have seldom seen such savage or sustained fighting in other waterfowl.

Nothing substantial has been recorded about the displays and pairing behaviour, but there are numerous superficial points of resemblance to the Wood Duck. Males of both species swim round the female rapidly, raising and lowering the head; the stretching of the neck by both birds during the mating display seems identical with the behaviour of the Wood Duck, as are the actions in preening the wing and turning the head sideways to the other bird in courtship.

The exact extent of, or the factors that determine, the breeding season have not been studied. On the subcoastal plains of the Northern Territory the birds are always paired and the simple displays intensify with the first rains of the wet season, usually in October. The breeding season itself, that is, the period when eggs are laid, extends from January until March near Darwin, according to the age of broods seen and the sexual state of birds dissected. The presence of sexual activity in the testes of males examined and the dates of the few nests that have been reported from Townsville, Queensland, show the same period is selected as the breeding seasons in this area.[69] I have never collected a bird showing any sexual activity in the dry season.

It seems that the Green Pigmy Goose breeds in the wet season, when the rapid and sudden rises in water-level are over and the lagoons are at their maximum extent or just beginning to decline. At this time the lilies and aquatic plants are undergoing their most luxuriant period of growth.

The male seems to take the initiative in selecting the nesting tree, but does not inspect the hollows. The pair swim among the timber and the male flies up to sit near hollows in trees; he is shortly joined by the female, who enters the hollow and inspects it. Many trees may be visited before a site is selected. When the eggs are laid the male remains in the vicinity and joins the female and brood when it hatches, remaining with them until the brood flies and the family party joins others in the breeding lagoon. At this time small groups of birds circulate among the local lagoons and the flocks increase in size. The parents and young brood spend the days in deep water, but swim to the edge of the lagoon at dawn and in the late afternoon to feed in very compact groups. When alarmed they move off slowly and carefully among the lilies; the young dive when approached and remain out of sight, presumably under water-lily leaves in the same area. This seems to be quite typical behaviour of Australian Cairinini ducklings; Wood Ducks scatter and freeze and pigmy geese do the aquatic equivalent, unlike the young of Anatini which scatter, dive, and continue swimming under water, surfacing and immediately diving again for considerable distances. When the cause of disturbance has gone the parents return and swim or fly over the area, whistling continuously until the brood reappears and reassembles. It is then led away in a compact group, the female usually leading and the male following.

Nests

Nests are found in swamp vegetation, on the ground and in tree hollows, but which is the commonest site is not known. The position is further complicated by the fact that few of the nests recorded have been properly authenticated. A typical unsatisfactory description is that by John Gilbert, Gould's collector, who described a nest "built up in the long grass about a foot above the water, the bottom of the nest resting on its surface"; it was "composed of long dried grasses slightly hollowed for the reception of the eggs". No one since has recorded such a nest, and since the eggs of the Green Pigmy Goose and the Water Whistle-duck, which sometimes does build such a nest, are quite similar in size and appearance, the possibility must remain that Gilbert was mistaken as to the species owning the two nests he saw. Eggs in the Gould collection are almost certainly of the Green Pigmy Goose but are not definitely referred to any particular nest description. Hill[55] records another unsatisfactory description—"a native brought me three eggs which were taken from a nest built in grass near a swamp"—and North refers to a nest found on the ground near the edge of a swamp, its identity authenticated by the female's skin. I can add to the records of ground nesting by mentioning young broods that I have seen on lagoons with no nearby timber at all. It is very unlikely that young of Green Pigmy Geese could or would travel overland to water.

On the other hand, Keartland stated that "they usually lay their eggs in a hollow branch sometimes far from water". Although the distance from water is doubtful, I have seen two nests in tree-holes, both in paperbarks standing in water. In neither case did the female flush, but in both there were enough pigmy goose feathers to leave little doubt about the identity of the bird. D. Tullock has seen a female leaving a tree hollow containing eggs in that same area. Ey has recorded tree nesting near Ayr, Queensland, and described a typical hollow: "The entrance of the hollow was about 7 inches in diameter, widening out to about 18 inches at the bottom. The depth was about 2 ft."

Eggs

Authenticated eggs are very rare in collections. They are white or creamy-white in colour, with a very hard, smooth, lustrous shell, and are only a little smaller than those of the Water Whistle-duck. Measurements of 106 eggs from 12 clutches were: length 35-49 mm. (average 44 mm.) and breadth 29-36 mm. (average 32 mm.).

Incubation

The incubation time is not known.

Clutch Size

There are no quantitative data on clutch size. According to North, the commonest clutch is 8 to 12 eggs.

Status

The Green Pigmy Goose has no effect on agriculture and is not sought after as a game bird, though it is shot along with other ducks by inexperienced shooters. It is legal game at present in the Northern Territory, though this is now under review. It is protected elsewhere.

It is nowhere numerous, but in some places, notably subcoastal areas of the Northern Territory, it is a common species and is found in every piece of suitable habitat. Despite its restricted range it seems well fitted to survive, and elaborate conservation measures, apart from protection from pointless shooting, are not essential at present. Much of its present range is almost in its primitive condition and extensive agricultural development seems only a remote possibility. Should this occur, however, experience in the Northern Territory shows that water-storage areas, which seem an essential adjunct to agricultural development in the region for dry-season irrigation purposes, create excellent pigmy goose habitat, and what is lost by drainage will, to some extent, be replaced in this way. Fogg Dam, one such water-storage area in Northern Territory, now has a large permanent breeding population of pigmy geese and supports several hundred others during the dry season.

There is no more attractive waterfowl in Australia, and for its beauty alone the authorities in the tropical States and Territories should ensure that the simple steps for its conservation are not neglected, so that it will remain common.

White Pigmy Goose

Nettapus coromandelianus (Gmelin)

References

Nettapus Brandt, Icon. An Russ. Nov., Av. 1, p. 5, 1836.
Anas coromandeliana, Gmelin, Syst. Nat., 1, p. 522, 1789, India. (Coromandel.)

Other Names

White-quilled Pigmy Goose, Cotton Teal, Australian Pigmy Goose, Pigmy Goose.

Description

ADULT MALE. Crown of head brown; scapulars brown; back glossy green; tail coverts and tail brown; chin white; neck white all around with some brown feathers, a black collar separates neck from abdomen; abdomen white; undertail coverts mottled brown and white; flanks white, freckled with brown; wing has glossy green coverts, primaries dark-brown with a broad white subterminal bar, secondaries have white tip; bill black; legs and feet olive-green; iris bright red.

ADULT FEMALE. Differs from male in being less green on the back, lacks the white collar and white bar across wings; it has a distinct brown eye stripe, and the breast is much barred with fine brown marks; iris brown.

IMMATURE: Juveniles of both sexes are similar to females, but have no green gloss at all, and the dark eye stripe is more distinct.

DUCKLING. Hind neck, back and tail, dark brown; underside light grey; underside of tail dark grey to black at tip; crown of head dark brown; face light grey, there is a dark-brown eye stripe; wing dark brown above and grey below with white trailing edge; bill, dark-

Green Pigmy Geese. *Upper*: Male in centre of water-lily lagoon, Humpty Doo, N.T. *Lower*: Small group feeding on pondweeds at the edge of a lagoon.

Photos by author

White Pigmy Geese near Townsville, north Queensland. *Photo by Ederic Slater*

grey culmen, yellow mandible; legs and feet dark grey with some yellow on webs.

Plumage

According to Phillips and later authors, the male of the Asiatic race assumes an eclipse plumage after breeding and retains it throughout the non-breeding season. The male in eclipse plumage is described as follows: "he resembles the female, losing the black collar and becoming mottled on head and breast with brown, but he retains the white band on the wing and some of his green gloss". No specimen of the Australian race in eclipse plumage has yet been secured and Lavery, who has seen fully coloured adult males at all seasons of the year, doubts if it exists. However, it would be remarkable if the Australian race had completely lost the eclipse plumage, and it is still possible that an eclipse exists, which is not strikingly different to the breeding plumage, and has not yet been detected. Only very recently has there been evidence that an eclipse plumage probably exists in the Green Pigmy Goose, a species that has been handled in very much greater numbers than the White Pigmy Goose.

Size

	Weight gm.	*Length** mm.	*Wing* mm.	*Bill* mm.
Adult Male				
Maximum	495	378	188	26
Minimum	311	355	172	25
Average	403	368	177	24
Number measured	*52*	*12*	*18*	*18*
Adult Female				
Maximum	439	376	186	26
Minimum	255	336	161	23
Average	380	363	174	24
Number measured	*37*	*9*	*15*	*15*

*The only published figures[69] refer to the distance between the tip of the bill and the vent (male 311-495 mm., average 403 mm.; female 255-439 mm., average 380 mm.). For the sake of uniformity in this book these are adjusted by adding the mean measurement from vent to tail tip of 31 museum skins.

Voice

The male has a loud staccato cackle uttered continuously in flight, but the female has only a very soft quack. There is no recording of the sounds.

Routine

The White Pigmy Goose is completely aquatic and only leaves the water to clamber onto fallen logs, as does the Green Pigmy Goose. The birds are usually found in pairs, or small groups, but flocks of up to one hundred occur in the dry season. Their general behaviour, in my limited experence, is very similar to that of the Green Pigmy Goose; they spend most of their time floating among water-lilies during the day and only coming near the shore in the early morning and late afternoon to feed. They fly swiftly and usually low down.

Field Recognition

White Pigmy Geese are usually found in pairs or small groups on water, frequently associated with other waterfowl. They are more often found in compact groups than are Green Pigmy Geese, but otherwise have very similar general behaviour, swimming in and out among the water-lilies and occasionally clambering out onto dead timber or mudbanks to rest.

On the water it is a small duck that floats high, and the males can be distinguished from those of Green Pigmy Geese by the white neck contrasted with the very dark one of the latter species and by the face being mainly white, so the striking contrast of the white face patch of the Green Pigmy Goose is not seen. The females of the two species are very difficult to distinguish on the water at a distance, apart from the fact that the Green Pigmy Goose is darker on the back and crown and the eye stripe is not so distinct. At short range the female White Pigmy Goose has a brown, not green, back and the white over the eye is obvious.

In flight, in addition to the white neck of the male, the white on the wing immediately distinguishes the two species. In the Green Pigmy Goose this is near the base of the wing, in the White Pigmy Goose it is near the tip. When overhead the white neck and throat, as well as the position of the white bars on the wing, still distinguish it readily from the Green Pigmy Goose.

In flight male White Pigmy Geese usually utter, continuously, a rapid staccato trumpeting, while Green Pigmy Geese almost always keep up a continuous chirrup.

Relationships

The relationship of the pigmy geese to the other waterfowl of the world has been described in the life history of the Green Pigmy Goose.

The White Pigmy Goose is an Asiatic species that has a wide range in that continent, Malaysia, and Indonesia, and in New Guinea and north-east Australia. Two subspecies have been recognized on the basis of size, birds from Australia being slightly larger than those from elsewhere.

Nettapus c. coromandelianus, the nominate subspecies, is common throughout India, where its main numbers are in Bengal. It is also common in Ceylon, Burma, Malaya, Thailand, and Vietnam, and in China as far north as Peking. It is also found in the Philippines, Borneo, Java, Sumatra, Celebes, and northern New Guinea.

N. c. albipennis, the Australian race, is restricted to north-east Australia, but formerly existed down the Queensland and New South Wales coasts, where occasional vagrants still occur.

Habitat

According to Lavery the principal habitats of the White Pigmy Goose are:

> . . . the deep lagoons associated with rivers and creeks along the coastal plains; these often are simulated by earth tanks and dams constructed as stock-watering sites, which in time become heavily vegetated with two predominant plant groups of lagoons–the blue waterlilies (*Nymphaea* species) and the submerged and floating aquatics such as hydrilla (*Hydrilla verticillata* Casp.), hornwort (*Coratophyllum domersum* L.), eelgrass (*Vallisneria* sp.), bushy pondweed (*Najas graminae* Del.), duckweed (*Lemna oligorrhiza* Kurz.), algae (*Chara* sp.), and others.

Other habitats noted by Lavery, frequently with both pigmy geese present, are the relatively few large freshwater lakes existing permanently within the species' range—for example, at "Valley of Lagoons" west of Ingham—and also the long deep rivers and small isolated creeks edged with water-lilies, water-snowflake *Nymphoides indica,* and, in particular, pondweeds of the *Potamogeton* species, which grow profusely during the drier months of the year. Finally there are the many shallow freshwater swamps, with their wide variety of vegetation, notably bulkuru sedge *Eleocharis dulcis.* Lavery further notes that swamps and creeks are inhabited during wet seasons, lagoons during the wet and early stages of dry seasons, and rivers and lakes mainly in the later months of dry seasons, that is, from September to November.

Distribution and Movements

The Asiatic race has a wide range, but, in many parts, its status is not well known. India is the undoubted stronghold and, according to Salim Ali,[2] it is common in most parts of the subcontinent,

Key to Plate V

DOWNY DUCKLINGS

1. Mountain Duck.
2. Magpie Goose.
3. Black Swan.
4. Cape Barren Goose.
5. Burdekin Duck.
6. Wood Duck.
7. Water Whistle-duck.
8. White Pigmy Goose.
9. Green Pigmy Goose.
10. Grass Whistle-duck.
11. Blue-billed Duck.
12. Musk Duck.
13. Freckled Duck.
14. Chestnut Teal.
15. Grey Teal.
16. Black Duck.
17. Pink-eared Duck.
18. Shoveler.
19. Hardhead.

B.T.W. 1965

being rare or absent only in the desert regions of Pakistan, Punjab, Sind, Baluchistan, and Rajputana. It is found wherever there is water, being especially numerous in the deltaic regions of Bengal, and has been recorded as far into the Himalayas as Bhutan. It is found throughout the lowlands of Ceylon[54] and throughout Burma.[5] It is not common in the Malay Peninsula, but might be found wherever there is water.[15] It occurs in Thailand and Vietnam, but there are no reliable notes on its status there. In China it occurs as far north as the Yangtze River and has been recorded in at least the following provinces of southern China, Kweichow, Yunnan, Fukien, and Kwantung, and as vagrants in Hainan and Taiwan.[95] In many of these places it is a summer migrant, but its breeding distribution is not well described. In Indonesia it is known only from Sumatra and West Java. In Borneo it is occasionally seen in Sarawak as a passage migrant and in Sabah, but there is no record from Kalimantan.[90] In the Philippines it is known to breed only in Northern Luzon, and in New Guinea it is known only on the Sepik River.[78]

In most of its range it is sedentary, but the northern populations, in China, are to some extent migratory and move south in the winter. This migratory tendency has led to some doubt as to its status in New Guinea where it has been infrequently collected, and earlier workers have inferred that it is a migrant from Asia, returning to breed in that continent. Seventeen specimens collected on the Sepik River in 1929 during the Northern Hemisphere breeding season were assumed to be winter migrants that had happened to remain in New Guinea. There is now evidence, however, that the White Pigmy Geese are present throughout the year in New Guinea. W. B. Hitchcock and K. Keith of the C.S.I.R.O. Division of Wildlife Research have collected in the Sepik district each year between 1961 and 1965. They have worked on the immense Chambrai Lake in the months of March, May, June, and December and seen White Pigmy Geese each time. I have inspected the lake from the air in November and also seen White Pigmy Geese. Two males collected there on 7th December 1962 had enlarged testes indicating breeding. In view of these observations there seems to be no reason to assume that the bird is not a permanent resident in New Guinea, even though no nest has yet been reported there.

The distribution and status of the Australian race has long been uncertain and confused and it is only in recent years that some accuracy has been brought into the discussion, mainly since Lavery began his systematic work based on Townsville, Queensland. Gould was unable to learn anything of its distribution north of Moreton

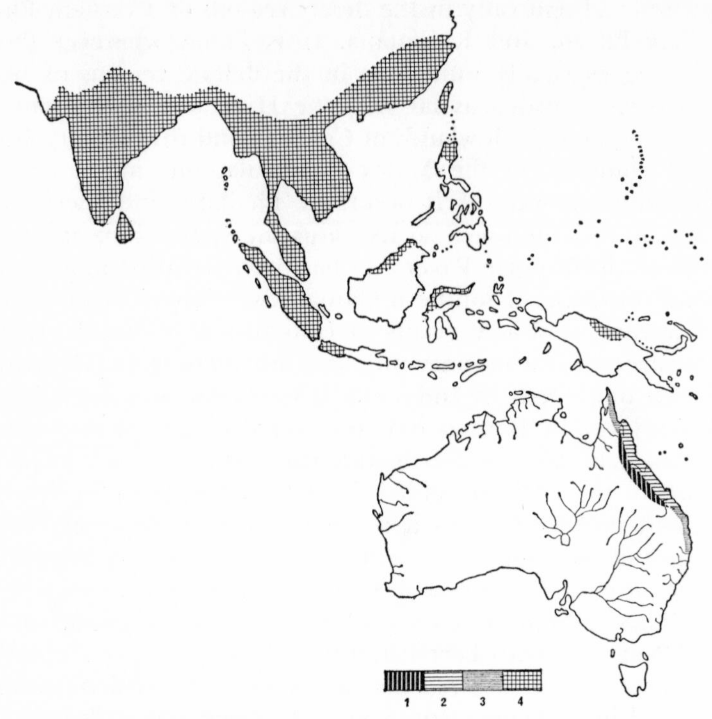

DISTRIBUTION OF THE WHITE PIGMY GOOSE

The square shading (No. 4) shows the range of *N. c. coromandelianus.* The linear shading shows the range of the Australian Pigmy Goose *N. c. albipennis*; the breeding range is shown by the darkest shading (No. 1); and the birds are distributed throughout the area with intermediate shading (No. 2) at other times, but rarely breed there. Vagrants occur in the areas with the lightest shading (No. 3).

Bay, but recorded that it was "tolerably abundant on the eastern portions of the Australian continent, inhabiting estuaries and rivers between the ranges and the coast from the Hunter to Moreton Bay". Although Gould was uncertain of its northern distribution his collector Gilbert was not and had noted it in the Burdekin Valley far to the north of Moreton Bay.[16] I have been unable to trace the source of Gould's information that it once extended as far south as the Hunter River. It is possible that vagrants did come down so far occasionally, though the habitat he mentions, "estuaries and rivers", is not typical of that favoured by the species today. The numbers mentioned—"tolerably abundant" for a district where the bird now occurs only in the northern part, and then as a very rare vagrant—suggest a great decline in its status in New South Wales.

According to Keartland, it occurred in the Northern Territory and was commoner than the Green Pigmy Goose in the eastern parts of the area. This is the only record of the bird in the Northern Territory and there is no other evidence that it has ever occurred even as far west as the west coast of Cape York Peninsula. One is fairly safe in assuming that Keartland was mistaken as to the species he discussed.

Jones[63] examined published records of its distribution and concluded that its original range was from the Clarence River, New South Wales, to Cardwell, Queensland, but he was unable to locate any incontestable records of its occurrence anywhere since 1895, an astonishing result when, at that time, the bird was quite numerous close to major towns and in some heavily settled districts. He concluded that the bird was possibly "exceedingly rare in Australia, and perhaps does not now occur there", and it "may be that the species has been vanquished throughout its known Australian districts". Happily not only have these dire forebodings been shown to be unfounded, but the bird has been found to be not uncommon in a range far exceeding that described.

The distribution in Australia is shown by Delacour to include the whole of Cape York, but he does not quote the authority for this westward extension of its range. Perhaps it was derived from Keartland's incorrect report. There is no evidence that the bird has ever been seen west of the Dividing Range on the Cape itself; north of Townsville it is strictly confined to the narrow coastal strip a few miles wide.

Although occasional birds may have been seen as far south as the Hunter River, the primitive distribution of the White Pigmy Goose seems to have extended from the Clarence River, where it was not uncommon in the Ulmarra Swamps, and the Richmond River, where until the mid 1930s it was an uncommon but fairly regular item in shooters' bags, wherever deep freshwater swamps occurred, to the tip of Cape York Peninsula. Reasoning from the distribution of suitable habitat, as well as the old records in this region, there were probably two particularly favourable areas, the northern rivers of New South Wales—the Tweed, Richmond, and Clarence—and the general neighbourhood of the Burdekin River, from Ayr to Ingham, North Queensland. Elsewhere there is little suitable habitat and the bird was probably never common, if it occurred at all.

The present-day range is similar, but the southern concentration has been destroyed by drainage and agriculture. It still visits north-eastern New South Wales, but rarely and as a vagrant, and does not breed there. The most recent records in the area are of one bird at Tucki on the Richmond River in 1956 and a pair shot at Tuckeyan Swamp on the same river in 1955; I saw the birds in each case. A further pair was reported near Murwillumbah, Tweed River, in 1964. It is occasionally seen near Brisbane, but elsewhere south of Bowen, north Queensland, there have been no recent reliable records. North of Ingham, Queensland, it occurs in small numbers wherever suitable habitat occurs, but is not common. In 1963 I travelled overland to the northern extremity of Cape York and returned by air. It was seen that suitable habitat for pigmy geese was restricted to a few isolated places in a very narrow strip near the coast, between the rain-forest and mangroves, and was very sparse. There is no reason to believe that pigmy geese were ever more abundant there than they are today, since the country, particularly the wetlands in the area, is virtually in its virgin state.

From Lavery's surveys in the Burdekin region, there is little doubt that the stronghold of the species today is from Rockhampton to Ingham, with the greatest numbers in the Ayr, Townsville, and Charters Towers district. Although not numerous, the bird is distributed throughout this district and is regularly encountered. In the immediate vicinity of Townsville a dry-season concentration of about three hundred birds regularly occurs. Smaller groups occur elsewhere, the largest of these recently seen was of a hundred near Charters Towers in March 1962.

Nothing substantial is known of the movement pattern, but the main local movements can be inferred from the annual cycle near Townsville. Here the local numbers increase each dry season, usually the concentration begins in February and March, and the numbers then decline to zero each wet season. The period of local abundance varies from year to year according to the rainfall. It was extended in 1959, an abnormally wet year, when the birds were present from March until November, there being abundant habitat in the area, but in a drought, in 1961, there was no concentration and only ten birds were in the area. No evidence of breeding has been seen near the coast, but ducklings have been seen several times inland near Charters Towers, and these events suggested to Lavery that the species retreats inland to breed. Although the present evidence for this is not substantial, the distribution map is drawn on that assumption.

From the above evidence it is probable that the White Pigmy

Goose is quite local and moves to a regular pattern according to the rainfall and consequent distribution of habitat. During the wet season White Pigmy Geese are comparatively widely dispersed inland and breeding. At the end of the wet, and as the inland waters decline or dry, they concentrate on the more permanent waters near the coast, to disperse again when the inland waters are renewed. Such a movement pattern is quite similar to that of many other ducks but on a much smaller scale both in numbers and distance.

Breeding

The breeding behaviour of the Australian race—or, for that matter, of the Asiatic race—has not yet been recorded. There is little information available on the breeding season or the factors that control it, but what there is is quite consistent with that recorded for most other tropical coastal waterfowl.

All clutches from the southern end of its range held in Australian Museums were collected in spring and early summer. The breeding season in that region was undoubtedly in the period September to November. From north Queensland broods have been recorded at ages that showed the eggs were laid in February and March, and a pair shot in December, in full breeding condition, suggested breeding in that month or January. There is no doubt that the main breeding season is in the period January to March, that is, from the middle to the end of the wet season. The nominate race in India breeds in the period June to September, but most nests are begun in July and August, the wet season, and when the rain begins early so does the nesting of the pigmy geese. The breeding season of the White Pigmy Geese seems to be timed to occur when the swamps are full after the wet season and breeding habitat, ultimately provided by rainfall, is abundant.

Feeding

The White Pigmy Goose is completely aquatic, as is the Green Pigmy Goose, and its feeding behaviour is similar. It cruises through the vegetation, frequently making short forward flights, but is more often in groups and perhaps not so pugnacious as the Green Pigmy Goose. The feeding actions are similar, dabbling the surface of the water or stripping the seeds and inflorescences from aquatic plants. It is frequently seen to dart its head deliberately at insects, an action I have not seen with Green Pigmy Geese, and it has not been seen diving for food as the latter species frequently does.

The food is almost entirely vegetable in origin, and in 77

gizzards collected on the coastal plains plant materials accounted for 99 per cent of the total food.[69] Pondweeds were by far the most important and accounted for 54 per cent of the total, *hydrilla* for 18 per cent, and the seeds of aquatic grasses, mainly barnyard-grass, for 12 per cent. The remainder was made up of a wide variety of seeds and other parts of aquatic plants. In a smaller sample of 12 birds, taken in the inland, there was very little pondweed, its place was taken by various sedges and a few insects were also eaten, providing 11 per cent of the total food.

It is of some interest how the pigmy geese, two very closely related species of similar size, general ecology and feeding habits, can coexist in the same habitat. The food found in the gizzards, though the samples are very small, does begin to suggest differences in food preferences. In 77 gizzards of the White Pigmy Goose from the coastal plains of north Queensland the food was similar to that in 32 gizzards of the Green Pigmy Goose from the same district, but there were two quite striking differences—the Green Pigmy Geese had eaten 30 per cent by volume of water-lilies and the White Pigmy Geese only one per cent, but the White had eaten 53 per cent of *Potamogeton* compared to only 11 per cent in the Green.[69] The two species probably have different food niches, the Green being more dependent on water-lilies and the White on *Potamogeton* and, in the dry season, on products of swamps rather than of lagoons.

Nest

The nominate race nests in elevated sites up to thirty feet from the ground, nearly always very close to water, but they have been found as far as two hundred yards away. The usual site is a tree-hole, usually in the trunk and rarely in a hollow branch. They also nest in holes in houses, temples, and ruined chimneys, in fact, in almost any elevated site.

Very few nests have been described in Australia and these have also all been in trees, but apart from this no detail has been recorded. In the Asiatic race, and probably also the Australian, the eggs are laid on the bare wood or debris in the hole and very little down is added.

Clutch Size

There are very few data on the clutch size. According to Delacour, the Indian race lays 8 to 15 eggs. Clutches of the Australian race as large as 16 and as small as 6 have been recorded.

Eggs

The eggs are pearly white, broad ovals without pointed ends. Very few measurements have been published; 30 eggs from four clutches measured in length 46-49 mm. (average 47 mm.) and in breadth 34-36 (average 35 mm.).

Incubation

The incubation time has not been recorded.

Status

The White Pigmy Goose has no effect on agriculture and is not a game bird. In north Queensland it is protected by law and is not shot; in northern New South Wales, although also protected, the rare vagrants are very liable to be shot on sight, as curiosities, so recolonization of the few remaining suitable areas of habitat in this district is unlikely under present conditions.

It is a rare and very beautiful bird and is content to live in closely settled districts, provided a few lagoons remain undrained. It is fortunate that in the tropical region, where it now remains, lagoon drainage is not so widespread as in other districts, and as newly constructed earth dams and impoundments quickly develop deep-water flora the amount of habitat can be easily increased, and is increased to some extent by normal agricultural and pastoral practices.

It has declined greatly in over-all range, but where it still persists it does so in reasonable numbers. The race is restricted to Australia and practically to one part of one State. As the custodians of most of the world population of the Australian race of the White Pigmy Goose, a solemn responsibility rests on the Queensland Government to preserve it.

Source of Data

I am indebted to Mr H. J. Lavery, Department of Primary Industry, Queensland, whose unpublished thesis[69] (University of Queensland) has been freely used in the preparation of the above account. My own experience with White Pigmy Geese in the wild is slight.

Blue-billed Duck

Oxyura australis Gould

References

Oxyura Bonaparte, Ann. Lyc. Nat. Hist. N.Y., 2, p. 390, 1828.
Oxyura australis Gould, P.Z.S. 1836, p. 85, 1837. (Swan River, W.A.)

Other Names

Blue-bill, Stiff-tail, Spine-tail, Diver, Diving-duck.

Description

ADULT MALE. Head and neck glossy black, sometimes with a chestnut tinge; foreneck, upper breast, flanks and back, rich chestnut; remainder of underside brown, flecked with black or dark brown; undertail black; tail coverts brownish black, flecked with chestnut; upper side of tail black; wings dark brown; bill, culmen slate-blue, sometimes vivid, lower mandible cream with brown centre; legs and feet grey; iris dark brown.

MALE IN ECLIPSE. Head loses the glossy black and becomes black and grey speckled; chin grey with some black speckles; breast loses chestnut and is dark grey, with each feather edged with pale brown; crown black, much speckled with light brown; upper neck black and grey speckled; back and scapulars lose chestnut and are dark brown, each feather fringed with light brown; bill slate-grey; legs and feet grey.

ADULT FEMALE. General colour above blackish brown, each feather barred with narrow bands of light brown; topside of tail black; chin and throat brown, speckled with black; foreneck, breast, and abdomen, mottled light brown and black, each feather being black with light tip; bill grey-brown; legs and feet grey-brown; iris brown.

IMMATURE. The immature plumage of both sexes resembles that of the female but is paler in colour; bill grey-green; legs and feet grey-brown; iris brown.

DUCKLING. Topside of head, neck, and back and tail, dark brown; there is a lighter brown line extending from eye backwards; underside light brown, except for neck and upper breast, which are dark brown; wings dark brown above, pale brown below; bills, legs and feet dark grey.

Plumage

It has long been known that the North American Ruddy Duck *Oxyura jamaicensis* enters eclipse plumage after breeding and, unlike most other ducks, in which the eclipse lasts only a short time, retains it throughout most of the winter.[67] That the Blue-billed Duck also has a similar sequence of moults and an eclipse plumage is reported here for the first time.

After the breeding season most birds leave the breeding swamps and congregate on large lakes and swamps elsewhere. Some males undergo the post-nuptial moult in the breeding swamps, but the majority do so in the winter flocking areas. The post-nuptial moult begins in December and most males have undergone it by March, though an occasional bird is still moulting in May. The moult involves the body, wings, and tail, and the duller eclipse or winter plumage is assumed. The pre-nuptial moult begins in July and the breeding plumage is assumed once more. In this period, unlike many other ducks, many males also change their wing and tail feathers again.

In females the post-nuptial moult begins in January and is complete by February and the pre-nuptial moult, involving the body feathers, occurs in June and July. That is, in females the moult periods are less extended than in the males.

Size

	Weight gm.	*Length* mm.	*Wingspread* mm.	*Wing* mm.	*Bill* mm.
Adult Male					
Maximum	965	440	692	173	48
Minimum	610	352	550	150	37
Average	812	409	606	160	41
Number measured	*241*	*236*	*205*	*222*	*231*
Adult Female					
Maximum	1300	441	630	163	47
Minimum	476	366	550	142	32
Average	852	403	600	153	41
Number measured	*140*	*124*	*104*	*121*	*122*

Voice

Blue-billed Ducks very rarely make any sound and the full range of calls has not been recorded. The female in alarm utters a weak quack. The male in display has a rapid, low-pitched, rattling note.

Relationships

The Blue-billed Duck is classified as a member of the Stiff-tailed Ducks, the tribe Oxyurini of the subfamily Anatinae. Stiff-tails are rather different to other ducks: the tail feathers are stiff, spine-like, and capable of erection, there is a distinct lobe on the hind toe, the neck is always short and thick and its skin is loose and can be inflated during display, and the trachea has no bulla.

The tribe includes four genera; three of them are monotypic, *Heteronetta* of South America, *Thassalornis* of Africa and Madagascar, and *Biziura*, the Australian Musk Duck. The other six species of the tribe belong to the genus *Oxyura* and are very similar in general appearance and habits. They are distributed throughout the world, but are most common in the Americas, which have three species; Africa, Australia, and Eurasia have one species each.

The Blue-billed Duck is uniform throughout its range and no races have been recognized.

Routine

During the winter many Blue-billed Ducks congregate in flocks of a thousand or more on large lakes and swamps; one unusually large concentration of eight thousand has been seen. At these times they prefer to remain in large rafts far from the shore during the day, they may be associated with very large numbers of Coots, *Fulica atra*, and overlooked. They move closer to the shore and feed by repeatedly diving in late afternoon and early morning.

In summer, in the breeding swamps, Blue-billed Ducks inhabit the densest places available and are very secretive. They are found in the deep, quiet pools among the tall cumbungi far from the shore. They swim silently along the edges of dense cover, are very alert, and dive swiftly with scarcely a ripple at the first hint of danger. They are very rarely seen without special and careful search, and this difficulty of observing them has led to exaggerated and erroneous ideas of their rarity; they are, in fact, common in most suitable habitat.

They are completely aquatic and, although they occasionally clamber onto a fallen log or cumbungi clump to rest or cross a mudbank from one pool to another, are rarely seen out of the water. Lowe has watched one repeatedly climbing onto a log and diving, presumably in play. On land they are awkward and almost helpless and can only move by propelling the abdomen along the ground. They swim swiftly and low in the water and dive repeatedly and expertly, to surface behind cover or twenty yards or more away, swimming rapidly.

In dense swamps they seldom fly, but occasionally do so, though when alarmed they prefer to escape by diving. In winter concentrations they fly more frequently and, in clear lakes, commonly escape by flying. Their take-off is laborious, the birds pattering along the surface for several yards, but once airborne they fly swiftly and well, though in a decidedly tail-heavy manner.

Field Recognition

In flight the Blue-billed Duck is most easily identified by posture, the tail-heavy appearance, and the very rapid, noisy beat of the wings.

On the water it appears as a small dark bird floating very low in the water; the head is heavy and the body compact. Males can be immediately distinguished by the brilliant blue bill and the stiff, erect tail. It can sometimes, but should not, be confused with the Coot and the Hardhead. The Coot floats much higher on the water and the bill lacks the brilliant blue colour, though in some lights it does appear bluish. The Coot's head, even at a distance, is also obviously smaller than that of the Blue-billed Duck. The Hardhead sometimes floats quite as low in the water as the Blue-billed Duck, and a very dark-coloured male can seem similar in appearance. Again the blue bill is the best distinguishing mark.

Females lack the blue colour of the bill but are easily identified by their characteristic shape. They are only a fraction of the size of female Musk Ducks, but apart from this size difference could be confused without due care.

Habitat

In winter Blue-billed Ducks congregate in large flocks and can then be seen in large clear lakes and on open water. For most of the year, however, they are confined to deep, densely vegetated swamps. The cover varies with the locality. In the inland it is nearly always cumbungi, though they sometimes occur in lignum swamps in small numbers; in coastal districts dense tea-tree thickets are favoured. Very occasionally a Blue-billed Duck can be found, and even breeding, in a river frontage, billabong, or flood-filled depression on the plains.

Distribution and Movements

Blue-billed Ducks are found throughout the better-watered parts of southern Australia wherever there is suitable habitat. It is a shy and retiring species and is not often observed in the dense vegetation that forms its habitat, unless a special and careful search is made. Consequently details of its exact range and numerical status are not certain. It is, however, much more common and widespread than is usually supposed. In the Murray-Darling Basin, for instance, in suit-

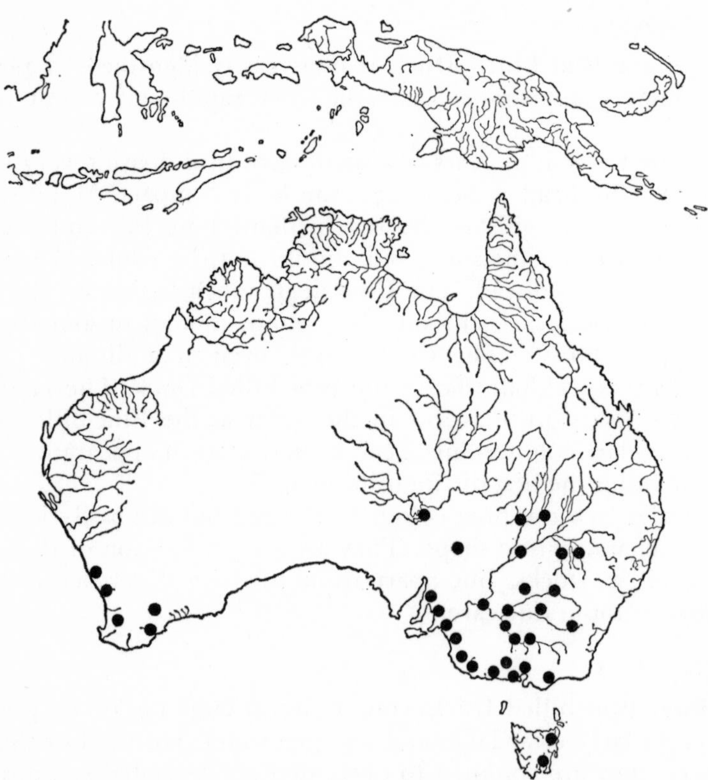

DISTRIBUTION OF THE BLUE-BILLED DUCK

The spots indicate districts in which the Blue-billed Duck is a permanent resident wherever suitable habitat occurs. No attempt is made to show every record for each district, in the interests of clarity.

Upper: Male (right) and female Musk Ducks, showing normal swimming posture. *Photo by author*

Lower: Male Musk Duck diving. Note powerful upward thrust of legs. *Photo by Ederic Slater*

Female Blue-billed Duck diving and swimming under water. As with the Musk Duck, diving and propulsion are entirely by the legs. *Photo by Ederic Slater*

able habitat, it can only be described as numerous and is found in every permanent swamp.

Its movements are basically regular, but have not been studied in detail, so it is not known to what extent the individual birds move. Wherever the numbers have been regularly observed on a given swamp they fluctuate annually. The most complete observations are those of J. Wheeler at Lake Wendouree, Ballarat, who has watched the birds for ten years.[99] Here the birds arrive each July or August and depart again in April or May, having bred in the meantime. The numbers present vary from year to year and are greater in the drier years. In 1958, a year of drought in eastern Australia, the greatest numbers were present on Lake Wendouree and they remained throughout the whole year. In 1955, a year of general rain, no birds came to the lake until January 1956—after the breeding season. At another near-coastal swamp, Bibra Lake near Perth, J. Ford also noted a regular rise and fall in numbers.[33] The birds increase in numbers in the lake each summer. In a wet year they disappeared completely during the winter, but in a dry year remained throughout the winter.

At Griffith, New South Wales, there is also a similar pattern of concentration. Blue-billed Ducks are numerous in the large cumbungi swamp, Barrenbox, and breed in large numbers. Here we have been engaged in a field study of the birds. Although, owing to the size of the swamp and its very dense vegetation, it is not possible to secure an accurate count of the birds, it has been noted each year that they decrease in numbers very greatly during the months of May, June, and July. The disappearance and later reappearance are abrupt and striking. At these times great but passing concentrations of Blue-billed Ducks appear on Lake Wyangan, a small open lake in the same district, and one such group numbered several thousands. These flocks are usually too great to be concentrations of local birds and are clearly flocks in passage.

A similar situation exists in the large swamps of the Murray River. Here Lowe has drawn attention to a great influx of Blue-billed Ducks to Kangaroo Lake and other lakes near Kerang each winter, flocks numbering up to a thousand being apparent.[73] John Hobbs noted similar conditions on Yanga Lake, Fletchers Lake, and other water areas farther down the river.[58] In all cases the situation is similar: where the habitat is suitable there is a resident breeding population and each winter an influx containing many juvenile birds arrives in May or June and departs again in August or September.

Impressed by the fact that these more southern concentrations occur at the time of the apparent decrease in numbers in inland New South Wales, a survey of the deep lakes in inland New South Wales —Wyangan, Barrenbox, Cowal, Brewster, and Cargelligo—was made in July 1965, and the situation compared with that on Kangaroo Lake. It was found that great numbers existed on the Murray River, but that the birds were uncommon on all the more northern lakes, in some of which a few weeks earlier they had been very numerous. A sample of birds collected near Kerang included adults, juveniles just assuming adult plumage, and eclipse males.

There is no longer any doubt that the Blue-billed Duck undertakes a partial migration each year, leaving the swamps of inland New South Wales to concentrate and moult on the Murray River and doubtless in more southern districts. The movement is not complete, since some birds remain in inland New South Wales at all times and some are resident and breeding in the wintering areas. It is, however, more complete, and more regular, and more closely resembles true migration, than the movement of any other Australian duck so far studied.

Despite this regular movement pattern the Blue-billed Duck has some nomadic tendency to occupy new areas of habitat as they are formed following floods. On the plains west of Booligal and south of Hay, New South Wales, where deep lignum swamps and creeks occur after floods and heavy rain, a few Blue-bills usually occupy them and sometimes breed there. They are, however, very much less commonly found to have undertaken such movements than are Musk Ducks.

It has been described how many inland waterfowl, such as Grey Teal and Pink-eared Ducks, take part in mass irruptions during inland droughts,[43] but this does not seem to occur so commonly with Blue-billed Ducks. During the large irruption of 1957 Blue-bills were not reported beyond their normal range, but some very large concentrations developed within it. However, despite the overall regularity of the birds' movements they can be modified by the climate. In dry years the numbers wintering on the Murray River and in Victoria are much greater than usual, and when there is abundant rainfall inland the movement south is comparatively small.

Feeding

Blue-billed Ducks are diving ducks and secure most of their food from the bottom of the swamp, diving deeply and skilfully and swimming under water. During the process they are often caught in gill nets set for fish. During dives they have been seen to remain under water for up to 30 seconds, but most commonly stay down for 10 to 15 seconds. I have seen them diving in water up to ten feet deep. In addition to diving, they swim alongside banks where plants overhang the deep water, stripping seeds and other parts, and frequently dabble after food items on the water surface. In cumbungi swamps there are numerous small islands of matted rotting cumbungi stalks on which many dry-land plants grow, so the presence of these plants in Blue-billed Ducks' stomachs does not necessarily indicate feeding close to the shore or in shallow water.

The stomach contents of 352 Blue-billed Ducks collected in Barrenbox Swamp, in all months of the year, showed that the food eaten was of about equal proportions of animal and vegetable material, 53 per cent plants and 47 per cent animal. Every stomach contained some plant items and all but four of them contained some animal material. There was a suggestion of a trend for less animal material to be eaten in autumn than at other seasons, but apart from this tendency, which might not prove significant in a larger sample, there were only minor variations from month to month, according to the cycle of abundance of various plant products.

The plant material eaten was very diverse and included seeds, buds, leaves, and stems of representatives of over twenty families of plants, but no one plant was of overriding importance, and no one family provided more than 6 per cent of the total food. About 4 per cent of the food was seeds of dry-land plants, including saffron thistle, clovers, and bindweed, all presumably collected from floating islands; 9 per cent of the food consisted of smartweeds, sedges, and nardoo, characteristic of water less than two feet deep, and the remainder of the plant food was derived from deep-water plants.

The plants that were most important, providing 6 per cent or more of the food, were the smartweeds found in half the stomachs, the submerged aquatic water-milfoil *Myriophyllum*, and duckweed *Azolla*, which was in 60 per cent of the stomachs. The only other individually important plant, which made up 4 per cent of the total food, was barnyard-grass *Echinochloa*. The remainder of the plant food consisted of a large number of plants, each of which, whilst only making up 1-2 per cent of the total volume of food, was found in 30 per cent or more of the stomachs, that is, they were very widely eaten but usually not in great quantities. These included algae, nardoo, ribbonweeds, pondweeds, knotweeds, thistles, legumes, and willow seed.

The animals eaten were all of small size, less than half an inch in length, and although they included a few spiders, mites, molluscs and crustaceans, were nearly all of insect origin; these insects provided 90 per cent of the total volume of animal food and were found in every stomach. The most important insect food was the aquatic larvae of Chironomidae, midges, which in some months were in every stomach and in no month were in less than 60 per cent of those examined; they comprised 25 per cent of the total food eaten, or half the total animals. This group of aquatic flies with free-swimming larvae are very common in inland cumbungi swamps and at times, particularly in summer, great concentrations of larvae are seen and hatchings of adults occur. Other valuable animal foods were the larvae of caddis-flies Trichoptera and of dragon-flies Odonata, each of which was found in most stomachs and contributed about 10 per cent of the total food.

The same water-beetles and water-boatmen that form a great part of the food of Dabbling Ducks were eaten by Blue-billed Ducks and were found in 30 per cent and 50 per cent of the stomachs respectively, but in over-all assessment they were not very important as they only provided 6 per cent and 2 per cent of the total food eaten.

Breeding

The courtship of the Blue-billed Duck has been studied in some detail by Mr J. R. Wheeler at Lake Wendouree, Ballarat, and this account is based largely on his notes.

The courtship display is vigorous and elaborate.[99] In an open pool and in the presence of the female the male splashes backwards suddenly with both feet and then springs erect, almost standing on the tail, with the head bent and bill pressed into the breast feathers. In this position the head and bill are rapidly jerked up and down. Finally the male gives a shallow dive and then the whole sequence is repeated several times. Suddenly the body is straightened out, and with the tail feathers held erect as a fan, the bird rocks vigorously up and down, dipping the head in and out of the water. The performance concludes with submerging the head and tail, arching the back, and skidding backwards for several feet. No other duck is quite so spectacular as this.

Copulation follows a vigorous chase; the male pursues the female across and around the pool at high speed and often completely under water. They frequently surface and fight in a flurry of water for a second or two, then submerge and rush on. Finally the male is able to, or allowed to, overtake, and copulation is effected with the female completely submerged. Finally the birds separate and vigorously preen the whole body.

The nest is built by the female, who is often then deserted by the male. Sometimes he remains and apparently defends the nest area and subsequently, when the female leads off the brood, sails along as escort in the rear. The female drives off intruding coots and other birds by fluffing the feathers and, with head moving backwards and forwards, swimming swiftly at the offender in a menacing manner, hissing.

So far as is known the breeding season is quite regular throughout the range of the species. At Ballarat J. Wheeler has recorded broods each year between October and March, which indicates that the eggs were laid between September and February, but most clutches were begun in September, October, and November. All the clutches from inland and south-east Australia in the collections of Australian Museums were collected in these months also. Farther afield, near Perth, Western Australia, R. Taylor has found all his nests in September, October, and November in a region having a very definite winter rainfall peak, unlike the irregular rainfall of the inland.

At Barrenbox Swamp regular monthly samples of Blue-billed Ducks have been collected throughout the past three years and their sexual state examined. Although the water-level in the swamp differed very greatly during the period the sexual cycle followed the same timetable each year. Even in 1964, when the swamp fell to a very low level indeed, neither the proportion of the population breeding nor the timing of the breeding season was noticeably affected. Presumably the Blue-billed Duck, unlike most other inland waterbirds, has a regular breeding season.

In males, each year the testes began to increase in size, and the spermatic tubules in diameter, in July. They reached their greatest size in December and thereafter underwent post-breeding regression. The testes of many birds contained sperms in late July, and those of most (85 per cent) in October, but few were producing sperms in November. The males then were capable of reproduction between July and October each year and were apparently controlled by a regular internal or external stimulus. The females were not sexually active for so long as the males. The first increase in the size of the oocytes occurred in August and the average size was greatest in September; thereafter it declined until by December no birds had enlarged oocytes, egg-laying having ceased. From this it is apparent that most females lay in late August, September, and October. The clutches and broods found in the area confirm this breeding season.

The pattern observed in Blue-billed Ducks is quite typical of birds with regular breeding seasons. The males are sexually active for a long period of potentially suitable time, perhaps their sexual cycle being mainly controlled by fixed seasonal factors. The females, however, control the actual breeding season and confine egg-laying to the most favourable time, probably receiving their stimulus partly from the displaying males but largely from less regular factors in the environment.

The study is continuing to determine the factors that control the breeding season and what advantage is conferred on the Blue-billed Duck by regular spring breeding. Of course, living in permanent swamps, it has the least need of any inland waterfowl to vary the breeding season annually.

Development of Young

After hatching the young remain in the nest for one day and may return to it for several days to rest. The young are led from the nest by the female; I have never seen a male with a brood, but J. Wheeler has observed one brood accompanied by both male and female. The young feed entirely by diving or dabbling the surface and in this respect, unlike young Musk Ducks, which are fed by the parents, are quite independent of them. The ducklings have not been seen riding on the back of the female, a common occurrence with Musk Ducks.

There have been no studies of the rate of growth or plumage development of the young beyond the observation that at eight weeks of age they are similar in size to the adults and fully feathered. By mid July of the year following hatching most young Blue-billed Ducks are in full adult plumage, but a few of those examined, presumably the latest hatched, were still undergoing the moult into adult plumage.

Nest

The nests are usually built in dense vegetation, in the inland in cumbungi or lignum, in more coastal areas in tea-trees or reeds, and occasionally on the ground or in the deserted nest of a coot or other waterbird. The herbage is trodden down and a deep cup-shaped nest is built on this platform; it is frequently covered by a dome of reeds. The cup is 8 or 9 inches in inside diameter and 3 or 4 inches deep, sometimes it is partly lined with dead herbage and a little down from the female's breast.

Eggs

The eggs are coarse-shelled and light green in colour. They are large for the size of the bird, larger than those of the Black Duck, though the bird is only little more than half the size. Sixty-two eggs from 12 nests measured in length 64-72 mm. (average 66 mm.) and in breadth 46-51 mm. (average 48 mm.).

Clutch Size

The clutch size varies from 3 to 12. It has been thought that the larger clutches might represent two females laying in the one nest but this is not known. The commonest number of eggs is 5 to 6.

Incubation

The incubation period is 26 to 28 days (Wheeler).

Status

The Blue-billed Duck is very rarely shot, and then only by accident as one bursts from under a shooter's feet. It is not considered a game bird in any State, and is excluded from lists of game species. It would, in any case, be a very unsatisfactory game bird, since it is seldom seen in the dense swamps and in the summer, when most shooting seasons occur, seldom flies. It does, however, fly quite freely on open lakes in the winter immediately before the breeding season. The flight is low to the water, slow and awkward. There seems little danger of Blue-billed Ducks ever being harassed by hunters.

It is usually believed to be a rare species, but this is entirely due to its secretive habits and dense habitat. It is, in fact, widely distributed in southern Australia and in suitable swamps is very numerous. Its numbers are only limited by the availability of deep permanent swamps, which in themselves are not widely distributed in the inland.

Many areas on the New South Wales, South Australian, and Western Australian coasts, which were formerly excellent habitat for Blue-billed Ducks, have been drained, and doubtless this trend will continue. It has been shown that the species readily adapts to drainage swamps of irrigation areas and reed-choked water-storage areas on some inland rivers, but the provision of these is not sufficient to completely compensate for the continuing loss of natural breeding habitat. Its conservation will demand the preservation of these areas.

Source of Data

The biology of the Blue-billed Duck is at present under study by C.S.I.R.O. Division of Wildlife Research. This account uses preliminary results of this study.

Musk Duck

Biziura lobata (Shaw)

References

Biziura Stephens, in Shaw's Gen. Zool. 12, p. 221, 1824.
Anas lobata Shaw, Nat. Misc. 8, p. 255, 1796. (Albany, W.A.)

Other Names

Diver, Diving Duck, Steamer, Mould Goose.

Description

ADULT MALE. General colour above, black brown, crossed with numerous fine lines of lighter brown; primaries and tail almost black; head and neck blackish brown, each feather with whitish tip; lower breast whitish brown; remainder of underside as back; bill black, there is a large pendulous lobe under the bill; legs and feet dark grey; iris dark brown.

ADULT FEMALE. As male, but the lobe under the bill is small and rudimentary, never more than half an inch wide.

IMMATURE. Juveniles of both sexes resemble the female. The front half of the lower mandible is, however, yellow.

DUCKLING. General colour above, uniform dark brown-grey, throat and neck dark brown-grey; remainder of underside light brown; wings dark brown; bill dark grey; legs and feet dark grey; iris brown.

Size

	Weight gm.	*Length* mm.	*Wingspread* mm.	*Wing* mm.	*Bill* mm.
Adult Male					
Maximum	3120	725	955	240	47
Minimum	1811	605	750	205	36
Average	2398	660	866	223	41
Number measured	*243*	*217*	*216*	*219*	*240*

	Weight gm.	Length mm.	Wingspread mm.	Wing mm.	Bill mm.
Adult Female					
Maximum	1844	595	780	202	41
Minimum	993	470	590	165	31
Average	1551	550	723	185	35
Number measured	*292*	*246*	*241*	*248*	*289*

Anatomy

Captain George Vancouver, in H.M.S. *Discovery* in 1791, while replenishing his larder on the south coast of Western Australia, first drew attention to two anatomical peculiarities of the Musk Duck. He wrote: "A very peculiar one was shot, of a darkish grey plumage, with a bag like that of a lizard hanging under its throat, which smelt so intolerably of musk that it scented nearly the whole ship."

The pendulous lobe varies in size with the age and the sexual activity of the bird. The measurements of about ten adult males each month for three years showed that the average diameter of the lobe steadily increased from 5·5 centimetres in March, before the breeding season, to 7·8 centimetres in November, at the height of the breeding season. During display periods the size of the lobe became turgid and further enlarged. At the end of the display it is loose and flaccid. There is an inflatable sack below the tongue that during display is distended, causing the cheeks and throat to swell. The lobe consists of thick, leathery skin enclosing a small amount of tissue provided with numerous blood vessels, but there is no apparent connection with oesophagus. In males shot in display the connecting tissue is separated, producing a cavity, although this does not contain blood or air. During the breeding season the blood vessels in the lobe are greatly enlarged, and in periods of sexual activity the turgidity of the lobe is due to blood-pressure.

The musky odour is a sex characteristic and is confined to the males. It is due to the secretion from the uropygian gland and becomes very much more intense during the breeding season, at which time Captain Vancouver's description is not exaggerated. The function of the odour is not known.

Plumage

The sequence of moult is similar to that of the Blue-billed Duck. From samples collected each month it has been determined that Musk Ducks have two moults each year and both involve the wings and tail. The post-nuptial moult occurs in the period April to June and the greatest number of moulting birds are collected in May. In males many are still undergoing post-nuptial moult in June. No eclipse plumage can be detected. In females the post-nuptial moult is complete in May. The pre-nuptial moult in males begins in December, but in females as early as October, though the greatest numbers are found in December.

The full sequence of the development of the plumage has not been studied yet, but the examination of birds collected shows that the earliest birds hatched in the breeding season begin their moult into adult plumage in February, and by July the whole population has achieved adult plumage.

Voice

The males make three characteristic sounds—a shrill whistle that is uttered throughout the year, a deep "plonk" that is almost confined to the breeding season, and a characteristic noisy splashing of water behind them. The whistle, to the ear, is a simple sound, but sonographic analysis shows it to be in three parts, a low-pitched thump, a higher-pitched hiss, and the whistle itself. The source of the thump is not known, but the hiss is thought to be swiftly indrawn breath. When males are displaying and whistling other Musk Ducks of

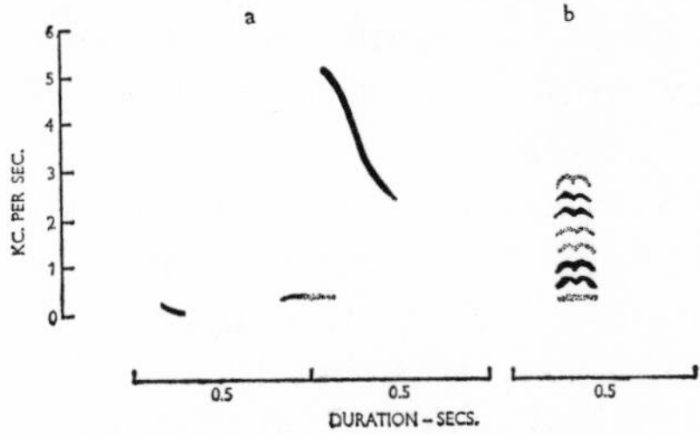

Diagram of sonograms of calls of the Musk Duck: (*a*) male, (*b*) female.

both sexes often approach and watch. The same response has been achieved by replaying tape recordings of the splashing and whistling in swamps, but it was surprising to find that the sound of the splashing was a powerful attractant whereas the whistle alone did not seem to be. More studies are needed on the function of the whistling.

The "plonk" has puzzled ornithologists, since no ready method of making the sound is evident from the anatomy of the bird's vocal apparatus. The sound is similar to that of a stone being dropped into very deep water and this has led to the suggestion that it is made by the feet hitting or being swiftly withdrawn from the water. There are numerous observations to suggest that this explanation is probably true. The position is complicated by the fact that some ornithologists in Western Australia refer to a low-pitched whistle, of undoubted vocal origin, as a "plonk". This particular sound has not been reported in the east.

Ducklings utter continuously a thin peep as a contact call, it becomes more rapid and higher-pitched in alarm; they also have a thin, soft quack, used when begging food from the female. Females seldom make any sound, but do have a soft quack similar to that of the ducklings.

Routine

Musk Ducks are usually far from the shore, floating motionless on the surface, each bird maintaining his distance from the others, or kicking great jets of water into the air. They are completely aquatic and never come on land, though they do sometimes crawl onto clumps of cumbungi to rest. When placed on land they slither along like seals and can only assume the semi-erect posture shown in most illustrations with very great difficulty. They often escape detection by slowly sinking under water and watching with only the nostrils and eyes above water. If closely pursued Musk Ducks usually dive or scramble rapidly across the water until far enough away to take stock, and dive to escape by swimming long distances under water. At these times they do not dive so effortlessly as when feeding, but disappear with a large splash.

Musk Ducks fly very much more commonly than textbooks imply. In the dense cumbungi swamps they seldom do so, being confined to small territories and easily escaping danger by diving and surfacing among the reeds. On clear lakes they frequently take off during the day, without being chased, and fly long distances. They need quite a long take-off distance to get the heavy body aloft, but this can be shortened to a few feet in windy weather. Landing is rough and heavy, the bird usually crashes and skids on contact with the water. Although small waves are no deterrent, and sometimes help in take-off, larger waves prevent it. Captive birds, even when pinioned, are capable of lifting over a seven-foot fence. Long-distance movements seem to be usually undertaken at night.

Field Identification

The low black silhouette with heavy head, large pendulous lobe and, frequently, erect stiff tail distinguishes the male from all other waterfowl; there is nothing quite so grotesque as a male Musk Duck. The females are more finely built, but are distinguished also by the low silhouette, heavy head, and erect tail. At a distance females can be confused with female Blue-billed Ducks.

Relationships

The Musk Duck belongs to the tribe Oxyurini, which has been described under the Blue-billed Duck. It has many anatomical and behavioural characteristics that separate it from the close-knit *Oxyura*.

Habitat

The ideal habitat for Musk Ducks is deep, permanent water with dense vegetation; the vegetation can, however, be too dense, since the birds need clear, open pools among the reeds for feeding and display. With this restriction, they seek the densest cover available and spend most of their time in it. In the inland, cumbungi swamps are the ideal, but very dense lignum is also suitable. On the coast the best Musk Duck habitat is in tea-tree swamps.

When not breeding many Musk Ducks are found on open water and frequently on high mountain lakes, clear lakes in the inland, and occasionally on lagoons, rivers, and ground tanks. They congregate in the winter on salt-water estuaries, particularly in Western Australia, and flocks have been seen in the ocean off southern New South Wales and South Australia, and in Bass Strait.

Distribution and Movements

Musk Ducks are widely distributed in southern Australia. That they were formerly more widespread is shown by the presence of sub-recent fossils of the present-day species and of an extinct related species *Biziura delautouri* in New Zealand.

Today their range extends from Fraser Island, Queensland, to North-west Cape, Western Australia.[13] They avoid the arid parts of the area and are most numerous where large swamps occur. In Western Australia the greatest numbers are in the south-west corner, from Esperance to Moora, but vagrants occasionally move up the coast as far as North-west Cape. In eastern Australia the Musk Duck is most numerous in the Murray-Darling Region and Tasmania. It is widely spread and common throughout Victoria and the Southern Tablelands, but elsewhere only occurs as small isolated colonies. It is not so closely tied to a specific habitat as is the related Blue-billed Duck, and vagrants can be found anywhere in southern Australia at times.

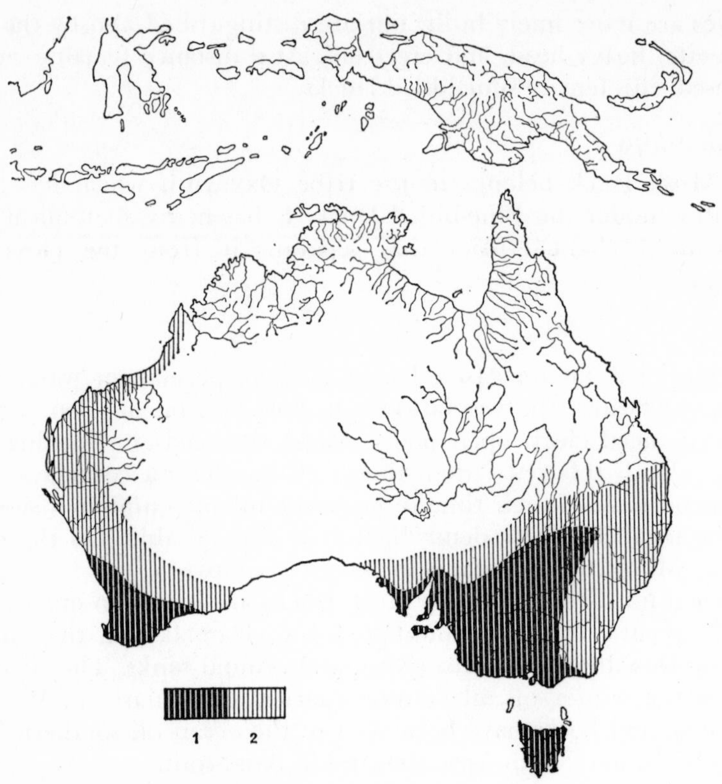

DISTRIBUTION OF THE MUSK DUCK

The heavier shading shows where Musk Ducks are numerous in appropriate habitat. They are widespread but less common in the area with lighter shading, but elsewhere in southern Australia only occur as vagrants.

Its movements are basically regular. During the summer, the breeding season, it is restricted to the dense breeding swamps, but in the autumn and winter there is some movement and at this season large concentrations form on clear lakes and swamps elsewhere. These concentrations are largely, but not entirely, due to local birds. At Griffith, New South Wales, the numbers of birds in the breeding swamps decrease sharply in March, but the birds that appear on the clear lakes in that district are not sufficient to account for the numbers involved. At this time, however, large numbers of Musk Ducks appear on lakes on the Murray River and farther south. It is a fair assumption that the birds from inland New South Wales are involved in these southern flocks, though none have yet been marked to prove the point.

At Griffith the exodus begins in March and April and continues until July. It consists mainly of the young of the year, though all the young leave the area and doubtless some adults also move. Lowe[73] has described considerable display among the birds in winter flocks in the south; although some of this is, no doubt, due to the local birds maintaining their position in the face of the large numbers of immigrants, there is also increasing sexual activity among the juvenile birds in the immigrant flocks. All juveniles, on return to Griffith, have evidence of considerable sexual activity in their testes. It seems then that the usual cycle is for Musk Ducks to breed throughout their range; the juveniles are forced out of the breeding swamps in the autumn and winter elsewhere, usually in the south; those that survive reach sexual maturity in the winter concentrations and move elsewhere to breed. It is not known if the birds that return to a particular breeding swamp are the same individuals that left it.

Unlike the Blue-billed Duck, the Musk Duck is well able to undertake wide movements to exploit newly formed habitat. When the inland rivers flood Musk Ducks move widely and breed in the deepest lignum swamps that are formed. They also colonize Lake Eyre and other distant, normally dry, inland lakes whenever these contain water. Birds involved in wide movements often appear temporarily in isolated ground tanks on the plains.

Food and Feeding

Musk Ducks feed almost entirely by diving in deep water. I have seen them dive in water twenty feet deep and remain submerged, commonly for 25 to 30 seconds, but sometimes for as long as 60 seconds. When they are feeding diving is continuous, and the birds remain on the surface only a few seconds between dives. They enter the water head first and disappear with hardly a ripple. Although diving in deep water is the commonest feeding method they also swim along banks with overhanging vegetation and strip the seed, and have also been seen catching large insects on the surface.

The food in 295 stomachs collected in a large cumbungi swamp near Griffith consisted of both animal and vegetable remains but was almost entirely of animal origin. Although some stomachs contained significant quantities of plants, in most cases there were just a few seeds, presumably collected casually or accidentally during bottom feeding. Of the 295 stomachs 75 per cent contained some plant material and 53 plants were represented. The plants most commonly found were nardoo *Marsilea,* found in 27 per cent of the birds, seeds of medicks *Medicago,* in 23 per cent, pondweeds *Potamogeton* and smartweeds *Polygonum* in 24 per cent, and *Aponogeton* in 19 per cent. Thirteen per cent had eaten cumbungi *Typha angustifolia,* the dominant vegetation of the swamp, and the remainder of the plant food was made up of a wide variety of seeds of grasses, sedges, herbs, freshwater sponges and algae.

The commonest animals eaten were insects which were found in every stomach examined. The usual insects were *Corixa,* water-boatmen, which also provide much of the food of the other inland ducks. Dragon-fly larvae, Odonata, were in 39 per cent, and the larvae of mayflies Ephemoptera, midges, Chironomidae, and caddis-flies Trichoptera, in 9, 14, and 10 per cent respectively. Water-beetles were an important source of food, being found in 19 per cent, and again were the same beetles that are important to the other ducks. The large freshwater crayfish *Cherax albidus* was easily caught and readily eaten, being in 30 per cent of the birds. Shells consisting of several freshwater snails and freshwater mussels *Corbiculena* were in more than half the stomachs, sometimes in large quantities. Surprisingly, fish were rarely caught, and only one bird had eaten one leech; all of these are very common animals in cumbungi swamps. There were no frogs in the samples studied, but Musk Ducks have been seen swallowing them.

Large numbers of Blue-billed Ducks collected in the same swamp at the same time allow the food of the two birds to be compared. Although these two related species live together in the same swamp and have the same general feeding methods their diets are very different. Both dive, but the Blue-billed Duck collects a large part of its food on the surface, unlike the Musk Duck, which uses little from this source. In the food secured under water there are very great differences; the items used by Blue-billed Ducks are smaller, mainly aquatic plants and the larvae of midges, those used by the Musk Duck are all animal and include many large crayfish and mussels that cannot be utilized by Blue-billed Ducks.

Breeding

The striking display of the Musk Duck occurs throughout the autumn and winter. The actions in this elaborate and bizarre display are well known, but their true significance has not yet been satisfactorily explained.

In a quiet pool the display usually begins by the male sailing out from the reeds with a series of strong, deliberate kicks with both feet, each kick throwing a large volume of water behind him. In the centre the action changes so that the bird remains more or less stationary whilst the jets of water are still thrown several feet behind. The kicks can be repeated thirty or forty times and continue for several minutes. The head is raised and the neck and cheeks puffed out and the lobe distended fully; the tail is raised and stiff feathers fanned over the back as the water splashing continues and deep, resonant "plonks" are heard. It is probable that the "plonk" is not vocal, but is caused by the feet and the water. The climax comes when the head is raised higher and the bill elevated almost vertically; the distended throat and lobe are very prominent; the tail is fanned and flattened on the back as the undertail coverts bristle; the bird sinks lower into the water and revolves, still kicking water jets and with each kick emitting the piercing whistle. The whistle is repeated many times and continues for several minutes.

The whole process is believed to be designed to advertise the male's presence and to assist pair formation; it is thought that copulation following the display is the only contact that occurs between the sexes. The solitary males continue their grotesque manoeuvres and gyrations, often alone but sometimes watched by other birds of both sexes. I have seen groups of females approach a displaying male and copulation with one of them follow. As the females approach, the intensity of the display ceases and the male moves closer to one, often splashing water over her as he manoeuvres. The copulation is sudden and rapid, the female being completely submerged; on surfacing she swims away and the male, almost completely submerged, swims swiftly across his territory. Lowe, watching a similar situation, saw the male distend his lobe and continue display, but in those cases I have seen this did not occur.

An occasional male in display can be found at most times of the year, but the frequency increases very greatly during the winter and early spring, and at this time encounters between males are often associated with quite savage fighting. The bird whose territorial space has been invaded lowers his head into the water and charges silently; the intruder usually flees. At other times they undertake shallow under-water dives until they meet and savagely fight with snapping beak and flapping wings until one retires.

For the past three years regular monthly samples of Musk Ducks have been examined from Barrenbox Swamp, near Griffith. The sexual cycle in the male begins in March when the spermatic tubules begin to increase in diameter and the testes to increase in size. At this time also the amount and intensity of the display increase and the lobes begin to increase in size. The maximum testes size, spermatic tubule diameter, and lobe size are achieved in November and thereafter they abruptly decline. A few males produce sperms in May, but most do so in June, and after September the percentage of males producing sperms declines. Most males then are sexually active in the period from mid May until the end of September.

In females there is a slight increase in the size of the oocytes in April, that is, after the males have intensified their display, but there is no really significant increase in the size of the oocytes until August, when all adult females collected are in egg-laying condition. After September the size of the oocytes declines until by December they are of the normal non-breeding size.

According to nests examined and the calculated hatching date of broods encountered, most clutches are begun in September and October, but in some years nests are begun as early as June and as late as December. In the Blue-billed Duck in this swamp, in the same period, the dates of the sexual cycle and the percentage of the population of birds breeding were not noticeably affected by annual differences in the level of the swamp. The breeding of the Blue-billed Duck is apparently largely controlled by fixed annual factors. In the Musk Duck, however, there were striking annual differences associated with the level of the swamp. In 1964, when the swamp was at a very low level, the period of spermatogenesis of the males was reduced to June to November, compared to 1963, a year when the swamp was at a high level, and the sexual period was April to December. The sexual period of the females was also restricted in 1963, the maximum oocyte development being between August and October; in 1964 it was restricted to September, but in 1965, when the swamp was high, some clutches were begun as early as June. The study is not complete yet, but the general conclusion emerging is that in inland New South Wales the breeding season of Musk Ducks is fairly regular in the spring, but, like that of many other inland waterfowl, its timing and extent are ultimately controlled by the water-level.

At other localities in southern Australia where Musk Duck breeding has been studied, the breeding season is generally similar to that at Griffith, that is, in the spring. J. Wheeler at Ballarat, Victoria, has examined many nests in the 1950-1957 period and found that most clutches were begun between September and November, but a few were begun as early as August and as late as December. R. Taylor at Benger, Western Australia, examined many nests in 1958-1963, and here also most clutches were begun in the period August to November, but few were outside the period September and October.

Out-of-season breeding occurs in years of exceptional water-level in the swamps. In 1956 Bullawarra Lake in south-west Queensland flooded in March and M. Schraeder found nests of Musk Ducks there in June. In the same year the Lachlan and Murrumbidgee rivers in south-western New South Wales flooded in March. I found Musk Duck nests in the deepest flooded lignum swamps near Hillston in May and in the permanent cumbungi swamps near Griffith in the same month; these swamps were still overfull in January 1957 and Musk Ducks were still breeding there. These events further support the conclusion that the timing of the breeding season of Musk Ducks is partly controlled by water-level.

Nest

The nest is well concealed and is usually built by breaking down the centre of a clump of cumbungi. It is usually a small clump standing alone or on the edge of a clear pool in the swamp. It is seldom far into a thicket. The beaten-down stems are woven into a rough cup that often is quite flimsy, so that the bottoms of the eggs are wet. Often some flags are pulled down or broken so that they overhang the nest and provide some top cover. It is usually thinly lined with a few leaves and down. The down is grey, each feather being lighter in the centre.

Nests are sometimes also built in low-hanging branches of tea-tree where they touch the water, in the tops of very low stumps, and occasionally on the ground or in clumps of grass on small islands.

Eggs

The eggs are pale greenish white with a thin coating of lime when fresh, but they soon become brown owing to nest staining. They are elliptical and a little pointed at each end, the shell is smooth and glossy.

Sixty-eight eggs in thirty-two clutches varied in length from 71 mm. to 88 mm. (average 79 mm.) and in breadth from 48 mm. to 58 mm. (average 54 mm.).

Clutch Size

The clutch size varies from 1 to 10, but 1 to 3 is the commonest size and 2·8 the mean clutch size. One clutch, numbering 9 eggs, collected at Griffith, was found to be comprised of two groups of eggs of different shape and quite different incubation states; perhaps all large clutches are the result of two females laying in the one nest. The clutch size in 49 nests was distributed as below.

Number of eggs:	1	2	3	4	5	6	7	8	9	10
Number of clutches:	12	16	13	3	1	1	2	0	1	1

Incubation

Incubation time has not been recorded.

Development of Young

Incubation is by the female alone and on hatching the young remain in the nest for at least one day before being led off. I have disturbed fresh-hatched ducklings from a nest one day and found them back in it the next day, an observation that suggests they later use it for a roosting site. Throughout their juvenile period they are fed by the female, probably entirely when very young but with decreasing regularity as they grow older. I have seen young nearly as large as the female still being fed and also diving for themselves. The female dives and surfaces carrying food in the bill; the young approach with their food-begging cry and remove it.

Ducklings hatched in incubators and placed in water have been unwilling to dive until several days old. Downy ducklings of Blue-billed Ducks dived immediately and continuously on touching the water, but the Musk Ducks swam around and made one or two attempts when frightened, but were unable to submerge. They were also unable, or unwilling, to pick up mealworms and other food from the bottom of water one inch deep and it was necessary to feed them; mealworms proffered with forceps were grasped and swallowed in the same way as by the nestlings of passerine birds. These observations suggest that downy Musk Ducks are largely dependent on the mother for food—a situation unique among waterfowl. They are very dependent on the mother in other ways, being frequently seen riding on her back, and Serventy[88] discusses the possibility that at the instant the mother dives the young sometimes cling to her and are carried with her under water until she surfaces again.

When moving through the dense cumbungi the family maintains contact with a high-pitched continuous "peeping", and if suddenly disturbed the brood scatters across the water rather than immediately diving as do the young of the Blue-billed Duck, a further observation suggesting ineptitude at diving when very young.

Status

Musk Ducks are never shot and have no value as game, they are pungent in odour and practically inedible. Some time ago, however, in Western Australia, they were netted and smoked for use as hard rations for bush travellers who could get nothing better. In lakes and estuaries where netting for fish is permitted and Musk Ducks abound many are caught under water and drown. Those that do not drown are usually killed, either to help extricate them from the net or to prevent them from being caught again. Losses of Musk Ducks and, less commonly, Blue-billed Ducks in this way occur widely inland and are very much higher than might be imagined.

Musk Ducks are very numerous in their correct habitat and in no danger of serious decline at present. However, the deep permanent swamps that they inhabit are not very numerous. Many have been drained and many more will be. This habitat is not ideal for the game ducks and one might not expect it to be preserved for this purpose; its retention, however, is essential for the conservation of Musk Ducks and Blue-billed Ducks.

Source of Data

The detailed study of the ecology and behaviour of the Musk Duck is at present in progress by the Division of Wildlife Research, C.S.I.R.O., and this account is based on preliminary results of that study.

BIBLIOGRAPHY

1. Alexander, W. B. (1916). History of Zoology in Western Australia: Part 2, 1791-1829. *J. Proc. Roy. Soc. W.A.* 1: 83-149.
2. Ali, Salim. (1941). *The Book of Indian Birds.* 440 pp. Bombay Nat. Hist. Soc.
3. Amadon, D. (1943). Birds collected during the Whitney South Sea Expedition No. 52. Notes on some non-passerine genera. 3. Am. Mus. Nov. 1237.
4. Anon (1953). *Checklist of New Zealand Birds.* Ornith. Soc. New Zealand. Reed, Wellington.
5. Baker, E. C. (1935). *The Nidification of Birds of the Indian Empire*: vol. iv. Pandionidae-Podicepidae. 546 pp. Taylor and Francis, London.
6. Balham, R. W. (1952). Grey and Mallard Ducks in the Manawatu District, New Zealand. *Emu* 52: 163-91.
7. Balham, R. W., and Miers, K. H. (1959). Mortality and survival of Grey and Mallard Ducks banded in New Zealand. N.Z. Dept. Int. Affairs Wildlife Pub. No. 5.
8. Bartels, M., and Franck, P. (1938). Eine neue Ente aus Java. *Treubia* 16 (3): 337-8.
9. Blaauw, F. E. (1894). *Ibis* ser. 6, 6: 317 (Quoted in Delacour).
10. Broinowski, G. J. (1885). *Birds and Mammals of Australia.* G. Murray, Sydney.
11. Campbell, A. J. (1899). *Ibis* ser. 7, 5: 362.
12. Campbell, A. J. (1901). *Nests and Eggs of Australian Birds.* Pub. by Author. Part II, pp. 525-1102. Sheffield, England.
13. Carter, T. (1903-4). Birds occurring in the region of the North-west Cape. *Emu* 3: 30-8, 89-96, 171-7; 4: 207-13.
14. Cayley, N. W. (1932). *What Bird is That?* 317 pp. Angus and Robertson Ltd., Sydney.
15. Chasen, F. N. (1939). *The Birds of the Malay Peninsula*: IV. The Birds of the Low-Country Jungle and Scrub. 485 pp. Witherby and Co. Ltd, London.
16. Chisholm, A. H. (1964). Some early letters in Australian Ornithology. *Emu* 63: 287-96, 373-82.

17. Christian, C. S., and Stewart, A. (1953). Survey of Katherine and Darwin Region 1946. Land Res. Ser. No. 1. CSIRO Aust.
18. Coombes, A. H. (1950). The Moult-Migration of the Sheld-duck. Int. Wild. Res. Ins. Pub. No. 2 Brit. Mus. England.
19. Crook, J. H. (1961). The basis of flock organization in Birds. pp. 125-49 in *Current Problems in Animal Behaviour,* ed. Thorpe, W., and Zangwill, O. L. Cambridge Univ. Press.
20. Cunningham, J. M., and Welch, E. O. (1955). The Grey Teal in New Zealand: Some nesting and plumage notes. *Emu* 55: 303-9.
21. Davies, S. J. J. F. (1961). The orientation of pecking in very young Magpie Geese, *Anseranas semipalmata. Ibis* 103a: 277-83.
22. Davies, S. J. J. F. (1962). The nest-building behaviour of the Magpie Goose, *Anseranas semipalmata. Ibis* 104: 147-57.
23. Davies, S. J. J. F. (1963). Aspects of the Behaviour of the Magpie Goose, *Anseranas semipalmata. Ibis* 105: 76-98.
24. Davies, S. J. J. F. (1962). The response of the Magpie Goose to aerial predators. *Emu* 62: 51-5.
25. Davies, S. J. J. F., and Frith, H. J. (1964). Some Comments on the Taxonomic Position of the Magpie Goose, *Anseranas semipalmata* (Latham). *Emu* 63: 265-72.
26. Delacour, J. (1954-1964). *The Waterfowl of the World.* 4 vols. Country Life, London.
27. Delacour, J., and Mayr, E. (1945). The Family Anatidae. *Wilson Bull.* 57: 3-55.
28. Dennis, R. V. (1907) . Ducks and Geese. *Emu* 6: 129-30.
29. D'Ombrain, A. F. (1945). Notes on Young of Plumed Tree-Duck. *Emu* 44: 324-7.
30. Delacour, J., and Mayr, E. (1946). *Birds of the Philippines.* 309 pp. Macmillan, New York.
31. Dorward, D. E., and Pizzey, G. M. (1965). Breeding of the Cape Barren Goose on the Anser and Glennie Islands, Vic. Wildfowl Trust 16th Annual Report, England.
32. Emlen, J. T., Jr. (1952). Flocking Behaviour in Birds. *Auk* 69: 160-70.
33. Ford, J. R. (1958). Seasonal Variation in Populations of Anatidae at the Bibra Lake District, Western Australia. *Emu* 58: 31-41.
34. Frith, H. J. (1955). The Downy Ducklings of the Pink-eared and White-eyed Ducks. *Emu* 55: 310-12.
35. Frith, H. J. (1957). Breeding and Movements of wild ducks in inland New South Wales. *CSIRO Wildl. Res.* 2: 19-31.
36. Frith, H. J. (1957). Wild ducks and the rice industry in New South Wales. *CSIRO Wildl. Res.* 2: 32-50.
37. Frith, H. J. (1959). The ecology of wild ducks in inland New South Wales: I. Waterfowl Habitats. *CSIRO Wildl. Res.* 4: 97-107.

38. Frith, H. J. (1959). The ecology of wild ducks in inland New South Wales: II. Movements. *CSIRO Wildl. Res.* 4: 108-30.

39. Frith, H. J. (1959). The ecology of wild ducks in inland New South Wales: III. Food Habits. *CSIRO Wildl. Res.* 4: 131-55.

40. Frith, H. J. (1959). The ecology of wild ducks in inland New South Wales: IV. Breeding. *CSIRO Wildl. Res.* 4: 156-81.

41. Frith, H. J. (1959). Ecology of wild ducks in inland Australia. In *Biogeography and Ecology in Australia* (Series Monographiae Biologicae, vol. VIII), pp. 383-95. June, 1959, The Hague.

42. Frith, H. J. (1960). Waterfowl Breeding Habitat in Australia. Australian Waterfowl Committee, mimeo report.

43. Frith, H. J. (1962). Movements of the Grey Teal, *Anas gibberifrons* Müller (Anatidae). *CSIRO Wildl. Res.* 7: 50-70.

44. Frith, H. J. (1963). Movements and Mortality Rates of the Black Duck and Grey Teal in South-eastern Australia. *CSIRO Wildl. Res.* 8: 119-31.

45. Frith, H. J. (1964). Taxonomic relationships of *Stictonetta naevosa* (Gould). *Nature* 202: 1352-3.

46. Frith, H. J. (1964). The Downy Young of the Freckled Duck, *Stictonetta naevosa*. *Emu* 64: 42-7.

47. Frith, H. J. (1965). Ecology of the Freckled Duck, *Stictonetta naevosa* (Gould). *CSIRO Wildl. Res.* 10: 125-39.

48. Frith, H. J., and Davies, S. J. J. F. (1961). Ecology of the Magpie Goose, *Anseranas semipalmata* Latham (Anatidae). *CSIRO Wildl. Res.* 6: 91-141.

49. Frith, H. J., and Davies, S. J. J. F. (1961). Breeding seasons of birds in subcoastal Northern Territory. *Emu* 61: 97-111.

50. Gould, J. (1865). *Handbook to the Birds of Australia*, vol. ii. 627 pp. 2 vols. Pub. by Author, London.

51. Guiler, E. R. (1961). The 1958-60 Cape Barren Goose aerial surveys. *Emu* 61: 61-4.

52. Guiler, E. R. (1966). The Cape Barren Goose: its numbers, environment, and breeding. *Emu* 66: in press.

53. Hall, R. (1909). Notes on Ducks. *Emu* 9: 77-9.

54. Henry, G. M. (1955). *A Guide to the Birds of Ceylon*. 432 pp. Oxford Univ. Press, London.

55. Hill, G. F. (1913). Ornithological Notes, Barclay Expedition. *Emu* 12: 238-62.

56. Hindwood, K. A., and McGill, A. R. (1958). The Birds of Sydney (County of Cumberland), New South Wales. Roy. Zool. Soc. N.S.W. 128 pp.

57. Hobbs, J. N. (1956). A Flood Year in the Riverina. *Emu* 56: 349-52.

58. Hobbs, J. N. (1961). The Birds of South-west New South Wales. *Emu* 61: 21-55.

59. Hoogerwerf, A. (1962). Some particulars on a research on harmful birds in rice crops in south New Guinea. Bull. Agr. Res. Stn. Manokwari, Agricultural Series No. 7.
60. Hoogerwerf, A. (1964). On birds new for New Guinea or with a larger range than previously known. *Bull. BOC.* 84: 70-84.
61. Jackson, S. W. (1907). Egg collecting and bird life in Australia. Catalogue and Data of the "Jacksonian Oological Collection". F. W. White: Sydney.
62. Johnsgard, P. A. (1960). Comparative behaviour of the Anatidae and its evolutionary implications. Wildlife Trust 11th Annual Report, England.
63. Jones, J. (1946). Australian distribution of two Pygmy-Geese. *Emu* 46: 128-32.
64. Jones, J. (1946). White-quilled Pygmy-Goose. *Emu* 46: 235.
65. Jones, Terry (1946). Waterfowl breeding season at Leckford. *Avicultural Magaz.* 52: 193-96.
66. Kinghorn, J. R. (1932). Wild ducks are not a serious pest of Rice crops. *Agr. Gaz. N.S.W.* 43: 603-8.
67. Kortright, F. H. (1942). *The Ducks, Swans, and Geese of North America.* 476 pp. Stackpole Co. Harrisburg Pa. and Wildl. Mgmt. Instit. Washington D.C.
68. Lack, D. (1954). *The Natural Regulation of Animal Numbers.* 343 pp. Clarendon Press, Oxford.
69. Lavery, H. J. (1964). An Investigation of the Biology and Ecology of Waterfowl (Anatidae: Anseriformes) in North Queensland. M.Sc. Thesis, Univ. of Queensland, 513 pp.
70. Littler, F. M. (1918). *A Handbook of the Birds of Tasmania.* 242 pp. Pub. by Author, Launceston.
71. Lorenz, K. (1941). Vergleichende Bewegungsstudien an Anatinen. *J. für Ornith.* Ergänzungsband iii, 194-293.
72. Lowe, V. T. (1958). Notes on ducks and duck-shooting. *Emu* 58: 26-30.
73. Lowe, V. T. (1966). Notes on the Musk Duck, *Biziura lobata. Emu* 65: 279-289.
74. Mathews, G. M. (1914-15). *The Birds of Australia*: IV. Anseriformes Pelecaniformes. London.
75. Mayr, E. (1940). Birds collected during the Whitney South Sea Expedition XLI. Notes on New Guinea Birds VI. Am. Mus. Nov. 1056.
76. Mayr, E. (1945). Birds collected during the Whitney South Sea Expedition LV. Notes on Birds of Northern Melanesia. Am. Mus. Nov. 1294. 12 pp.
77. Mayr, E. (1941). List of New Guinea Birds. A systematic list of the birds of New Guinea and adjacent islands. Am. Mus. Nat. Hist. 260 pp. New York.

78. Mayr, E., and Camras, S. (1937). Birds of the Crane Pacific Expedition. Fld. Mus. Nat. Hist. Zoo. Series 20 (34): 453-73.

79. Miles, J. A. R. (1964). Notes on the status of certain birds in Fiji. *Emu* 63: 422.

80. Morgan, D. G. (1954). Seasonal changes in populations of Anatidae at the Laverton Saltworks, Victoria, 1950-1953. *Emu* 54: 263-78.

81. Morse, F. C. (1922). Birds of the Moree District. *Emu* 22: 24-36.

82. North, A. J. (1901-14). Nests and eggs of birds found breeding in Australia and Tasmania. 4 vols. Aust. Mus. Special Catalogue No. 1.

83. Oliver, W. R. B. (1955). *New Zealand Birds.* 661 pp. Reed, Wellington.

84. Philips, J. C. (1926). *A Natural History of the Ducks.* 4 vols. Houghton Mifflin Co., Boston.

85. Rand, A. L. (1942). Results of the Archbold Expeditions, No. 4. Birds of the 1938-39 New Guinea Expedition. Bull. Am. Mus. Nat. Hist. 79: 425-516, part VII.

86. Ripley, S. D. (1942). A review of the species *Anas castanea. Auk* 59: 90-9.

86a. Ripley, S. D. (1964). A Systematic and Ecological Study of Birds of New Guinea. Bull. 19, Peabody Museum of Natural History, Yale University.

87. Serventy, V. N. (1952). The Archipelago of the Recherche: Part 2. Birds. Aust. Geogr. Soc. Rep. No. 1. 24 pp.

88. Serventy, D. L., and Whittell, H. M. (1951). *A Handbook of the Birds of Western Australia.* 384 pp. Paterson Brokensha, Perth.

89. Sharland, M. (1945). *Tasmanian Birds.* 175 pp. Angus and Robertson Ltd, Sydney.

90. Smythies, B. E. (1960). *The Birds of Borneo.* 562 pp. Oliver and Boyd, Edinburgh.

91. Stone, A. C. (1912). Birds of Lake Boga, Victoria. *Emu* 12: 112-22.

92. Storr, G. M. (1965). The Avifauna of Rottnest Island, Western Australia: II. Lake and Littoral Birds. *Emu* 64: 105-13.

93. Thomson, D. F. (1935). Birds of Cape York Peninsula. Ecological Notes, Field Observations and Catalogue of Specimens collected on three Expeditions to North Queensland. Melbourne.

94. Ticehurst, N. F. (1957). *The Mute Swan in England.* 131 pp. Cleaver-Hume Press Ltd., London.

95. Tsen Choh Lin (1955). Index to Classification of Chinese Birds. 329 pp. Pub. Inst. Sc. Peking.

96. Verheyen, R. (1955). La systematique des Anseriformes basée sur l'osteologie comparée. Bull. Inst. Roy. Sci. Nat. Belgique 31: No. 35, 1-18; No. 36, 1-16; No. 37, 1-22; No. 38, 1-16.

97. de Vis, C. W. (1897). Annual Report: British New Guinea, 1896-97, p. 90.

98. Von Boetticher, H. (1943). Die phylogenetisch-systematische Stellung von *Anseranas. Zool. Ans.* 142: 55-8.
99. Wheeler, J. R. (1953). Notes on the Blue-billed Ducks at Lake Wendouree, Ballarat. *Emu* 53: 280-82.
100. Williams, G. R. (1964). Extinction and the Anatidae of New Zealand. Wildfowl Trust 15th Annual Report, England.
101. Woolfenden, G. E. (1961). Postcranial osteology of the Waterfowl. Bull. Fla. St. Mus.: 6, No. 1.

INDEX